PURE MATHEMATICS

2. TRIGONOMETRY

Third Edition

By

Anthony Nicolaides

P.A.S.S. PUBLICATIONS

Private Academic & Scientific Studies Limited

First Published in Great Britain 1991 by
Private Academic & Scientific Studies Limited

ISBN–13 978–1–872684–87–1

THIRD EDITION 2008

Titles by the same author.

Revised and Enhanced

1. Algebra. GCE A Level ISBN–13 978–1–872684–82–6 £11–95
2. Trigonometry. GCE A Level ISBN–13 978–1–872684–87–1 £11–95
3. Complex Numbers. GCE A Level ISBN–13 978–1–872684–92–5 £9–95
4. Differential Calculus and Applications. GCE A Level ISBN–13 978–1–872684–97–0 £9–95
5. Cartesian and Polar Curve Sketching. GCE A Level ISBN–13 978–1–872684–63–5 £9–95
6. Coordinate Geometry in two Dimensions. GCE A Level ISBN–13 978–1–872684–68–0 £9–95
7. Integral Calculus and Applications. GCE A Level ISBN–13 978–1–872684–73–4 £14–95
8. Vectors in two and three dimensions. GCE A Level ISBN–13 978–1–872684–15–4 £9–95
9. Determinants and Matrices. GCE A Level ISBN–13 978–1–872684–16–1 £9–95
10. Probabilities. GCE A Level ISBN–13 978–1–872684–17–8 £8–95
    This book includes the full solutions
11. Success in Pure Mathematics: The complete works of GCE A Level. (1–9 above inclusive) ISBN 978–1–872684–93–2 £39–95
12. Electrical & Electronic Principles. First year Degree Level ISBN–13 978–1–872684–98–7 £16–95
13. GCSE Mathematics Higher Tier Third Edition. ISBN–13 978–1–872684–69–7 £19–95

All the books have answers and a CD is attached with FULL SOLUTIONS of all the exercises set at the end of the book.

Preface

This book, which is part of the GCE A level series in Pure Mathematics covers the specialized topic of Trigonometry.

The GCE A level series success in Pure Mathematics is comprised of nine books, covering the syllabuses of most examining boards. The books are designed to assist the student wishing to master the subject of Pure Mathematics. The series is easy to follow with minimum help. It can be easily adopted by a student who wishes to study it in the comforts of his home at his pace without having to attend classes formally; it is ideal for the working person who wishes to enhance his knowledge and qualification. Trigonometry book, like all the books in the series, the theory is comprehensively dealt with, together with many worked examples and exercises. A step by step approach is adopted in all the worked examples. A CD is attached to the book with FULL SOLUTIONS of all the exercises set at the end of each chapter.

This book develops the basic concepts and skills that are essential for the GCE A level in Pure Mathematics.

Chapter 21 indicates in order the modules of C1, C2, C3, C4, FP1, FP2, FP3 dealing with Trigonometry with Questions and Full solutions.

A. Nicolaides

2. TRIGONOMETRY

Contents

1

Introduction to Trigonometry

The word "trigonometry" comes from the Greek word "trigonometria", the former part of the word "trigono" means "triangle", a three-sided figure, and the latter part of the word "metria" denotes "measure", hence the whole word denotes "measurement of triangles".

Angles, Degrees, Radians

Angles

When a straight line AB with centre A and radius AB revolves about the point A from AB to AC as shown, the angle BAC is described. An angle thus measures the amount of turning between two positions of a straight line.

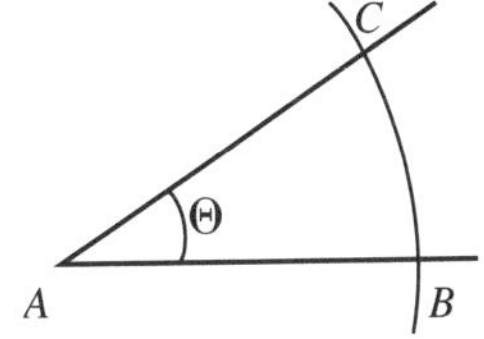

Fig. 2-I/1 $\angle BAC$ = Angle Θ

The magnitude of the angle is independent of the lengths AB and AC. A is known as the vertex of the angle. When two straight lines intersect, two angles are formed, one angle is called "acute" and the other angle "obtuse", unless the two lines are perpendicular to each other, then the angles are right angles. Two angles which add up to two right angles are called "supplementary angles".

Let α and β be two supplementary angles, $\alpha+\beta = 180°$, α is the supplement of β, or β is the supplement of α. If $\alpha = \beta$ and α and β are supplementary, then $\alpha = \beta =$ one right angle.

$\beta =$ acute angle

$\alpha =$ obtuse angle

α is the supplement of β and β is the supplement of α

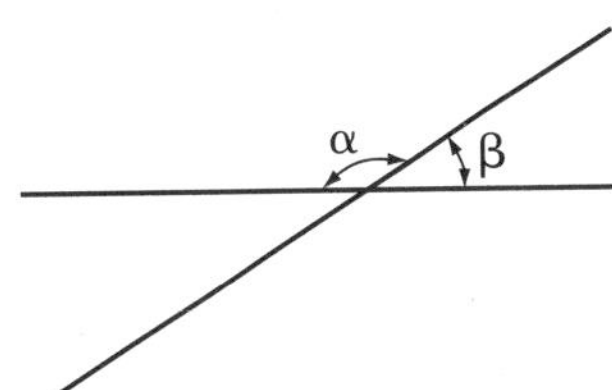

Fig. 2-I/2

If angles α and β together equal one right angle, these angles are complementary angles.

$$\alpha + \beta = \text{one right angle}$$

Sexagesimal

One right angle = 90 degrees, denoted by $90°$.

One degree ($1°$) = 60 minutes, denoted by $60'$.

One minute ($1'$) = 60 seconds, denoted by $60''$.

Angles in Degrees and Radians

The angles may be measured in degrees or radians. Degrees have units, as we have seen above; although radians are dimensionless, they have no units, they are merely numbers.

The Degree

One complete revolution of the circle is divided into 360 degrees. The degrees are measured with a protractor, a semicircular, normally a plastic transparent instrument with a centre and 180 equally spaced degrees.

The Radian

A radian is the angle subtended at the centre of a circle by an arc equal to the length of the radius.

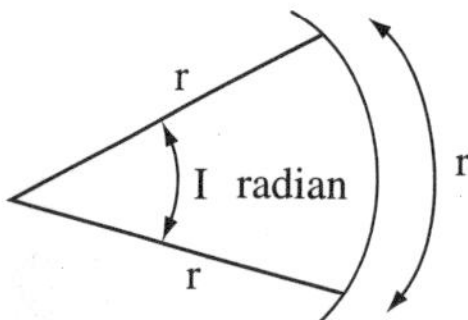

Fig. 2-I/3

To illustrate the radian further, draw a circle with a certain radius, using a compass. Take a piece of thread and measure the radius to size with this thread. Accommodate the piece of thread along the circumference, it will be observed that about 6.28 times this thread will fit around the circumference, that is, one complete revolution is equal to $2\pi \approx 6.28$ radians, therefore $\pi = 3.14$ radians to three significant figures. Therefore, one complete revolution of the circle is 2π radians.

$$\text{One radian} = \frac{360^\circ}{2\pi} = \frac{180^\circ}{\pi} = 57.29578^\circ$$
$$= 57^\circ\ 17'\ 44.8'',$$

that is, 57° 17 minutes and 44.8 seconds.

Convention of the Angle

A POSITIVE angle is measured from the reference line OA in an anticlockwise direction as shown in the diagram of Fig. 2-I/4

Conversion of Degrees to Radians and Radians to Degrees

It is absolutely necessary to learn the conversion table below:-

x°	0	30	45	60	90	120	135	150	180
x^c	0	$\frac{\pi}{6}$	$\frac{\pi}{4}$	$\frac{\pi}{3}$	$\frac{\pi}{2}$	$\frac{2\pi}{3}$	$\frac{3\pi}{4}$	$\frac{5\pi}{6}$	π
x°	210	225	240	270	300	315	330	360	
x^c	$\frac{7\pi}{6}$	$\frac{5\pi}{4}$	$\frac{4\pi}{3}$	$\frac{3\pi}{2}$	$\frac{5\pi}{3}$	$\frac{7\pi}{4}$	$\frac{11\pi}{6}$	2π	

The angle, in degrees, 30° means 30 degrees, and the angle, in radians, $\left(\frac{\pi}{6}\right)^c$ means $\frac{\pi}{6} = 0.5235987$ radians; the former has units, the latter is a number.
Radians are converted to degrees by multiplying by the factor $\frac{360}{2\pi}$.
Degrees are converted to radians by multiplying by the factor $\frac{2\pi}{360}$.
Earlier, it was mentioned that an angle may be measured in degrees or radians, for example: sin 30° $= \sin\left(\frac{\pi}{6}\right)^c = 0.5$. It is observed that the sine of 30 degrees is the same as the sine of $\frac{\pi}{6}$ radians, namely 0.5, but in the expression e^x, x must be in radians and not in degrees in order to give e^x as a number with no dimension; also $\sinh x$, where x is expressed in radians only, then $\sinh x$ is a number where

$$\sinh x = \frac{(e^x - e^{-x})}{2} \text{ is the definition.}$$

It is therefore advisable to think in general in degrees because they are easier to manipulate, and to work the results in radians.
In general, there are certain difficulties in converting degrees, minutes, seconds to radians and vice versa.

$$1^\circ = \frac{\pi^c}{180} = \frac{\pi}{180} \text{ radians} = 0.017453292 \text{ radians}$$

$$1' = \frac{\pi^c}{(180)(60)} = 0.0002908882087 \text{ radians}$$

$$1'' = \frac{\pi^c}{(180)(3600)} = 0.000004848136811 \text{ radians.}$$

WORKED EXAMPLE 1

Express (i) 17° 25′ 37″ in radians, and

(ii) 1.55 radians in degrees.

Solution 1

(i) $17^\circ\ 25'\ 37'' = 17^\circ 25\left(\frac{37}{60}\right)'$

$$= 17\left(\frac{25.616667}{60}\right)^\circ$$
$$= 17.4269444^\circ$$
$$= 17.4269444 \times \frac{\pi}{180} \text{ radians}$$
$$= 0.3041575 \text{ radians.}$$

Therefore, $17^\circ\ 25'\ 37'' = 0.304$ radians to three decimal places.

Check that 0.304 radians equals 17° 25′ 37″.

(ii) $1.55 \text{ radians} = 1.55 \times \frac{180}{\pi} = 88.808458^\circ$

$$= 88^\circ\ (0.808458 \times 60)'$$
$$= 88^\circ\ (48.5)' = 88^\circ\ 48'\ 30''$$

Check that 88° 48′ 30″ = 1.55 radians.

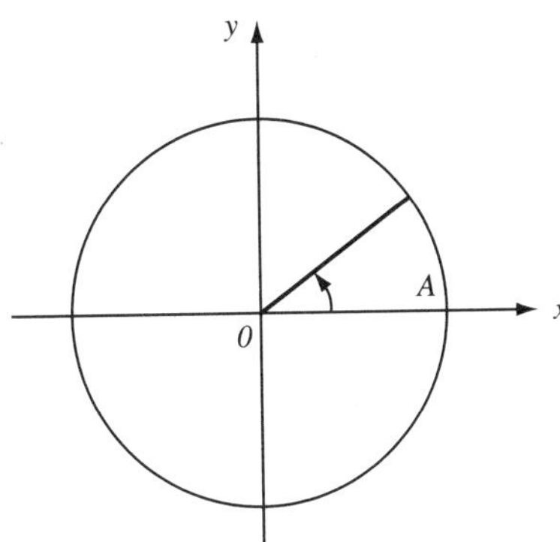

Fig. 2-I/4

Angle x is in the range $0^\circ \leq x \leq 360^\circ$, in degrees, or in radians $0^c \leq x \leq (2\pi)^c$.

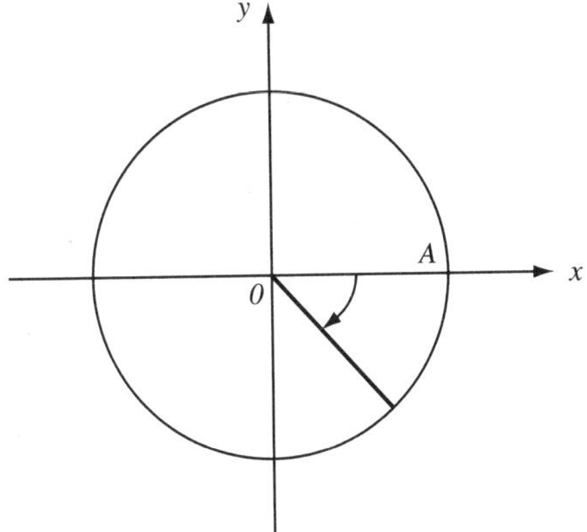

Fig. 2-1/5

A NEGATIVE angle is measured from the reference line *OA* in a clockwise direction shown in the diagram.

The principal values of x are defined as follows:

$-180^\circ \leq x \leq +180^\circ$ in degrees

or $-\pi \leq x \leq \pi$ in radians

that is, the angles which are measured in the anticlockwise direction 0° to 180° or 0^c to π^c, and the angles which are measured in the clockwise direction 0° to -180° or 0^c to $-\pi^c$.

Exercise 1

1. Convert the following angles to radians:
   (i) 30°
   (ii) 45°
   (iii) 15°
   (iv) 75°
   (v) 105°.

2. Convert the following angles to radians:
   (i) $12^\circ\,35'$
   (ii) $42^\circ\,05'$
   (iii) $56^\circ\,33'$
   (iv) $89^\circ\,01'$
   (ii) $93^\circ\,35'$.

3. Express in degrees the following angles in radians:
   (i) $\frac{\pi}{10}$
   (ii) $\frac{\pi}{4}$
   (iii) $\frac{\pi}{3}$
   (iv) $\frac{4\pi}{3}$
   (v) $\frac{7\pi}{8}$.

4. Express in degrees the following angles in radians:
   (i) 1^c
   (ii) 2^c
   (iii) 3^c
   (iv) 3.14^c
   (v) 7^c.

2

Mensuration of a Circle

Length of Arc

The circumference of the circle equals $2\pi r$, that is, the angle subtended is $2\pi^c$ or $360°$. If an angle x is subtended, the length of arc will be a portion of the circumference.

Let s be the length of an arc, then

$$s = 2\pi r\left(\frac{x}{2\pi}\right) = rx.$$

Let r be expressed in metres and the angle in radians (a number), then the length of arc will be in metres. For this expression $s = rx$, x cannot be measured in degrees.

Area of a Sector

The area enclosed by the two radii OA and OB, and the arc AB is called **a sector**.

Let A_1 be the area of a sector OAB of arc AB subtending an angle x at the centre O.

$$A_1 = \text{area of sector} = \pi r^2\left(\frac{x}{2\pi}\right) = \text{area of circle}\left(\frac{x}{2\pi}\right).$$

$$A_1 = \text{area of sector} = \frac{1}{2}r^2 x.$$

If $x = 2\pi$, then the area of the sector is that of the whole circle.

$$A = r^2\frac{2\pi}{2} = \pi r^2.$$

Let A_1 be the minor sector of the circle and $A_2 = r^2\,\frac{(2\pi - x)}{2}$ the major sector of the circle.

$$A = A_1 + A_2 = \frac{1}{2}r^2 x + \frac{1}{2}r^2(2\pi - x)$$

$$= \pi r^2 = \text{area of circle.}$$

Area of a Segment

The hatched area is called 'a segment'. The chord AB divides the circle into two segments, the minor segment and the major segment.

If S_1 is the area of the minor segment and S_2 is the area of the major segment then $S_1 + S_2 = A_1 + A_2 =$ area of the circle A.

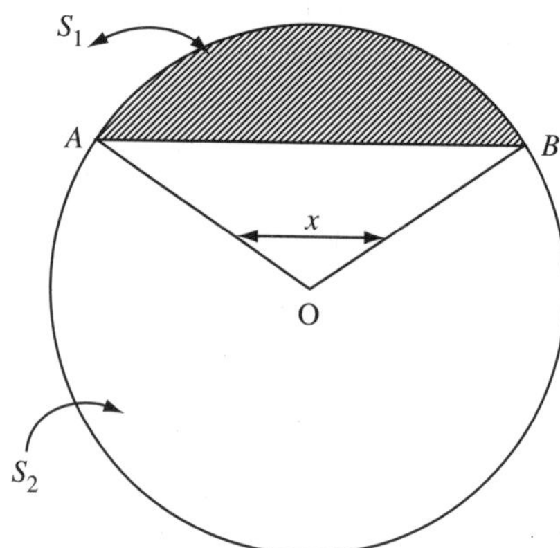

Fig. 2-I/6 Minor and major segments.

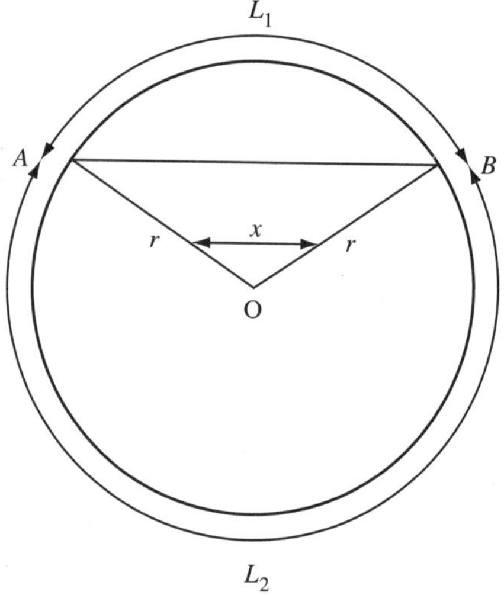

Fig. 2-I/7 Minor and major arcs.

Area of minor segment
$= A_1$ area of minor sector − area of the triangle.

$S_1 = A_1 - \frac{1}{2} r^2 \sin x$; where Δ_1

$= \text{area of triangle} = \frac{1}{2} r^2 \sin x,$

$S_1 = A_1 - \Delta_1.$

Consider the two segments S_1 and S_2. A problem of general interest is to find the angle x such that the ratio $\frac{S_1}{S_2} = K$ where $K < 1$.

WORKED EXAMPLE 2

A chord AB divides a circle of radius r and centre O, into two segments S_1 and S_2.

(i) If $K = \frac{1}{2}$, show that $\sin x = x - \frac{2\pi}{3}$

(ii) If $K = \frac{1}{3}$, show that $\sin x = x - \frac{2\pi}{4}$

(iii) If $K = \frac{1}{4}$, show that $\sin x = x - \frac{2\pi}{5}$

(iv) If $K = \frac{1}{5}$, show that $\sin x = x - \frac{2\pi}{6}$

(v) If $K = \frac{1}{n}$, show that $\sin x = x - \frac{2\pi}{(n+1)}$.

Solution 2

(i) $K = \frac{1}{2}$ $\qquad \frac{(x - \sin x)}{(2\pi - x) + \sin x} = \frac{1}{2}$

$2x - 2\sin x = 2\pi - x + \sin x$

$3 \sin x = 3x - 2\pi$

$$\boxed{\sin x = x - \frac{2\pi}{3}}$$

(ii) If $K = \frac{1}{3}$,

$$\frac{1}{3} = \frac{\frac{r^2 x}{2} - \frac{(r^2 \sin x)}{2}}{r^2 \frac{(2\pi - x)}{2} - \frac{r^2 \sin (2\pi - x)}{2}}$$

$$= \frac{x - \sin x}{(2\pi - x) - \sin (2\pi - x)}$$

$2\pi - x + \sin x = 3x - 3\sin x$

$4 \sin x = 4x - 2\pi$

$$\boxed{\sin x = x - \frac{\pi}{2}}$$

where x is the angle of the minor sector subtended at O and $(2\pi - x)$ is the angle of the major sector subtended at O.

(iii) If $K = \frac{1}{4}$, $\qquad \frac{(x - \sin x)}{\{(2\pi - x) + \sin x\}} = \frac{1}{4}$

$4x - 4\sin x = 2\pi - x + \sin x$

$5x - 2\pi = 5 \sin x$

$$\boxed{\sin x = x - \frac{2\pi}{5}}$$

(iv) If $K = \frac{1}{5}$, $\qquad \frac{(x - \sin x)}{\{(2\pi - x) + \sin x)\}} = \frac{1}{5}$

therefore $2\pi - x + \sin x = 5x - 5\sin x$
$6x - 2\pi = 6 \sin x$

$$\boxed{\sin x = x - \frac{\pi}{3}}$$

(v) If $K = \frac{1}{n}$, $\qquad \frac{(x - \sin x)}{\{(2\pi - x) + \sin x)\}} = \frac{1}{n}$

$nx - n \sin x = 2\pi - x + \sin x$

$(n+1)x - 2\pi = (n+1) \sin x$

$$\boxed{\sin x = x - \frac{2\pi}{(n+1)}}$$

WORKED EXAMPLE 3

A chord AB divides a circle, of radius r and centre O, into two segments. The perimeter of the major segment is $7r$ and the angle AOB is x radians.
Find a relationship between $\sin \frac{x}{2}$ and x.

Solution 3

The major segment is shown in Fig. 2-I/6 hatched.

The major arc AB has a length of $(2\pi - x)r$.

The perimeter of the major segment

$$= (2\pi - x)r + AB = (2\pi - x)r + 2r \sin \frac{x}{2} = 7r.$$

$2\pi - x + 2 \sin \frac{x}{2} = 7 \qquad 2 \sin \frac{x}{2} = 7 - 2\pi + x$

Therefore $\boxed{\sin \frac{x}{2} = \frac{7}{2} - \pi + \frac{x}{2}}$

Worked Example 4

Two points A and B are on the circumference of a circle with centre O.

The tangent to the circle at A meets OB produced at Q.

The angle AOQ is $2x$ radians and the length of the line OQ is equal to the perimeter of the sector AOB.

Show that $\dfrac{\sec 2x}{2} = x + 1$.

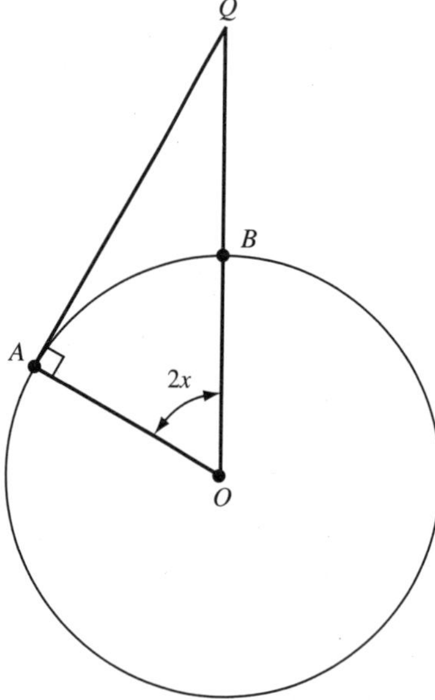

Fig. 2-I/8 Tangent to the circle at A.

Solution 4

$$\cos 2x = \frac{r}{OQ} = \frac{r}{(2rx + 2r)}$$

$$\sec 2x = 2x + 2 \qquad \frac{1}{2}\sec 2x = x + 1.$$

Worked Example 5

An arc AB of a circle subtends an angle of $2x$ radians at the centre O.

The length of the arc is S and the length of the chord AB is l.

If $\dfrac{l}{S} = \dfrac{5}{8}$, show that $x = \dfrac{8 \sin x}{5}$.

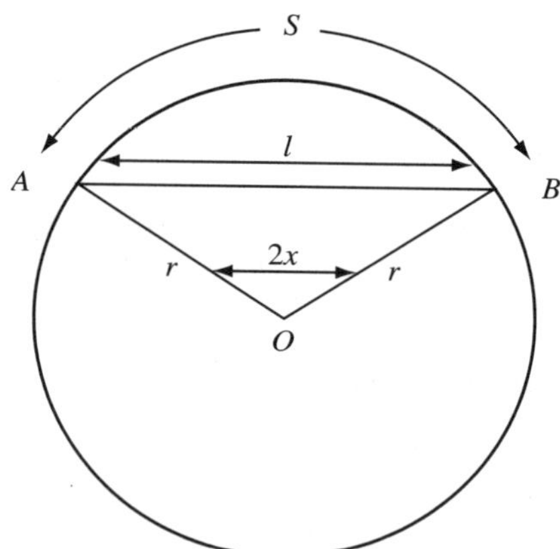

Fig. 2-I/9 Length of arc and length of chord.

Solution 5

$S = r2x$ and $l = 2r \sin x$, therefore

$$\frac{l}{S} = \frac{2r \sin x}{2rx} = \frac{5}{8} \qquad \boxed{x = \frac{8}{5}\sin x}$$

Worked Example 6

Two circles intersect orthogonally at A and B, the centres are C_1 and C_2, and their corresponding radii are r_1 and $r_2 (r_1 > r_2)$.

Determine the area enclosed by the two circles and the perimeter of the loop.

If $r_1 = 12$ m and $r_2 = 5$ m, determine the area enclosed and the perimeter of the loop of this area.

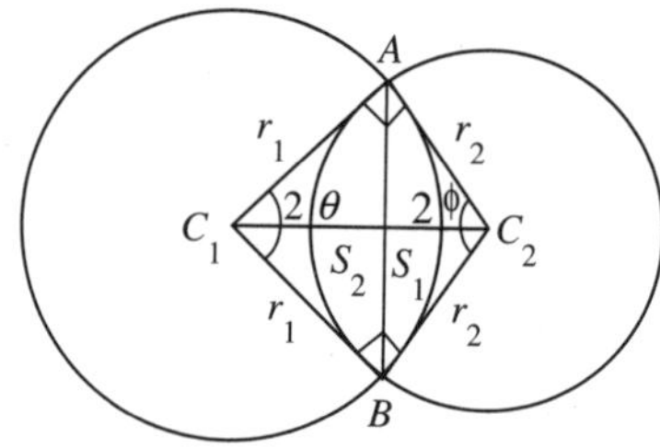

Fig. 2-I/10 Circles intersecting orthogonally.

Solution 6

Referring to Fig. 2-I/10

The right angled triangle C_1AC_2 has $r_2{}^2 + r_1{}^2 = C_1C_2{}^2$, $\tan \Phi = \dfrac{r_1}{r_2}$ and $\tan \Theta = \dfrac{r_2}{r_1}$

$\Phi = \tan^{-1}\left(\frac{r_1}{r_2}\right)$ and $\Theta = 90° - \Phi$.

The area of the segment

S_1 = area of sector − area of triangle

$= \frac{1}{2}r_1^2\, 2\Theta - \frac{1}{2}r_1^2 \sin 2\Theta.$

The area of the segment $S_2 = \frac{1}{2}r_2^2 2\Phi - \frac{1}{2}r_2^2 \sin 2\Phi.$

The area enclosed by the two circles

$= \pi r_1^2 + \pi r_2^2 - (S_1 + S_2).$

The area enclosed by the two circles

$$= \pi r_1^2 - \frac{1}{2}r_1^2\, 2\Theta + \frac{1}{2}r_1^2 \sin 2\Theta + \pi r_2^2$$

$$- \frac{1}{2}r_2^2\, 2\Phi + \frac{1}{2}r_2^2 \sin\, 2\Phi.$$

The arc subtending the 2Φ angle $= r_2 2\Phi$.

The arc subtending the 2Θ angle $= r_1 2\Theta$.

The perimeter of the loop

$= 2\pi r_1 - 2r_1\Theta - 2r_2\Phi + 2\pi r_2.$

The numerical value of the area

$$\pi 12^2 + \pi 5^2 - \frac{1}{2}12^2 2\Theta - \frac{1}{2}5^2 2\Phi + \frac{1}{2}12^2 \sin 2\Theta$$

$$+ \frac{1}{2}5^2 \sin 2\Phi$$

$\tan\Phi = \frac{12}{5}$ hence $\Phi = 67°22'\,48'' = 1.176^c$ and

$\Theta = 90° - 67°22'48'' = 22°37'\,12'' = 0.395^c$

$$\text{area} = \pi 12^2 + \pi 5^2 - 144\Theta - 25\Phi + 72\sin 2\Theta$$

$$+ 12.5 \sin 2\Phi$$

$$= 144\pi + 25\pi - 144 \times 0.395 - 25 \times 1.176$$

$$+ 72 \sin 45.23° + 12.5 \sin 134.77$$

$$= 169\pi - 56.88 - 29.44 + 51.11 + 8.874$$

$$= 504.6 = 505\,\text{m}^2.$$

The numerical value of the perimeter:

$$2\pi r_1 + 2\pi r_2 - 2r_1\Theta - 2r_2\Phi$$

$$= 2\pi 12 + 2\pi 5 - 2 \times 12 \times 0.395 - 2 \times 5 \times 1.176$$

$$= 24\pi + 10\pi - 9.48 - 11.76$$

$$= 85.57 \approx 85.6\,\text{m}.$$

Exercises 2

1. Find the angle in radians subtended at the centre of a circle of radius 10 cm by a chord of length

   (i) 1 cm

   (ii) 5 cm

   (iii) 10 cm.

   Express your answer to the nearest four decimal places.

2. Find the length of arc of a circle of radius 12 cm which subtends an angle at the centre of:

   (i) 45°

   (ii) $\frac{\pi}{3}$

   (iii) 95°

   (iv) $\frac{3\pi}{2}$

   (v) 312°.

   Express your answer to the nearest three decimal places and in cm.

3. An arc of a circle of radius 15 cm subtends an angle of

   (i) $\frac{7\pi}{6}$

   (ii) $\frac{\pi}{6}$

   (iii) $\frac{\pi}{3}$.

   Calculate the length of the arc in each case.

   Express your answer in cm to three significant figures.

4. Calculate the area of a sector of a circle of radius 5 cm subtending an angle of

   (i) 30°

   (ii) 44°

   (iii) $\frac{\pi}{4}$

   (iv) $\frac{3\pi}{4}$

   (v) 307°.

   Express your answer in cm^2 to three significant figures.

5. The area of a sector of a circle of 7 cm radius is $5\pi\ \text{cm}^2$.
   Calculate the angle in radians subtended to three decimal places.

6. A belt goes round two wheels as shown in Fig. 2-I/11 of radii 10 cm and 5 cm whose centres are 25 cm apart. Calculate the length of the belt to 3 decimal places, and hence to three significant figures.

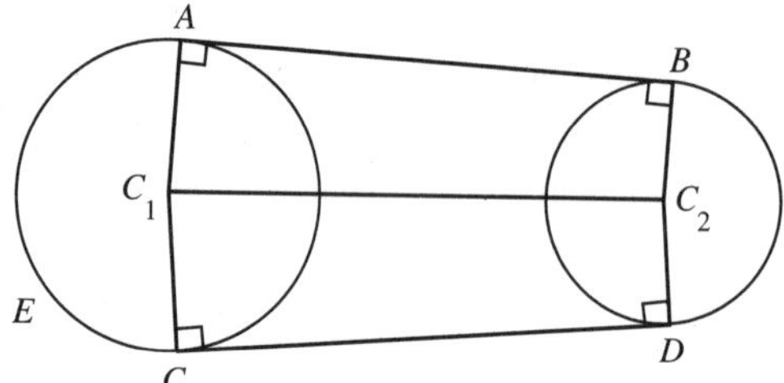

Fig. 2-I/11 A belt around 2 wheels
$BC_2 = 5$ cm $AC_1 = 10$ cm.

7. A wheel of radius 5 cm is rotating at 500 revolutions per minute. Calculate the speed of the wheel.

8. A sector of a circle of radius 10 cm has an area of 150 cm^2.

   Find the length of the arc of the sector in cm.

9. AB is an arc of length 15 cm in a circle of radius 8 cm.

   Find the area of the sector, in cm.

10. A sector of a circle of radius 12 cm has an area of 200 cm^2.
    Calculate the perimeter of the sector.

11. AP and BP are tangents at A and B which are points on the circumference of a circle of radius 5 cm.

    If the angle APB is 36°, calculate:-

    (i) the length of the arc AB subtended by the angle APB;

    (ii) the area enclosed by the tangents and the arc AB.

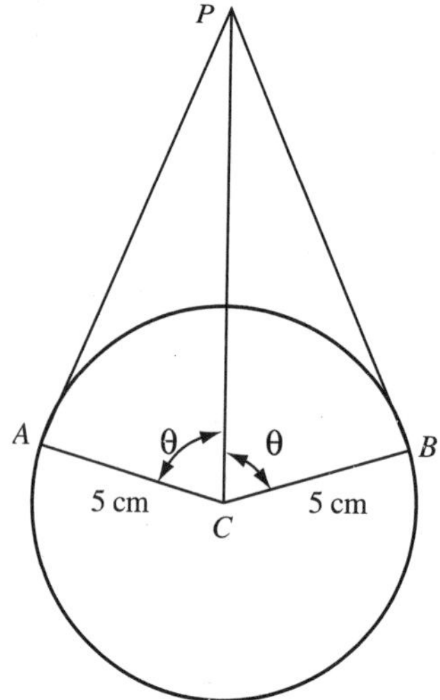

Fig. 2-I/12 Tangents at A and B

12. Referring to Fig. 2-I/13.
    (i) Calculate the length of the common chord:
    (ii) Calculate the hatched area:
    (iii) Calculate the perimeter of the inner loop and the perimeter of the outer loop.

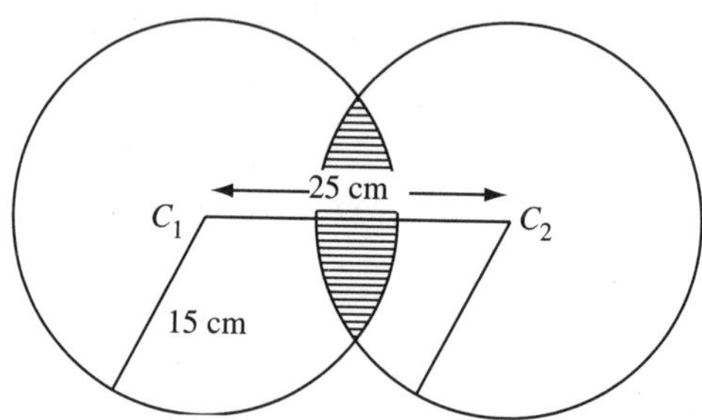

Fig. 2-I/13 Two intersecting circles.

13. A chord AB of length 1 cm divides a circle of radius 3 cm into 2 segments.
    Calculate the area of the minor and major segments.

3

The Basic Trigonometric Functions

The sine, cosine, tangent, cotangent, secant, cosecant.

Consider the right-angled triangle where c is the hypotenuse, the side opposite the right angle, the largest side of the triangle, side b is adjacent to the angle x and a is the opposite side to the angle x.
The six basic trigonometric functions are:

$$\text{sine } x = \sin x = \frac{a}{c}$$

$$= \frac{\text{the side opposite to angle } x}{\text{hypotenuse of the right-angle triangle}}.$$

$$\text{cosine } x = \cos x = \frac{b}{c}$$

$$= \frac{\text{the side adjacent to angle } x}{\text{hypotenuse of the right-angle triangle}}.$$

$$\boxed{\tan x = \frac{\sin x}{\cos x}}$$

$$\text{tangent } x = \tan x = \frac{a}{b} = \frac{\text{opposite}}{\text{adjacent}}$$

$$\text{cotangent } x = \cot x = \frac{\text{adjacent}}{\text{opposite}}$$

$$\boxed{\cot x = \frac{\cos x}{\sin x}}$$

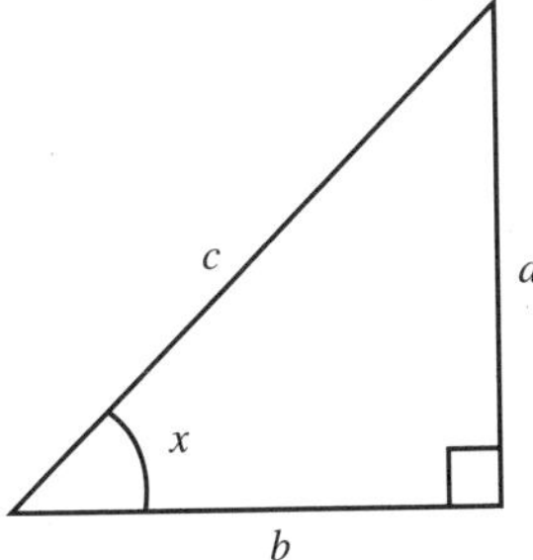

Fig. 2-I/14 The right angled triangle

$$\text{secant } x = \sec x = \frac{c}{b} = \frac{\text{hypotenuse}}{\text{adjacent}}$$

$$\text{cosecant } x = \text{cosec } x = \frac{c}{a} = \frac{\text{hypotenuse}}{\text{opposite}}.$$

Each of the above ratios is independent of the triangle, and depends only on the value of the angle x.

$$\sin x = \frac{1}{\text{cosec } x} \qquad \text{cosec } x = \frac{1}{\sin x}$$

$$\cos x = \frac{1}{\sec x} \qquad \sec x = \frac{1}{\cos x}$$

$$\tan x = \frac{1}{\cot x} \qquad \cot x = \frac{1}{\tan x}.$$

The reciprocals of sine, cosine and tangent are the cosecant, secant and cotangent respectively.

From the above, we have:

$\sin x \text{ cosec } x = 1$

$\sec x \cos x = 1$

$\cot x \tan x = 1.$

Where $OA = 1$, $\sin x = \frac{AB}{1}$

therefore $\boxed{AB = \sin x}$

$\cos x = \frac{OB}{1}$ therefore $\boxed{OB = \cos x}$

Two perpendicular lines are drawn to intersect at O, the origin of the cartesian set, ox and oy are the positive x and y axes, that is to the right of O and up from O respectively and ox and oy, are the negative x and y axes, that is, to the left of O and down from O, respectively. Any length along the positive OB measures the cosine of the angle x, i.e. $0^c \le x \le \frac{\pi}{2}^c$ and $\left(3\frac{\pi}{2}\right)^c \le x \le (2\pi)^c$

and any length along the negative OB measures thc cosine of the angle x

i.e. $\left(\frac{\pi}{2}\right)^c \le x \le \left(3\frac{\pi}{2}\right)^c$.

The cosine is positive when the angle lies in the first and fourth quadrants.
The cosine is negative when the angle lies in the second and third quadrants.

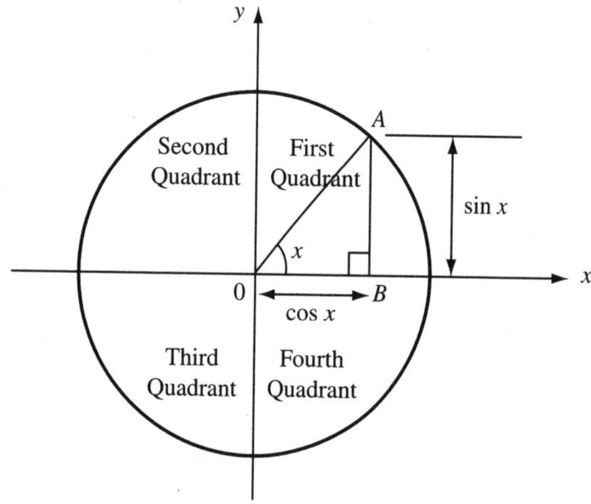

Fig. 2-I/15 The unit radius circle

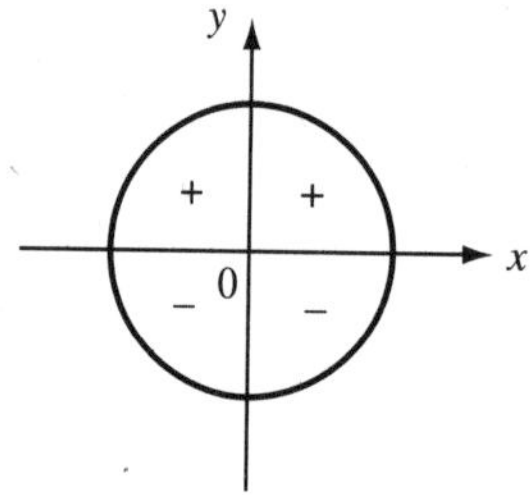

Fig. 2-I/16 sine

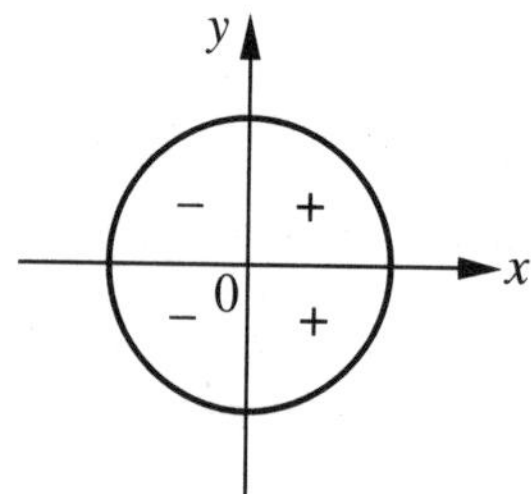

Fig. 2-I/17 cosine

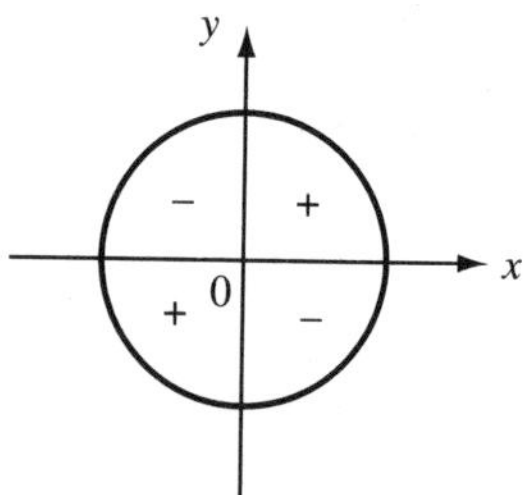

Fig. 2-I/18 tangent

The right-angled triangle and the unit radius circle are extremely useful in finding the various trigonometric functions.

Worked Example 7

Given that cosec $\Theta = \frac{25}{7}$, evaluate the trigonometric functions of $\sin\Theta, \cos\Theta, \cot\Theta$, $\sec\Theta$ and $\tan\Theta$, without the use of a calculator or trigonometric tables.

Solution 7

By definition of cosec $\Theta = \frac{25}{7}$, where the hypotenuse is 25 and the opposite side 7, using Pythagoras, the adjacent side is 24.

$$b^2 = c^2 - a^2 = 25^2 - 7^2 = 32 \times 18 \text{ or } b = 24.$$

$$\sin\Theta = \frac{7}{25} \qquad \sec\Theta = \frac{25}{24}$$

$$\cos\Theta = \frac{24}{25} \qquad \cot\Theta = \frac{24}{7}$$

$$\tan\Theta = \frac{7}{24}.$$

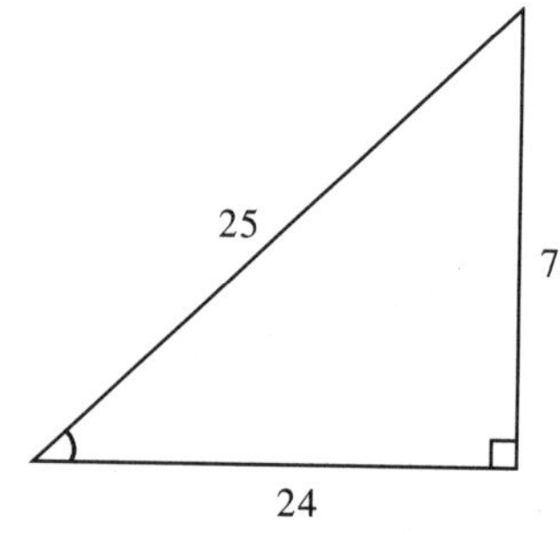

Fig. 2-I/19 Right angled triangle

ANGLE Θ IN DEGREES (∘)	ANGLE Θ IN RADIANS (C)	sin Θ	cos Θ	tan Θ	cot Θ	sec Θ	cosecΘ
0	0	0	1	0	∞	1.000	∞
30	$\frac{\pi}{6}$	$0.5\left(\frac{1}{2}\right)$	$0.866\left(\frac{\sqrt{3}}{2}\right)$	$0.577\left(\frac{1}{\sqrt{3}}\right)$	$1.732\left(\sqrt{3}\right)$	1.155	2
45	$\frac{\pi}{4}$	$0.707\left(\frac{1}{\sqrt{2}}\right)$	$0.707\left(\frac{1}{\sqrt{2}}\right)$	1	1	1.414	1.414
60	$\frac{\pi}{3}$	$0.866\left(\frac{\sqrt{3}}{2}\right)$	$0.5\left(\frac{1}{2}\right)$	$1.732\left(\sqrt{3}\right)$	$0.577\left(\frac{1}{\sqrt{3}}\right)$	2.000	1.155
90	$\frac{\pi}{2}$	1	0	∞	0	∞	1
120	$\frac{2\pi}{3}$	$0.866\left(\frac{\sqrt{3}}{2}\right)$	$-0.5\left(\frac{-1}{2}\right)$	$-1.732\left(-\sqrt{3}\right)$	$-0.577\left(\frac{-1}{\sqrt{3}}\right)$	−2.000	1.155
135	$\frac{3\pi}{4}$	$0.707\left(\frac{1}{\sqrt{2}}\right)$	$-0.707\left(\frac{-1}{\sqrt{2}}\right)$	−1	−1	−1.414	1.414
150	$\frac{5\pi}{6}$	$0.5\left(\frac{1}{2}\right)$	$-0.866\left(\frac{-\sqrt{3}}{2}\right)$	$-0.577\left(\frac{-1}{\sqrt{3}}\right)$	$-1.732(-\sqrt{3})$	−1.155	2

ANGLE Θ IN DEGREES (∘)	ANGLE Θ IN RADIANS (C)	sin Θ	cos Θ	tan Θ	cot Θ	sec Θ	cosec Θ
180	π	0	−1	0	∞	−1	∞
210	$\frac{7\pi}{6}$	$-0.5\left(\frac{-1}{2}\right)$	$-0.866\left(\frac{-\sqrt{3}}{2}\right)$	$0.577\left(\frac{1}{\sqrt{3}}\right)$	$1.732\left(\sqrt{3}\right)$	−1.155	−2
225	$\frac{5\pi}{4}$	$-0.707\left(\frac{-1}{\sqrt{2}}\right)$	$-0.707\left(\frac{-1}{\sqrt{2}}\right)$	1	1	−1.414	−1.414
240	$\frac{4\pi}{3}$	$-0.866\left(\frac{-\sqrt{3}}{2}\right)$	$-0.5\left(\frac{-1}{2}\right)$	$1.732\left(\sqrt{3}\right)$	$0.577\left(\frac{1}{\sqrt{3}}\right)$	−2.000	−1.155
270	$\frac{3\pi}{2}$	−1	0	∞	0	∞	−1
300	$\frac{5\pi}{3}$	$-0.866\left(\frac{-\sqrt{3}}{2}\right)$	$+0.5\left(\frac{1}{2}\right)$	$-1.732(-\sqrt{3})$	$-0.577\left(\frac{-1}{\sqrt{3}}\right)$	2.000	−1.155
315	$\frac{7\pi}{4}$	$-0.707\left(\frac{-1}{\sqrt{2}}\right)$	$+0.707\left(\frac{1}{\sqrt{2}}\right)$	−1	−1	1.414	−1.414
330	$\frac{11\pi}{6}$	$-0.5\left(\frac{-1}{2}\right)$	$+0.866\left(\frac{\sqrt{3}}{2}\right)$	$-0.577\left(\frac{-1}{\sqrt{3}}\right)$	$-1.732\left(-\sqrt{3}\right)$	1.155	−2
360	2π	0	1	∞	0	1.000	∞

WORKED EXAMPLE 8

If $\sin\Theta = \frac{1}{3}$ and the angle is obtuse, determine $\cos\Theta$, $\tan\Theta$, $\sec\Theta$, $\cot\Theta$, $\operatorname{cosec}\Theta$.

Solution 8

The adjacent side $b = \sqrt{c^2 - a^2} = \sqrt{9-1} = 2\sqrt{2}$

$$\cos\Theta = -\frac{2\sqrt{2}}{3} \quad \sec\Theta = -\frac{3}{2\sqrt{2}} \quad \operatorname{cosec}\Theta = 3$$

$$\tan\Theta = -\frac{1}{2\sqrt{2}} \quad \cot\Theta = -2\sqrt{2}.$$

Since the angle is obtuse, it lies in the second quadrant where the cosine, secant, cotangent, tangent are negative and cosecant is positive.

The sine of an angle is measured along AB where it is positive above the x-axis and is also measured along AB where it is negative below the x-axis.

The sine of an angle is positive when the angle lies in the first and second quadrants and the sine of an angle is negative when the angle lies in the third and fourth quadrants.

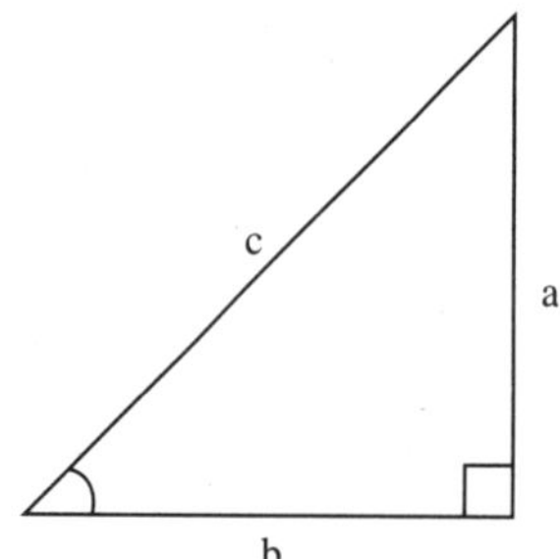

Fig. 2-I/20 Right angled triangle

Complementary Angles

In the right-angled triangle ABC the sum of the angles A and B is $90°$, $x + 90° - x = 90°$, and the angles are called *complementary angles*.

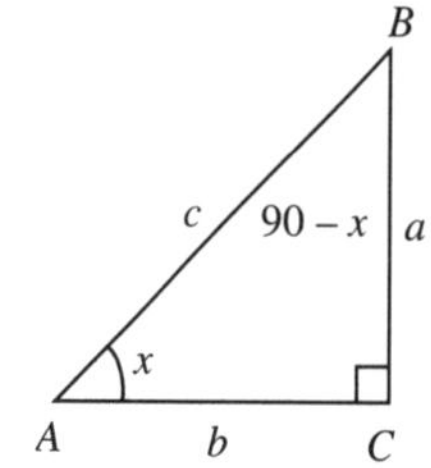

Fig. 2-I/21 Complementary angles.

The complement of angle x is therefore $90° - x$ and the complement of angle $90° - x$ is therefore x.

$$\sin(90° - x) = \frac{b}{c} = \cos x$$

$$\sec(90° - x) = \frac{c}{a} = \operatorname{cosec} x$$

$$\cos(90° - x) = \frac{a}{c} = \sin x$$

$$\cot(90° - x) = \frac{a}{b} = \tan x$$

$$\tan(90° - x) = \frac{b}{a} = \cot x$$

$$\operatorname{cosec}(90° - x) = \frac{c}{b} = \sec x.$$

Therefore,

cosine of any angle

= sine of its complement;

cotangent of any angle

= tangent of its complement

cosecant of any angle

= secant of its complement.

$\sin(-x) = -\sin x$ $\quad$ $\sin(180° - x) = \sin x$

$\cos(-x) = \cos x$ $\quad$ $\cos(180° - x) = -\cos x$

$\tan(-x) = -\tan x$ $\quad$ $\tan(180° - x) = -\tan x$

$\cot(-x) = -\cot x$ $\quad$ $\cot(180° - x) = -\cot x$

$\sin(90° - x) = \cos x$ $\quad$ $\sin(180° + x) = -\sin x$

$\cos(90° - x) = \sin x$ $\quad$ $\cos(180° + x) = -\cos x$

$\tan(90° - x) = \cot x$ $\quad$ $\tan(180° + x) = \tan x$

$\cot(90° - x) = \tan x$ $\quad$ $\cot(180° + x) = \cot x$

$\sin(90° + x) = \cos x$ $\quad$ $\sin(270° - x) = -\cos x$

$\cos(90° + x) = -\sin x$ $\quad$ $\cos(270° - x) = -\sin x$

$\tan(90° + x) = -\cot x$ $\quad$ $\tan(270° - x) = \cot x$

$\cot(90° + x) = -\tan x$ $\quad$ $\cot(270° - x) = \tan x.$

Useful triangles for remembering the values of sin 30°, cos 30°, tan 30°, cos 45°, sin 45° etc.

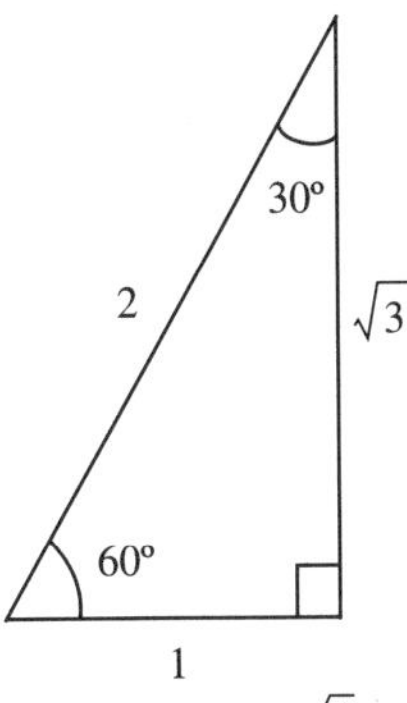

Fig. 2-I/22 $\sin 60° = \dfrac{\sqrt{3}}{2} = \cos 30°$

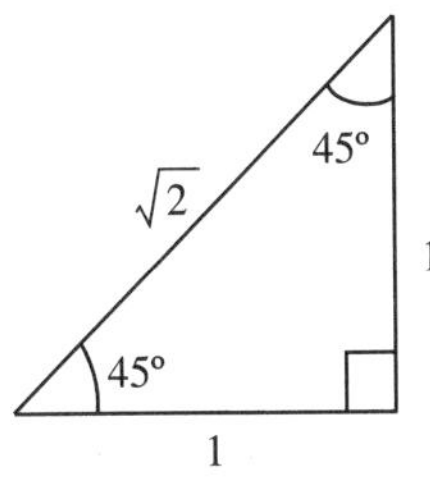

Fig. 2-I/23 $\sin 45° = \cos 45° = \dfrac{1}{\sqrt{2}}$

Worked Example 9

If $\sin\alpha = \frac{3}{5}$, and α lies in the second quadrant, find the values of the following:

(i) $\cot\alpha - \operatorname{cosec}\alpha$
(ii) $\tan\alpha + \cos\alpha$
(iii) $\sec\alpha - \sin\alpha$
(iv) $\tan\alpha + \cot\alpha$
(v) $\sec\alpha + \operatorname{cosec}\alpha$.

Solution 9

(i) $\cot\alpha - \operatorname{cosec}\alpha = \dfrac{\cos\alpha}{\sin\alpha} - \dfrac{1}{\sin\alpha} = \dfrac{-\frac{4}{5}}{\frac{3}{5}}$

$$-\frac{1}{\frac{3}{5}} = -\frac{4}{3} - \frac{5}{3} = -3.$$

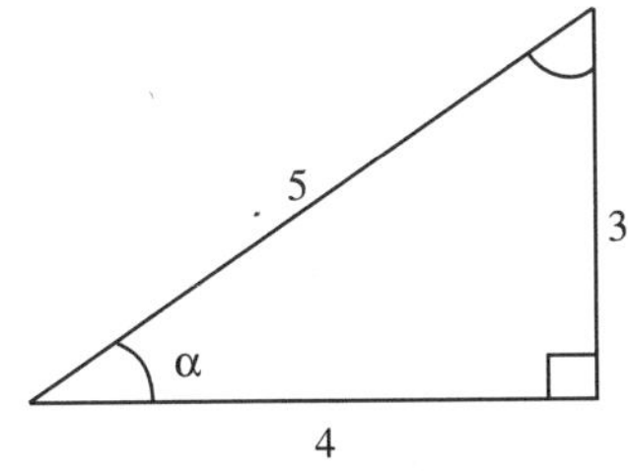

Fig. 2-I/24 $\sin\alpha = \dfrac{3}{5}$

(ii) $\tan\alpha + \cos\alpha$

$$= \frac{\sin\alpha}{\cos\alpha} + \cos\alpha = \frac{\frac{3}{5}}{\frac{-4}{5}} + \left(\frac{-4}{5}\right)$$

$$= -\frac{3}{4} - \frac{4}{5} = -\frac{15}{20} - \frac{16}{20} = -\frac{31}{20}.$$

(iii) $\sec\alpha - \sin\alpha$

$$= \frac{1}{\cos\alpha} - \sin\alpha = \frac{1}{\frac{-4}{5}} - \frac{3}{5}$$

$$= -\frac{5}{4} - \frac{3}{5} = -\frac{25}{20} - \frac{12}{20} = -\frac{37}{20}.$$

(iv) $\tan\alpha + \cot\alpha$

$$= \frac{\sin\alpha}{\cos\alpha} + \frac{\cos\alpha}{\sin\alpha} = \frac{\sin^2\alpha + \cos^2\alpha}{\sin\alpha\cos\alpha}$$

$$= \frac{1}{\sin\alpha\cos\alpha} = \frac{1}{\left(\frac{3}{5}\right)\left(-\frac{4}{5}\right)} = -\frac{25}{12}.$$

(v) $\sec\alpha + \operatorname{cosec}\alpha = \dfrac{1}{\cos\alpha} + \dfrac{1}{\sin\alpha} = -\dfrac{5}{4} + \dfrac{5}{3}$

$$= \frac{-15+20}{12} = \frac{5}{12}.$$

Worked Example 10

Write all the angles between 720° and 1080° which have the same:

(i) cosine as 60°
(ii) sine as 30°
(iii) tan as 45°
(iv) secant as 60°
(v) cosecant as 45°.

Solution 10

The angles between 720° and 1080° are those in the third revolution.

(i) $\cos 60° = \cos 780° = \cos 1020°$

(ii) $\sin 30° = \sin 750° = \sin 870°$

(iii) $\tan 45° = \tan 765° = \tan 945°$

(iv) $\sec 60° = \dfrac{1}{\cos 60°} = \dfrac{1}{\cos 780°} = \dfrac{1}{\cos 1020°}$

(v) $\operatorname{cosec} 45^\circ = \dfrac{1}{\sin 45^\circ} = \dfrac{1}{\sin 765^\circ} = \dfrac{1}{\sin 855^\circ}$

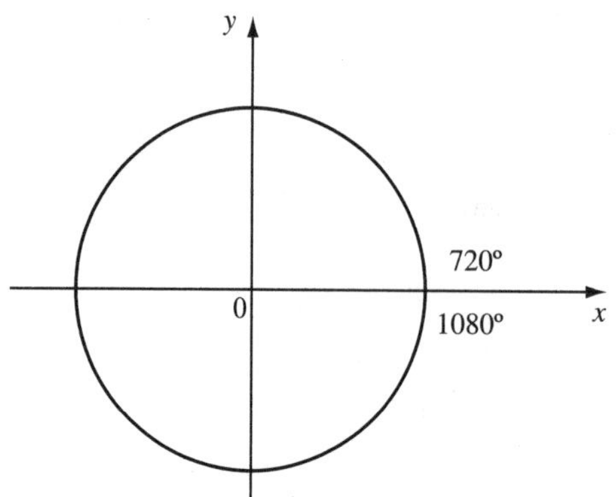

Fig. 2-I/25 Third revolution

WORKED EXAMPLE 11

Evaluate without tables or calculators:

(i) $\dfrac{\sin 315^\circ + \cos 45^\circ}{\sin 315^\circ - \cos 45^\circ}$

(ii) $\dfrac{\cos 135^\circ + \sin 30^\circ}{\cos 135^\circ - \sin 30^\circ}$

(iii) $\sin \dfrac{2\pi}{3} + \sin \dfrac{\pi}{3} + \sin \dfrac{4\pi}{3} + \sin \dfrac{5\pi}{3}$

(iv) $\tan \dfrac{\pi}{3} + \tan \dfrac{2\pi}{3} + \tan \dfrac{4\pi}{3}$

(v) $\dfrac{\tan 60^\circ + \tan 30^\circ}{\tan 60^\circ - \tan 30^\circ}$.

Solution 11

(i) $\dfrac{\sin 315^\circ + \cos 45^\circ}{\sin 315^\circ - \cos 45^\circ} = \dfrac{-\dfrac{1}{\sqrt{2}} + \dfrac{1}{\sqrt{2}}}{-\dfrac{1}{\sqrt{2}} - \dfrac{1}{\sqrt{2}}} = 0$

(ii) $\dfrac{\cos 135^\circ + \sin 30^\circ}{\cos 135^\circ - \sin 30^\circ}$

$$= \frac{-\dfrac{1}{\sqrt{2}} + \dfrac{1}{2}}{-\dfrac{1}{\sqrt{2}} - \dfrac{1}{2}} = \frac{\dfrac{1}{\sqrt{2}} - \dfrac{1}{2}}{\dfrac{1}{\sqrt{2}} + \dfrac{1}{2}} \times \frac{\dfrac{1}{2} - \dfrac{1}{\sqrt{2}}}{\dfrac{1}{2} - \dfrac{1}{\sqrt{2}}}$$

$$= \frac{\dfrac{1}{2\sqrt{2}} - \dfrac{1}{4} - \dfrac{1}{2} + \dfrac{1}{2\sqrt{2}}}{\dfrac{1}{4} - \dfrac{1}{2}}$$

$$= \frac{\dfrac{1}{\sqrt{2}} - \dfrac{3}{4}}{\dfrac{-1}{4}} = \frac{\dfrac{4 - 3\sqrt{2}}{4\sqrt{2}}}{-\dfrac{1}{4}} = \frac{3\sqrt{2} - 4}{\sqrt{2}}$$

$$= 3 - \left(\frac{4}{\sqrt{2}}\right)\left(\frac{\sqrt{2}}{\sqrt{2}}\right) = 3 - 2\sqrt{2}.$$

(iii) $\sin \dfrac{2\pi}{3} + \sin \dfrac{\pi}{3} + \sin \dfrac{4\pi}{3} + \sin \dfrac{5\pi}{3}$

$$= \frac{\sqrt{3}}{2} + \frac{\sqrt{3}}{2} - \frac{\sqrt{3}}{2} - \frac{\sqrt{3}}{2} = 0$$

(iv) $\tan \dfrac{\pi}{3} + \tan \dfrac{2\pi}{3} + \tan \dfrac{4\pi}{3}$

$$= \sqrt{3} - \sqrt{3} + \sqrt{3} = \sqrt{3}.$$

(v) $\dfrac{\tan 60^\circ + \tan 30^\circ}{\tan 60^\circ - \tan 30^\circ} = \dfrac{\sqrt{3} + \dfrac{1}{\sqrt{3}}}{\sqrt{3} - \dfrac{1}{\sqrt{3}}} = \dfrac{\dfrac{3+1}{\sqrt{3}}}{\dfrac{3-1}{\sqrt{3}}} = 2.$

Exercises 3

1. If $\sec x = -\frac{\sqrt{3}}{\sqrt{2}}$, find the values of $\cos x$, $\sin x$, $\operatorname{cosec} x$, $\tan x$, and $\cot x$, when x is:
   (i) in the second quadrant
   (ii) in the third quadrant.

2. If $\cot x = -\frac{1}{5}$, find the values of $\tan x$, $\sin x$, $\cos x$, $\sec x$ and $\operatorname{cosec} x$, when x is:
   (i) in the second quadrant
   (ii) in the fourth quadrant.

3. If $\operatorname{cosec} x = -\sqrt{2}$, find the values of $\sin x$, $\cos x$, $\tan x$, $\cot x$ and $\sec x$, when x is:
   (i) in the third quadrant
   (ii) in the fourth quadrant.

4. If $\tan x = 7$, find the values of $\sin x$, $\cos x$, $\sec x$, $\cot x$ and $\operatorname{cosec} x$ when x is:
   (i) in the third quadrant
   (ii) in the first quadrant.

5. If $\tan x = -\sqrt{3}$, find the values of $\sin x$, $\cos x$, $\sec x$, $\cot x$ and $\operatorname{cosec} x$ when x lies in the fourth quadrant.
6. If $\sin x = \frac{1}{2}$, find the values of $\cos x$, $\tan x$, $\operatorname{cosec} x$, $\sec x$ and $\cot x$ when x lies in the second quadrant.

7. State in which quadrants do the following exist:

   (i) $\operatorname{cosec} x$ is negative
   (ii) $\sin x$ is positive
   (iii) $\cot x$ is negative
   (iv) $\sec x$ is positive
   (v) $\cos x$ is negative
   (vi) $\tan x$ is positive.

8. Simplify the following:

   (i) $\sin(90° - \alpha)$
   (ii) $\cos(90° - \alpha)$
   (iii) $\sec(90° - \alpha)$
   (iv) $\tan(90° - \alpha)$
   (v) $\cot(90° - \alpha)$
   (vi) $\operatorname{cosec}(90° - \alpha)$

   if α is a small acute angle.

9. Simplify the following:

   (i) $\sin(90° + \alpha)$
   (ii) $\cos(90° + \alpha)$
   (iii) $\tan(90° + \alpha)$
   (iv) $\cot(90° + \alpha)$
   (v) $\sec(90° + \alpha)$
   (vi) $\operatorname{cosec}(90° + \alpha)$

   if α is a small acute angle.

10. Simplify the following:

    (i) $\sin(180° - \alpha)$
    (ii) $\cos(180° - \alpha)$
    (iii) $\tan(180° - \alpha)$
    (iv) $\cot(180° - \alpha)$
    (v) $\sec(180° - \alpha)$
    (vi) $\operatorname{cosec}(180° - \alpha)$

    if α is a small acute angle.

11. Simplify the following:

    (i) $\sin(\pi^c + \alpha)$
    (ii) $\cos(\pi^c + \alpha)$
    (iii) $\tan(\pi^c + \alpha)$
    (iv) $\cot(\pi^c + \alpha)$
    (v) $\sec(\pi^c + \alpha)$
    (vi) $\operatorname{cosec}(\pi^c + \alpha)$
    (vii) $\sin(270° - \alpha)$
    (viii) $\cos(270° - \alpha)$
    (ix) $\tan(270° - \alpha)$
    (x) $\cot(270° - \alpha)$
    (xi) $\sec(270° - \alpha)$
    (xii) $\operatorname{cosec}(270° - \alpha)$
    (xiii) $\sin\left(\frac{3\pi^c}{2} + \alpha\right)$
    (xiv) $\cos\left(\frac{3\pi^c}{2} + \alpha\right)$
    (xv) $\tan(\alpha - 270°)$
    (xvi) $\cot(\alpha + 270°)$
    (xvii) $\operatorname{cosec}\left(\alpha + \frac{3\pi^c}{2}\right)$
    (xviii) $\sec\left(\alpha + \frac{3\pi^c}{2}\right)$.

    if α is a small acute angle.

12. Simplify the following circular functions by considering the unit radius circle where $0 < \alpha < \frac{\pi}{2}$.

    (i) $\sec(3\pi^c - \alpha)$
    (ii) $\cot(\alpha + 3\pi^c)$
    (iii) $\tan\left(\frac{5\pi^c}{2} - \alpha\right)$
    (iv) $\cot\left(\alpha + \frac{\pi^c}{2}\right)$
    (v) $\cos\left(\alpha - \frac{3\pi^c}{2}\right)$
    (vi) $\sin\left(\frac{3\pi^c}{2} + \alpha\right)$
    (vii) $\operatorname{cosec}\left(\alpha + \frac{3\pi^c}{2}\right)$
    (viii) $\operatorname{cosec}\left(\alpha - \frac{5\pi^c}{2}\right)$
    (ix) $\tan\left(\alpha - \frac{\pi^c}{2}\right)$
    (x) $\sin\left(\frac{5\pi^c}{2} - \alpha\right)$.

13. Write down without using tables or calculators the value of:

    (i) $\cot \frac{3\pi}{4}$
    (ii) $\operatorname{cosec} \frac{7\pi}{4}$
    (iii) $\sin \frac{7\pi}{4}$
    (iv) $\tan \frac{5\pi}{4}$
    (v) $\cos \frac{5\pi}{3}$
    (vi) $\sin \frac{\pi}{3}$
    (vii) $\sin \frac{17\pi}{4}$.

4

The Sum and Difference of Two Angles

Compound Angles

It is convenient sometimes to express the sine of the sum of two angles in terms of the sines and cosines of the individual angles. It is required to show that $\sin(\Theta + \Phi) = \sin\Theta\cos\Phi + \sin\Phi\cos\Theta$.
Although this proof is not required for examination purposes, it is however interesting to note this proof which is somewhat tedious.
Let AOB and BOC be two angles such as Θ and Φ respectively, as shown in the diagram, and AOC be the angle $\Theta + \Phi$.

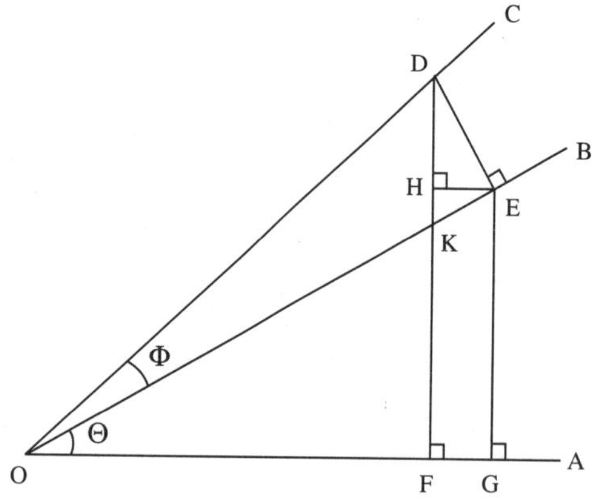

Fig. 2-I/26

From a point D on OC a perpendicular DE on OB is constructed and DF is drawn perpendicular to OA.
From E, two perpendiculars to OA and DF are dropped, EG and EH respectively.
EH is parallel to OA which is horizontal

$$\sin(\Theta + \Phi) = \frac{DF}{OD} = \frac{DH + HF}{OD} = \frac{DH + EG}{OD}$$

$$= \frac{DH}{OD} + \frac{EG}{OD} = \frac{DH}{DE}\cdot\frac{DE}{OD} + \frac{EG}{OE}\cdot\frac{OE}{OD}$$

$$= \cos\Theta\sin\Phi + \sin\Theta\cos\Phi$$

$$\cos(\Theta + \Phi) = \frac{OF}{OD} = \frac{OG - FG}{OD} = \frac{OG - HE}{OD}$$

$$= \frac{OG.OE}{OE.OD} - \frac{EH.DE}{DE.OD}$$

$\cos(\Theta + \Phi) = \cos\Theta\cos\Phi - \sin\Theta\sin\Phi$.
If Φ is negative:

$$\sin(\Theta - \Phi) = \cos\Theta\sin(-\Phi) + \sin\Theta\cos(-\Phi)$$
$$= \cos\Phi\sin\Theta - \sin\Phi\cos\Theta.$$
$$\cos(\Theta - \Phi) = \cos\Theta\cos(-\Phi) - \sin\Theta\sin(-\Phi)$$
$$= \cos\Theta\cos\Phi + \sin\Theta\sin\Phi.$$

Therefore:

$$\sin(\Theta + \Phi) = \sin\Theta\cos\Phi + \sin\Phi\cos\Theta$$
$$\sin(\Theta - \Phi) = \sin\Theta\cos\Phi - \sin\Phi\cos\Theta$$
$$\cos(\Theta + \Phi) = \cos\Theta\cos\Phi - \sin\Phi\sin\Theta$$
$$\cos(\Theta - \Phi) = \cos\Theta\cos\Phi + \sin\Phi\sin\Theta.$$

WORKED EXAMPLE 12

Find the values of $\sin 15°$, $\sin 75°$, $\cos 15°$, $\cos 75°$, $\tan 15°$ and $\tan 75°$ in surd form.

Solution 12

$$\sin 15° = \sin(45° - 30°)$$
$$= \sin 45°\cos 30° - \sin 30°\cos 45°$$
$$= \left(\frac{1}{\sqrt{2}}\right)\left(\frac{\sqrt{3}}{2}\right) - \left(\frac{1}{2}\right)\left(\frac{1}{\sqrt{2}}\right)$$
$$= \frac{\sqrt{3} - 1}{2\sqrt{2}} = \frac{\left(\sqrt{3} - 1\right)\sqrt{2}}{2\sqrt{2}\sqrt{2}} = \frac{\sqrt{6} - \sqrt{2}}{4}$$

or $\sin 15° = \cos(90° - 15°) = \cos 75° = \dfrac{\sqrt{6} - \sqrt{2}}{4}$

$$\sin 75^\circ = \sin(45^\circ + 30^\circ)$$
$$= \sin 45^\circ \cos 30^\circ + \sin 30^\circ \cos 45^\circ$$
$$= \left(\frac{1}{\sqrt{2}}\right)\left(\frac{\sqrt{3}}{2}\right) + \left(\frac{1}{2}\right)\left(\frac{1}{\sqrt{2}}\right)$$
$$= \frac{\sqrt{3}+1}{2\sqrt{2}} \cdot \frac{\sqrt{2}}{\sqrt{2}} = \frac{\sqrt{6}+\sqrt{2}}{4}$$

or $\sin 75^\circ = \cos(90^\circ - 75^\circ) = \cos 15^\circ = \dfrac{\sqrt{6}+\sqrt{2}}{4}$

$$\tan 15^\circ = \frac{\sin 15^\circ}{\cos 15^\circ}$$
$$= \frac{\frac{\sqrt{6}-\sqrt{2}}{4}}{\frac{\sqrt{6}+\sqrt{2}}{4}} = \frac{\sqrt{6}-\sqrt{2}}{\sqrt{6}+\sqrt{2}} \cdot \frac{\sqrt{6}-\sqrt{2}}{\sqrt{6}-\sqrt{2}}$$
$$= \frac{6+2-2\sqrt{12}}{4} = 2-\sqrt{3}$$

$$\tan 75^\circ = \tan(30^\circ + 45^\circ) = \frac{\tan 30^\circ + \tan 45^\circ}{1 - \tan 30^\circ \tan 45^\circ}$$
$$= \frac{\frac{1}{\sqrt{3}}+1}{1-\frac{1}{\sqrt{3}}} = \frac{1+\sqrt{3}}{\sqrt{3}-1} \cdot \frac{\sqrt{3}+1}{\sqrt{3}+1}$$
$$= \frac{\left(\sqrt{3}+1\right)^2}{2} = \frac{3+1+2\sqrt{3}}{2} = 2+\sqrt{3}$$

$\tan 75^\circ = 2+\sqrt{3}.$

Worked Example 13

Evaluate in surd forms the following:

(i) $\cos 15^\circ$
(ii) $\cos 75^\circ$
(iii) $\sin 300^\circ$
(iv) $\tan 105^\circ$
(v) $\sin 105^\circ$
(vi) $\operatorname{cosec} 75^\circ$
(vii) $\sin 75^\circ$
(viii) $\sec 105^\circ$
(ix) $\cos 105^\circ$
(x) $\sin 15^\circ$

using the expansions for $\sin(A+B)$ and/or $\cos(A+B)$ and without the use of trigonometrical tables or calculators.

Solution 13

(i) $\cos 15^\circ = \cos(60^\circ - 45^\circ)$
$$= \cos 60^\circ \cos 45^\circ + \sin 60^\circ \sin 45^\circ$$
$$= \frac{1}{2} \cdot \frac{1}{\sqrt{2}} + \frac{\sqrt{3}}{2} \cdot \frac{1}{\sqrt{2}}$$
$$= \frac{1}{2\sqrt{2}}\left(1+\sqrt{3}\right)\frac{\sqrt{2}}{\sqrt{2}} = \frac{\sqrt{2}+\sqrt{6}}{4}.$$

(ii) $\cos 75^\circ = \cos(45^\circ + 30^\circ)$
$$= \cos 45^\circ \cos 30^\circ - \sin 45^\circ \sin 30^\circ$$
$$= \frac{1}{\sqrt{2}}\left(\frac{\sqrt{3}}{2} - \frac{1}{2}\right)$$
$$= \frac{1}{2\sqrt{2}}\left(\sqrt{3}-1\right)\frac{\sqrt{2}}{\sqrt{2}} = \frac{\sqrt{6}-\sqrt{2}}{4}.$$

(iii) $\sin 300^\circ = \sin(360^\circ - 60^\circ)$
$$= \sin 360^\circ \cos 60^\circ - \sin 60^\circ \cos 360^\circ$$
$$= -\frac{\sqrt{3}}{2} \cdot 1 = -\frac{\sqrt{3}}{2}.$$

(iv) $\tan 105^\circ = \dfrac{\sin 105^\circ}{\cos 105^\circ} = \dfrac{\sin(60^\circ + 45^\circ)}{\cos(60^\circ + 45^\circ)}$
$$= \frac{\cos 45^\circ \sin 60^\circ + \sin 45^\circ \cos 60^\circ}{\cos 60^\circ \cos 45^\circ - \sin 60^\circ \sin 45^\circ}$$
$$= \frac{\frac{1}{\sqrt{2}}\left(\frac{\sqrt{3}}{2} + \frac{1}{2}\right)}{\frac{1}{\sqrt{2}}\left(\frac{1}{2} - \frac{\sqrt{3}}{2}\right)}$$
$$= \frac{1+\sqrt{3}}{1-\sqrt{3}} \times \frac{1+\sqrt{3}}{1+\sqrt{3}}$$
$$= \frac{\left(1+\sqrt{3}\right)^2}{1-3} = \frac{1+3+2\sqrt{3}}{-2}$$
$$= -\left(2+\sqrt{3}\right).$$

(v) $\sin 105^\circ = \sin(60^\circ + 45^\circ)$
$$= \sin 60^\circ \cos 45^\circ + \sin 45^\circ \cos 60^\circ$$
$$= \frac{1}{\sqrt{2}}\left(\frac{\sqrt{3}}{2} + \frac{1}{2}\right) = \frac{1}{2\sqrt{2}}\left(1+\sqrt{3}\right)\frac{\sqrt{2}}{\sqrt{2}}$$
$$= \frac{\sqrt{2}+\sqrt{6}}{4} = \cos 15^\circ.$$

(vi) $\operatorname{cosec} 75° = \dfrac{1}{\sin 75°} = \dfrac{1}{\sin(45° + 30°)}$

$$= \frac{1}{\sin 45° \cos 30° + \sin 30° \cos 45°}$$

$$= \frac{1}{\frac{1}{\sqrt{2}}\left(\frac{\sqrt{3}}{2} + \frac{1}{2}\right)}$$

$$= \frac{2\sqrt{2}}{1+\sqrt{3}} \times \frac{1-\sqrt{3}}{1-\sqrt{3}}$$

$$= \frac{2\sqrt{2} - 2\sqrt{6}}{1-3}$$

$$= \sqrt{6} - \sqrt{2}$$

Hence $\operatorname{cosec} 75° = 4 \sin 15° = 4 \cos 75°$.

(vii) $\sin 75° = \sin(45° + 30°)$

$$= \sin 45° \cos 30° + \sin 30° \cos 45°$$

$$= \frac{1}{\sqrt{2}}(\cos 30° + \sin 30°)$$

$$= \frac{1}{\sqrt{2}}\left(\frac{\sqrt{3}}{2} + \frac{1}{2}\right)$$

$$= \frac{1}{2\sqrt{2}}\left(\sqrt{3}+1\right)$$

$$= \frac{\sqrt{2}}{2\sqrt{2}\sqrt{2}}\left(\sqrt{3}+1\right)$$

$$= \frac{\sqrt{6}+\sqrt{2}}{4}.$$

(viii) $\sec 105° = \dfrac{1}{\cos 105°} = \dfrac{1}{\cos(60° + 45°)}$

$$= \frac{1}{\cos 60° \cos 45° - \sin 60° \sin 45°}$$

$$= \frac{1}{\frac{1}{2} \cdot \frac{1}{\sqrt{2}} - \frac{\sqrt{3}}{2}\,\frac{1}{\sqrt{2}}}$$

$$= \frac{1}{\frac{1}{2\sqrt{2}}\left(1-\sqrt{3}\right)}$$

$$= \frac{2\sqrt{2}}{1-\sqrt{3}} \times \frac{1+\sqrt{3}}{1+\sqrt{3}}$$

$$= \frac{2\left(\sqrt{2}+\sqrt{6}\right)}{1-3} = -\left(\sqrt{2}+\sqrt{6}\right).$$

(ix) $\cos 105° = \dfrac{1-\sqrt{3}}{2\sqrt{2}}$

$$= -\frac{1}{\left(\sqrt{2}+\sqrt{6}\right)} \times \frac{\left(\sqrt{2}-\sqrt{6}\right)}{\left(\sqrt{2}-\sqrt{6}\right)}$$

$$= \frac{\sqrt{6}-\sqrt{2}}{2-6} = \frac{\sqrt{2}-\sqrt{6}}{4}.$$

(x) $\sin 15° = \sin(60° - 45°)$

$$= \sin 60° \cos 45° - \sin 45° \cos 60°$$

$$= \frac{1}{\sqrt{2}}\left(\frac{\sqrt{3}}{2} - \frac{1}{2}\right)$$

$$= \frac{1}{2\sqrt{2}}\left(\sqrt{3}-1\right)$$

$$= \frac{\sqrt{2}}{2\sqrt{2}\sqrt{2}}\left(\sqrt{3}-1\right)$$

$$= \frac{\sqrt{6}-\sqrt{2}}{4} = -\cos 105°.$$

WORKED EXAMPLE 14

If $\sin A = \dfrac{3}{5}$ and $\cos B = \dfrac{5}{13}$, find $\sin(A+B)$, $\sin(A-B)$, $\cos(A+B)$ and $\cos(A-B)$ where A and B are acute angles.

Solution 14

$\sin(A+B) = \sin A \cos B + \sin B \cos A$

$$= \frac{3}{5} \cdot \frac{5}{13} + \frac{12}{13} \cdot \frac{4}{5} = \frac{15}{65} + \frac{48}{65} = \frac{63}{65}$$

$\sin(A+B) = \dfrac{63}{65}$.

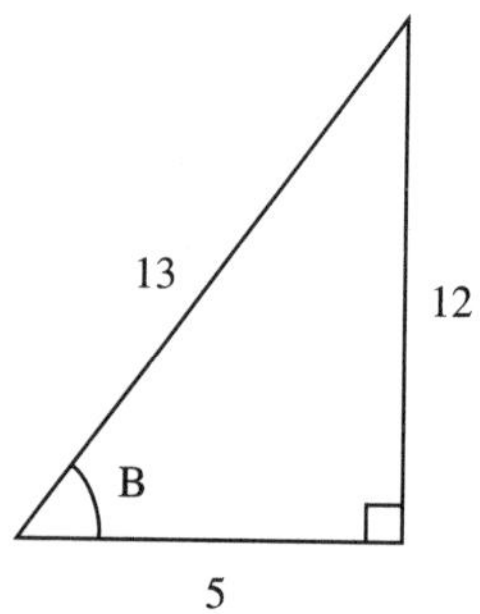

Fig. 2-I/27 $\cos B = \dfrac{5}{13}$

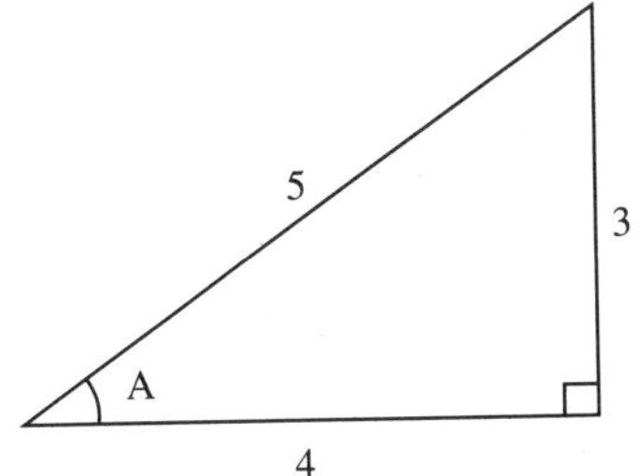

Fig. 2-I/28 $\sin A = \frac{3}{5}$

$$\sin(A - B) = \sin A \cos B - \sin B \cos A$$

$$= \frac{3}{5} \cdot \frac{5}{13} - \frac{12}{13} \cdot \frac{4}{5} = \frac{15}{65} - \frac{48}{65} = \frac{-33}{65}$$

$$\cos(A + B) = \cos A \cos B - \sin A \sin B$$

$$= \frac{4}{5} \cdot \frac{5}{13} - \frac{3}{5} \cdot \frac{12}{13} = \frac{20}{65} - \frac{36}{65} = -\frac{16}{65}$$

$$\cos(A - B) = \cos A \cos B + \sin A \sin B$$

$$= \frac{4}{5} \cdot \frac{5}{13} + \frac{3}{5} \cdot \frac{12}{13} = \frac{20}{65} + \frac{36}{65} = \frac{56}{65}.$$

Worked Example 15

Simplify the following circular functions by considering:

(a) the expansion of formulae

(b) the unit radius circle, $0 < \alpha < \frac{\pi}{2}$.

(i) $\cos\left(\frac{3\pi}{2} + \alpha\right)$

(ii) $\sin\left(\frac{3\pi}{2} + \alpha\right)$

(iii) $\operatorname{cosec}\left(\alpha - \frac{\pi}{2}\right)$

(iv) $\sec(\pi - \alpha)$

(v) $\cot\left(\frac{\pi}{2} + \alpha\right)$

(vi) $\tan\left(\frac{\pi}{2} - \alpha\right)$

(vii) $\tan\left(5\frac{\pi}{2} + \alpha\right)$

(viii) $\operatorname{cosec}\left(\frac{3\pi}{2} - \alpha\right)$

(ix) $\tan\left(\frac{\pi}{2} + \alpha\right)$

(x) $\cot(\alpha - 3\pi)$.

Solution 15

(a) (i) $\cos\left(\frac{3\pi}{2} + \alpha\right)$

$$= \cos\frac{3\pi}{2}\cos\alpha - \sin\frac{3\pi}{2}\sin\alpha$$

$$= 0 - (-1)\sin\alpha = \sin\alpha.$$

(ii) $\sin\left(\frac{3\pi}{2} + \alpha\right)$

$$= \sin\frac{3\pi}{2}\cos\alpha + \sin\alpha\cos\frac{3\pi}{2} = -\cos\alpha.$$

(iii) $\operatorname{cosec}\left(\alpha - \frac{\pi}{2}\right)$

$$= \frac{1}{\sin\left(\alpha - \frac{\pi}{2}\right)}$$

$$= \frac{1}{\sin\alpha\cos\frac{\pi}{2} - \sin\frac{\pi}{2}\cos\alpha} = -\sec\alpha$$

(iv) $\sec(\pi - \alpha)$

$$= \frac{1}{\cos(\pi - \alpha)}$$

$$= \frac{1}{\cos\pi\cos\alpha + \sin\pi\sin\alpha} = -\sec\alpha.$$

(v) $\cot\left(\frac{\pi}{2} + \alpha\right) = \frac{\cos\left(\frac{\pi}{2} + \alpha\right)}{\sin\left(\frac{\pi}{2} + \alpha\right)}$

$$= \frac{-\sin\alpha}{\cos\alpha} = -\tan\alpha$$

(vi) $\tan\left(\frac{\pi}{2} - \alpha\right) = \frac{\sin\left(\frac{\pi}{2} - \alpha\right)}{\cos\left(\frac{\pi}{2} - \alpha\right)}$

$$= \frac{\cos\alpha}{\sin\alpha} = \cot\alpha$$

(vii) $\tan\left(\frac{5\pi}{2}+\alpha\right) = \frac{\sin\left(\frac{5\pi}{2}+\alpha\right)}{\cos\left(\frac{5\pi}{2}+\alpha\right)}$

$$= \frac{\cos\alpha}{-\sin\alpha} = -\cot\alpha$$

(viii) $\operatorname{cosec}\left(\frac{3\pi}{2}-\alpha\right)$

$$= \frac{1}{\sin\left(\frac{3\pi}{2}-\alpha\right)}$$

$$= \frac{1}{\sin\frac{3\pi}{2}\cos\alpha - \sin\alpha\cos\frac{3\pi}{2}}$$

$$= \frac{1}{(-1)\cos\alpha - \sin\alpha(0)} = -\sec\alpha.$$

(ix) $\tan\left(\frac{\pi}{2}+\alpha\right) = \frac{\sin\left(\frac{\pi}{2}+\alpha\right)}{\cos\left(\frac{\pi}{2}+\alpha\right)}$

$$= \frac{\cos\alpha}{-\sin\alpha} = -\cot\alpha$$

(x) $\cot(\alpha - 3\pi) = \frac{\cos(\alpha-3\pi)}{\sin(\alpha-3\pi)}$

$$= \frac{-\cos\alpha}{-\sin\alpha} = \cot\alpha$$

(b) (i) The angles are measured anti-clockwise, $\frac{3\pi}{2}$ lies at A.

The angle $\frac{3\pi}{2}+\alpha$ lies at B.

$AB = \alpha$ or $OBC = \alpha$,

therefore $\cos\left(\frac{3\pi}{2}+\alpha\right) = OC.$

From the triangle OBC,

$OC = \sin\alpha$

$OB =$ unit radius.

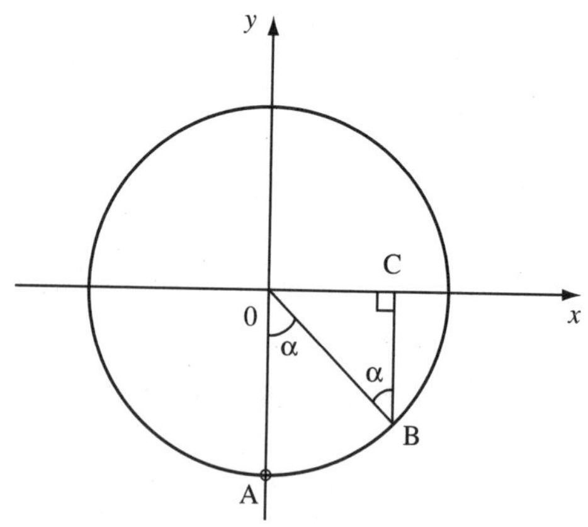

Fig. 2-I/29 $AB = OBC = \alpha$

$$\cos\left(\frac{3\pi}{2}+\alpha\right) = \sin\alpha$$

(ii) The angle $\frac{3\pi}{2}$ is measured anticlockwise from ox, it lies at A, $\frac{3\pi}{2}+\alpha$ lies at B.

$\sin\left(\frac{3\pi}{2}+\alpha\right) = CB$

$= -\cos\alpha$

since $\cos\alpha$ in the triangle OBC is equal to $\frac{BC}{OB} = BC$ which is negative.

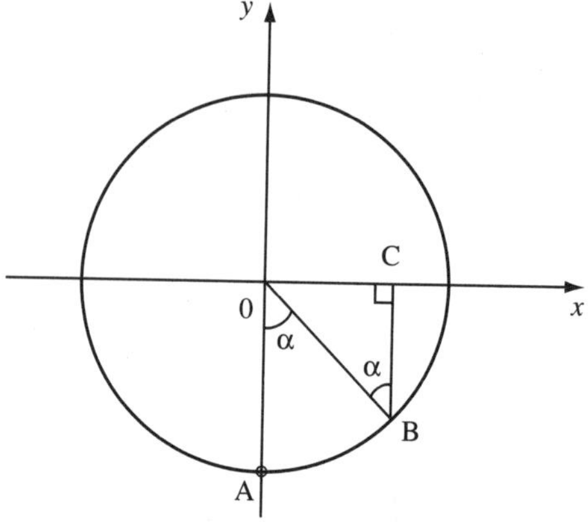

Fig. 2-I/30 $\sin\left(\frac{3\pi}{2}+\alpha\right) = -\cos\alpha$

(iii) $\operatorname{cosec}\left(\alpha - \frac{\pi}{2}\right)$

$$= \frac{1}{\sin\left(\alpha - \frac{\pi}{2}\right)}$$

$$= \frac{1}{-\cos\alpha} = -\sec\alpha.$$

The angle $\frac{-\pi}{2}$ lies at A, the angle $\alpha - \frac{\pi}{2}$ lies at B, therefore $\sin\left(\alpha - \frac{\pi}{2}\right) = -\cos\alpha$.

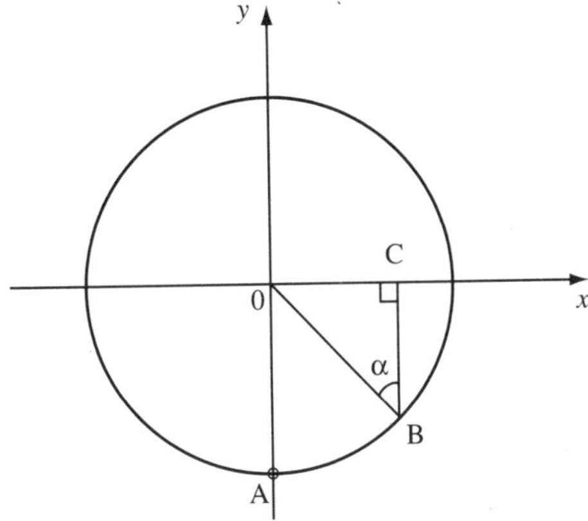

Fig. 2-I/31 $\sin\left(\alpha - \frac{\pi}{2}\right) = -\cos\alpha$

(iv)

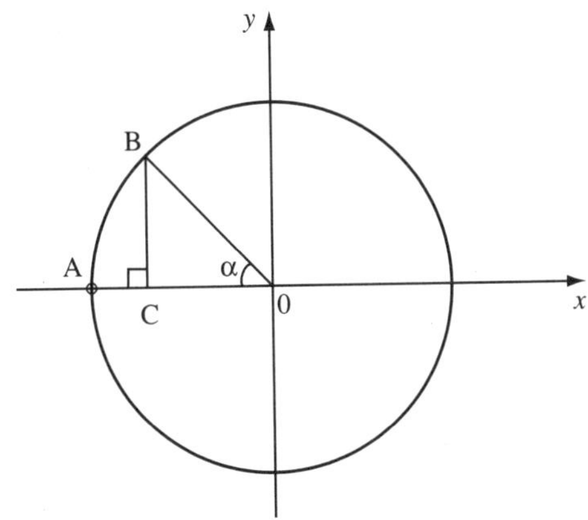

Fig. 2-I/32 $\cos(\pi - \alpha) = -\cos\alpha$

$\sec(\pi - \alpha) = -\sec\alpha$

(v)

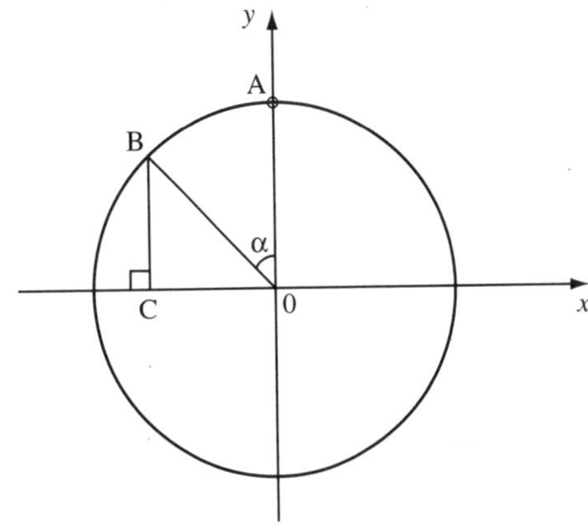

Fig. 2-I/33

$$\sin\left(\frac{\pi}{2} + \alpha\right) = \cos\alpha$$

$$\cos\left(\frac{\pi}{2} + \alpha\right) = -\sin\alpha$$

$$\cot\left(\frac{\pi}{2} + \alpha\right) = \frac{-\sin\alpha}{\cos\alpha} = -\tan\alpha$$

(vi) $\tan\left(\frac{\pi}{2} - \alpha\right) = \frac{\sin\left(\frac{\pi}{2} - \alpha\right)}{\cos\left(\frac{\pi}{2} - \alpha\right)}$

$$= \frac{\cos\alpha}{\sin\alpha} = \cot\alpha$$

The angle $\frac{\pi}{2} - \alpha$ lies at B, $\sin\left(\frac{\pi}{2} - \alpha\right) = BC = \cos\alpha$, $\cos\left(\frac{\pi}{2} - \alpha\right) = OC = \sin\alpha$ **see Fig. 2-I/34**.

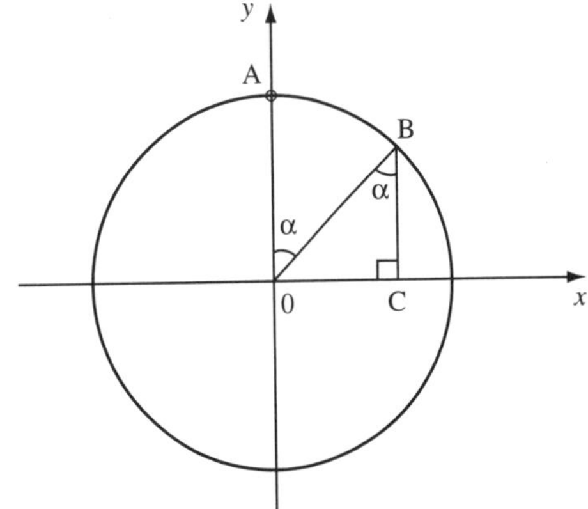

Fig. 2-I/34

$$\cos\left(\frac{\pi}{2}-\alpha\right)=\sin\alpha,$$

$$\sin\left(\frac{\pi}{2}-\alpha\right)=\cos\alpha,$$

$$\tan\left(\frac{\pi}{2}-\alpha\right)=\cot\alpha$$

(vii) $\tan\left(\frac{5\pi}{2}+\alpha\right)$

$$=\frac{\sin\left(\frac{5\pi}{2}+\alpha\right)}{\cos\left(\frac{5\pi}{2}+\alpha\right)}=\frac{\cos\alpha}{-\sin\alpha}=-\cot\alpha.$$

The angle $\frac{5\pi}{2}+\alpha$ lies at B, $\sin\left(\frac{5\pi}{2}+\alpha\right)=BC=\cos\alpha$

$\cos\left(\frac{5\pi}{2}+\alpha\right)=OC=-\sin\alpha$.
See Fig. 2-I/35.

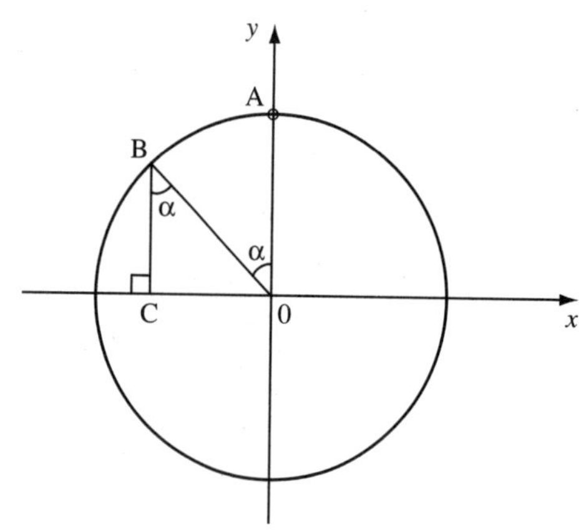

Fig. 2-I/35

$$\cos\left(\frac{5\pi}{2}+\alpha\right)=-\sin\alpha$$

$$\sin\left(\frac{5\pi}{2}+\alpha\right)=\cos\alpha$$

$$\tan\left(\frac{5\pi}{2}+\alpha\right)=-\cot\alpha$$

(viii) $\operatorname{cosec}\left(\frac{3\pi}{2}-\alpha\right)$

$$=\frac{1}{\sin\left(\frac{3\pi}{2}-\alpha\right)}=\frac{1}{-\cos\alpha}=-\sec\alpha.$$

The angle $\frac{3\pi}{2}-\alpha$ lies at B, $\sin\left(\frac{3\pi}{2}-\alpha\right)=BC=-\cos\alpha$. **See Fig. 2-I/36.**

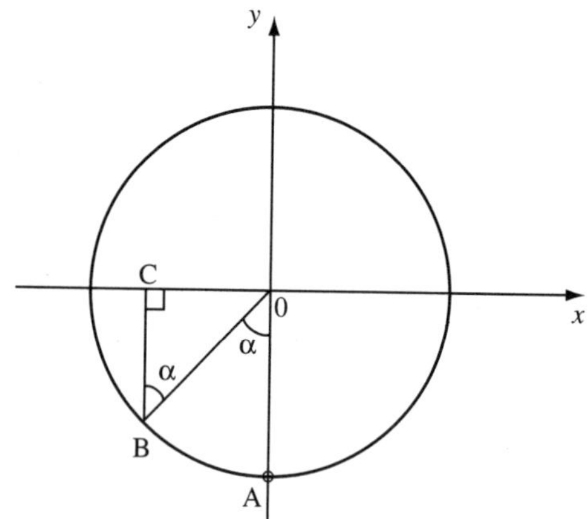

Fig. 2-I/36 $\sin\left(\frac{3\pi}{2}-\alpha\right)=-\cos\alpha$

(ix) $\tan\left(\frac{\pi}{2}+\alpha\right)=\frac{\sin\left(\frac{\pi}{2}+\alpha\right)}{\cos\left(\frac{\pi}{2}+\alpha\right)}$

$$=\frac{\cos\alpha}{-\sin\alpha}=-\cot\alpha.$$

The angle $\frac{\pi}{2}+\alpha$ lies at B, $\sin\left(\frac{\pi}{2}+\alpha\right)=BC=\cos\alpha$, $\cos\left(\frac{\pi}{2}+\alpha\right)=OC=-\sin\alpha$. **See Fig. 2-I/37.**

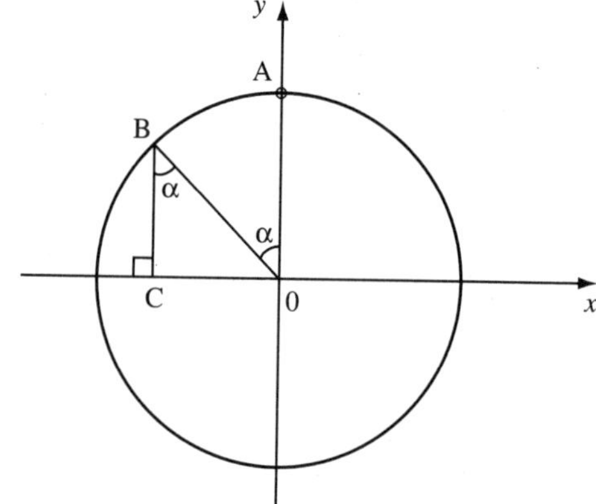

Fig. 2-I/37 $\cos\left(\frac{\pi}{2}+\alpha\right)=-\sin\alpha$

(x) $\cot(\alpha-3\pi)=\frac{\cos(\alpha-3\pi)}{\sin(\alpha-3\pi)}$

$$=\frac{-\cos\alpha}{-\sin\alpha}=\cot\alpha.$$

The angle $(\alpha-3\pi)$ lies at B, $\cos(\alpha-3\pi)=OC=-\cos\alpha$

$\sin(\alpha-3\pi)=BC=-\sin\alpha$.
See Fig. 2-I/38.

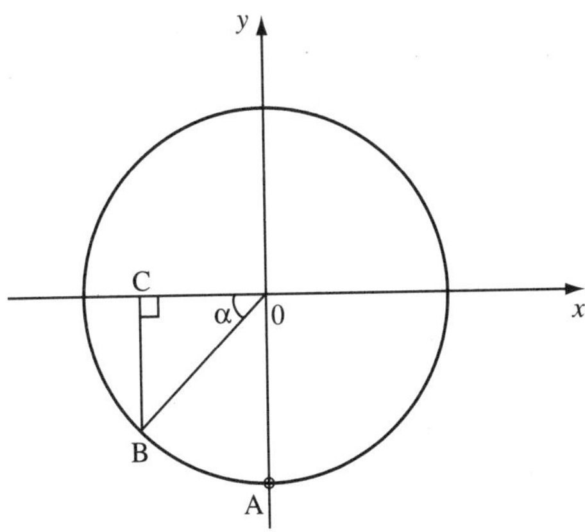

Fig. 2-I/38 $\sin(\alpha - 3\pi) = \sin\alpha$

To prove that

$$\tan(\Theta + \phi) = \frac{\tan\Theta + \tan\phi}{1 - \tan\Theta\tan\phi}$$

$$\tan(\Theta + \phi) = \frac{\sin(\Theta + \phi)}{\cos(\Theta + \phi)}$$

$$= \frac{\sin\Theta\cos\phi + \sin\phi\cos\Theta}{\cos\Theta\cos\phi - \sin\Theta\sin\phi}$$

dividing numerator and denominator by $\cos\Theta\cos\phi$

$$\tan(\Theta + \phi) = \frac{\frac{\sin\Theta\cos\phi}{\cos\Theta\cos\phi} + \frac{\sin\phi\cos\Theta}{\cos\Theta\cos\phi}}{\frac{\cos\Theta\cos\phi}{\cos\Theta\cos\phi} - \frac{\sin\Theta\sin\phi}{\cos\Theta\cos\phi}}$$

$$\tan(\Theta + \phi) = \frac{\tan\Theta + \tan\phi}{1 - \tan\Theta\tan\phi}.$$

If ϕ is negative $\tan(\Theta - \phi)$

$$= \frac{\tan\Theta + \tan(-\phi)}{1 - \tan\Theta\tan(-\phi)} = \frac{\tan\Theta - \tan\phi}{1 + \tan\Theta\tan\phi}$$

where $\sin(-\phi) = -\sin\phi$ (an odd function).

Worked Example 16

Determine that $\cot(\Theta + \alpha) = \dfrac{\cot\Theta\cot\alpha - 1}{\cot\Theta + \cot\alpha}$.

If $\cot\Theta = 3$, find without using tables or calculators, the value of $\cot\alpha$ in surd form given that $\Theta + \alpha = \frac{\pi}{3}$.

Solution 16

$$\cot(\Theta + \alpha) = \frac{1}{\tan(\Theta + \alpha)}$$

$$= \frac{1}{\frac{\tan\Theta + \tan\alpha}{1 - \tan\Theta\tan\alpha}} = \frac{1 - \tan\Theta\tan\alpha}{\tan\Theta + \tan\alpha}$$

$$= \frac{1 - \frac{1}{\cot\Theta}\cdot\frac{1}{\cot\alpha}}{\frac{1}{\cot\Theta} + \frac{1}{\cot\alpha}}$$

$$\cot(\Theta + \alpha) = \frac{\cot\Theta\cot\alpha - 1}{\cot\alpha + \cot\Theta}.$$

$$\cot(\Theta + \alpha) = \cot\frac{\pi}{3} = \frac{3\cot\alpha - 1}{\cot\alpha + 3} = \frac{1}{\sqrt{3}}$$

$$\Rightarrow 3\sqrt{3}\cot\alpha - \sqrt{3} = \cot\alpha + 3$$

$$\cot\alpha = \frac{3 + \sqrt{3}}{3\sqrt{3} - 1} \times \frac{-1 - 3\sqrt{3}}{-1 - 3\sqrt{3}}$$

$$= \frac{-3 - \sqrt{3} - 9\sqrt{3} - 9}{(-1)^2 - 27} = \frac{-12 - 10\sqrt{3}}{-26}$$

$$\boxed{\cot\alpha = \frac{6}{13} + \frac{5\sqrt{3}}{13}}$$

$$\cot(\Theta - \alpha) = \frac{\cot\Theta\cot(-\alpha) - 1}{\cot(-\alpha) + \cot\Theta}$$

$$= \frac{-\cot\Theta\cot\alpha - 1}{-\cot\alpha + \cot\Theta} = \frac{\cot\Theta\cot\alpha + 1}{\cot\alpha - \cot\Theta}.$$

Worked Example 17

Express $\cot(A + B)$ in terms of $\cot A$ and $\cot B$ and hence without the use of a calculator, find the values of $\cot 22\frac{1}{2}^\circ$ and $\cot 67\frac{1}{2}^\circ$ in surd form.

Solution 17

$$\cot(A + B) = \frac{\cot A\cot B - 1}{\cot A + \cot B}$$

and similarly $\cot(A - B) = \dfrac{\cot A\cot B + 1}{\cot B - \cot A}$.

If $A = B = 22\frac{1}{2}^\circ$: $\cot 45^\circ = \dfrac{\cot^2 22\frac{1}{2}^\circ - 1}{2\cot 22\frac{1}{2}^\circ} = 1$

$c^2 - 1 - 2c = 0$ where $c = \cot 22\frac{1}{2}°$

$c^2 - 2c - 1 = 0$

$$c = \frac{2 \pm \sqrt{4+4}}{2} = 1 \pm \sqrt{2}$$

$$c = \boxed{\cot 22\tfrac{1}{2}° = 1 + \sqrt{2}}$$

the negative sign is disregarded since the angle lies in the first quadrant and its contagent is positive.

$$\cot 67\tfrac{1}{2}° = \cot\left(90 - 22\tfrac{1}{2}°\right) = \frac{\cot 90° \cot 22\frac{1}{2}° + 1}{\cot 22\frac{1}{2}° - \cot 90°}$$

$$= \frac{1}{\cot 22\frac{1}{2}°} = \frac{1}{1+\sqrt{2}} \times \frac{1-\sqrt{2}}{1-\sqrt{2}}$$

$$\Rightarrow \cot 67\tfrac{1}{2}° = \sqrt{2} - 1$$

or $\cot(A + B) = \dfrac{\cot A \cot B - 1}{\cot A + \cot B}$.

If $A = 45°$ and $B = 22\frac{1}{2}°$,

$$\cot 67.5 = \frac{\cot 45° \cot 22.5° - 1}{\cot 45° + \cot 22.5°}$$

$$= \frac{1.(1+\sqrt{2}) - 1}{1 + 1 + \sqrt{2}} = \frac{\sqrt{2}}{2+\sqrt{2}}$$

$$\times \frac{2-\sqrt{2}}{2-\sqrt{2}}; \cot 67\tfrac{1}{2}° = \frac{2\sqrt{2}-2}{4-2} = \sqrt{2} - 1$$

$$\boxed{\cot 67\tfrac{1}{2}° = \sqrt{2} - 1}$$

Exercises 4

Simplify the following expressions:

1. $\sin 30° \cos 60° + \sin 60° \cos 30°$
2. $\sin 10° \cos 20° + \sin 20° \cos 10°$
3. $\sin 20° \cos 30° - \sin 30° \cos 20°$
4. $\cos 45° \cos 15° + \sin 45° \sin 15°$
5. $\cos 60° \cos 30° + \sin 60° \sin 30°$
6. $\cos 3\alpha \cos \beta + \sin 3\alpha \sin \beta$
7. $\cos 5x \cos x - \sin 5x \sin x$
8. $\sin 7x \cos x - \cos 7x \sin x$
9. $\dfrac{\tan 60° - \tan 30°}{1 + \tan 60° \tan 30°}$
10. $\dfrac{\cot 45° \cot 30° - 1}{\cot 45° + \cot 30°}$
11. $\dfrac{\cot 60° \cot 45° + 1}{\cot 45° - \cot 60°}$
12. $\dfrac{2 \tan 45°}{1 - \tan^2 45°}$
13. $\dfrac{\tan 3x - \tan x}{1 + \tan 3x \tan x}$
14. $\dfrac{\cot 4\alpha \cot \alpha + 1}{\cot \alpha - \cot 4\alpha}$
15. $\dfrac{\tan 90° - \tan 30°}{1 + \tan 90° \tan 30°}$.
16. Find the values of $\sin \frac{\pi^c}{12}$, $\cos \frac{\pi^c}{12}$, $\tan \frac{\pi^c}{12}$, $\sec \frac{\pi^c}{12}$, $\cot \frac{\pi^c}{12}$ and $\operatorname{cosec} \frac{\pi^c}{12}$ using the sum or difference formulae of two angles

    $\{\sin(A \pm B) = \sin A \cos B \pm \sin B \cos A$,
    $\cos(A \pm B) = \cos A \cos B \mp \sin A \sin B\}$.

    Your answers may be in decimal or surd form.
17. Evaluate in surd form the following:

    (i) $\cos 150°$
    (ii) $\sin 330°$
    (iii) $\sec 75°$
    (iv) $\tan 315°$
    (v) $\operatorname{cosec} 405°$

    using the expansions.
18. Employing the expansions of $\sin(A - B) = \sin A \cos B - \sin B \cos A$ and $\cos(A - B) = \cos A \cos B + \sin A \sin B$, find expressions for the following:

    (i) $\cot(A - B)$ in terms of cotangents, hence
    (ii) $\tan(A - B)$ in terms of tangents.
19. Simplify the following using the sum and difference formulae of two angles:

    (i) $\sin 45° \cos 60° + \sin 60° \cos 45°$
    (ii) $\dfrac{\tan 49° - \tan 48°}{1 + \tan 49° \tan 48°}$
    (iii) $\cos 90° \sin 90° + \sin 90° \cos 90°$

(iv) $\cos 45° \cos 35° - \sin 45° \sin 35°$

(v) $\cos 62° \cos 58° + \sin 62° \sin 58°$

(vi) $\dfrac{\tan 25° + \tan 65°}{1 - \tan 25° \tan 65°}$

(vii) $\cos 30° \cos 45° - \sin 30° \sin 45°$

(viii) $\cos 60° \cos 30° + \sin 60° \sin 30°$

(ix) $\dfrac{\tan 50° + \tan 60°}{1 - \tan 50° \tan 60°}$

(x) $\sin 75° \cos 65° - \sin 65° \cos 75°$.

20. If $\sin A = \frac{2}{3}$, and $\cos B = \frac{4}{7}$, find the values of $\sin(A+B)$, $\sin(A-B)$, $\cos(A+B)$ and $\cos(A-B)$ where A and B are acute angles.

21. Express $\sin 4x$ and $\cos 4x$ in terms of $\sin x$ and $\cos x$.

22. Simplify the following:

(i) $\sin\left(x - \dfrac{3\pi}{2}\right)$

(ii) $\tan\left(2x + \dfrac{\pi}{2}\right)$

(iii) $\cos\left(3x - \dfrac{3\pi}{2}\right)$.

5

Sums or Differences into Products

To prove that

$$\boxed{\sin\Theta + \sin\Phi = 2\sin\frac{\Theta+\Phi}{2}\cos\frac{\Theta-\Phi}{2}}$$

Let $\Theta = P + Q \quad \Phi = P - Q$

$$P = \frac{\Theta+\Phi}{2} \text{ and } Q = \frac{\Theta-\Phi}{2}$$

$$\begin{aligned}\sin\Theta + \sin\Phi &= \sin(P+Q) + \sin(P-Q)\\ &= \sin P\cos Q + \sin Q\cos P\\ &\quad + \sin P\cos Q - \sin Q\cos P\\ &= 2\sin P\cos Q.\end{aligned}$$

$$\sin\Theta + \sin\Phi = 2\sin\frac{\Theta+\Phi}{2}\cos\frac{\Theta-\Phi}{2}$$

To prove that

$$\sin\Theta - \sin\Phi = 2\sin\frac{\Theta-\Phi}{2}\cos\frac{\Theta+\Phi}{2}$$

$$\begin{aligned}\sin\Theta - \sin\Phi &= \sin(P+Q) - \sin(P-Q)\\ &= \sin P\cos Q + \sin Q\cos P\\ &\quad - \sin P\cos Q + \sin Q\cos P\end{aligned}$$

$$\boxed{\sin\Theta - \sin\Phi = 2\sin\frac{\Theta-\Phi}{2}\cos\frac{\Theta+\Phi}{2}}$$

To prove that

$$\cos\Theta + \cos\Phi = 2\cos\frac{\Theta+\Phi}{2}\cos\frac{\Theta-\Phi}{2}$$

$$\begin{aligned}\cos\Theta + \cos\Phi &= \cos(P+Q) + \cos(P-Q)\\ &= \cos P\cos Q - \sin P\sin Q\\ &\quad + \cos P\cos Q + \sin P\sin Q\\ &= 2\cos P\cos Q\end{aligned}$$

$$\boxed{\cos\Theta + \cos\Phi = 2\cos\frac{\Theta-\Phi}{2}\cos\frac{\Theta+\Phi}{2}}$$

To prove that

$$\cos\Theta - \cos\Phi = -2\sin\frac{\Theta+\Phi}{2}\sin\frac{\Theta-\Phi}{2}$$

$$\begin{aligned}\cos\Theta - \cos\Phi &= \cos(P+Q) - \cos(P-Q)\\ &= \cos P\cos Q - \sin P\sin Q\\ &\quad - \cos P\cos Q - \sin P\sin Q\\ &= -2\sin P\sin Q.\end{aligned}$$

$$\boxed{\cos\Theta - \cos\Phi = -2\sin\frac{\Theta+\Phi}{2}\sin\frac{\Theta-\Phi}{2}}$$

The sum or differences expressed as products are extremely useful formulae in order to simplify quotients such as:

$$\frac{(\sin\Theta - \sin\Phi)}{(\cos\Theta + \cos\Phi)}.$$

WORKED EXAMPLE 18

Simplify $\dfrac{\sin 3\Theta - \sin 3\Phi}{\cos 3\Theta + \cos 3\Phi} = a.$

If $\Theta = 45°$ and $\Phi = 30°$, find the value of a in surd form.

Solution 18

$$\begin{aligned}\frac{\sin 3\Theta - \sin 3\Phi}{\cos 3\Theta + \cos 3\Phi} &= \frac{2\sin 3\dfrac{(\Theta-\Phi)}{2}\cos 3\dfrac{(\Theta+\Phi)}{2}}{2\cos 3\dfrac{(\Theta+\Phi)}{2}\cos 3\dfrac{(\Theta-\Phi)}{2}}\\ &= \tan\frac{3}{2}(\Theta-\Phi)\end{aligned}$$

$$a = \tan\frac{3}{2}(45^\circ - 30^\circ) = \tan 22\frac{1}{2}^\circ.$$

Consider $\tan 45^\circ = \dfrac{2\tan 22\frac{1}{2}^\circ}{1-\tan^2 22\frac{1}{2}^\circ} = 1,$

$2t = 1 - t^2$ or $t^2 + 2t - 1 = 0$

$$t = \frac{-2 \pm \sqrt{4+4}}{2} = \frac{-2 \pm 2\sqrt{2}}{2}$$

$= -1 \pm \sqrt{2}$ where $t = \tan 22\frac{1}{2}^\circ$

$\tan 22\frac{1}{2}^\circ = -1 + \sqrt{2}$, therefore $a = \sqrt{2} - 1$.

Worked Example 19

If $\cot(x+y) = \frac{1}{a}$ and $\cot(x-y) = \frac{1}{b}$ determine the following expressions in terms of a and b:

(i) $\dfrac{\cos 2x + \cos 2y}{\cos 2x - \cos 2y}$

(ii) $\dfrac{\sin 4x + \sin 4y}{\sin 4x - \sin 4y}$

(iii) $\dfrac{\cos 2x - \cos 2y}{\sin 2x - \sin 2y}$

(iv) $\dfrac{\sin 4x - \sin 4y}{\sin 4x + \sin 4y}$

(v) $\dfrac{\sin 2x - \sin 2y}{\sin 2x + \sin 2y}$.

Solution 19

(i) $$\frac{\cos 2x + \cos 2y}{\cos 2x - \cos 2y} = \frac{2\cos(x+y)\cos(x-y)}{-2\sin(x+y)\sin(x-y)}$$

$$= -\cot(x+y)\cot(x-y)$$

$$= -\frac{1}{a}.\frac{1}{b} = -\frac{1}{ab}.$$

(ii) $$\frac{\sin 4x + \sin 4y}{\sin 4x - \sin 4y}$$

$$= \frac{2\sin 2(x+y)\cos 2(x-y)}{2\sin 2(x-y)\cos 2(x+y)}$$

$$= \tan 2(x+y)\cot 2(x-y)$$

$$= \frac{\tan 2(x+y)}{\tan 2(x-y)} = \frac{\dfrac{2\tan(x+y)}{\{1-\tan^2(x+y)\}}}{\dfrac{2\tan(x-y)}{\{1-\tan^2(x-y)\}}}$$

$$= \frac{\dfrac{2a}{(1-a^2)}}{\dfrac{2b}{(1-b^2)}} = \frac{a}{b}.\frac{(1-b^2)}{(1-a^2)}.$$

(iii) $$\frac{\cos 2x - \cos 2y}{\sin 2x - \sin 2y} = \frac{-2\sin(x+y)\sin(x-y)}{2\sin(x-y)\cos(x+y)}$$

$$= -\tan(x+y) = -a.$$

(iv) $$\frac{\sin 4x - \sin 4y}{\sin 4x + \sin 4y}$$

$$= \frac{2\sin 2(x-y)\cos 2(x+y)}{2\sin 2(x+y)\cos 2(x-y)}$$

$$= \tan 2(x-y)\cot 2(x+y)$$

$$= \frac{\tan 2(x-y)}{\tan 2(x+y)} = \frac{\dfrac{2\tan(x-y)}{\{1-\tan^2(x-y)\}}}{\dfrac{2\tan(x+y)}{\{1-\tan^2(x+y)\}}}$$

$$= \frac{b}{a}.\frac{1-a^2}{1-b^2}$$

(v) $$\frac{\sin 2x - \sin 2y}{\sin 2x + \sin 2y} = \frac{2\sin(x-y)\cos(x+y)}{2\sin(x+y)\cos(x-y)}$$

$$= \tan(x-y)\cot(x+y) = \frac{b}{a}.$$

Worked Example 20

Show that $\dfrac{\sin 8x + \sin 2x}{\cos 7x - \cos 3x} = 2\sin x - \dfrac{1}{2}\operatorname{cosec} x.$

Solution 20

$$\frac{\sin 8x + \sin 2x}{\cos 7x - \cos 3x}$$

$$= \frac{2\sin 5x \cos 3x}{-2\sin 5x \sin 2x}$$

$$= \frac{-\cos 3x}{\sin 2x} = -\cos 3x \operatorname{cosec} 2x$$

$$= -(4\cos^3 x - 3\cos x)\operatorname{cosec} 2x$$

$$= \frac{3\cos x - 4\cos^3 x}{2\sin x \cos x}$$

$$= \left(\frac{3}{2}\right)\operatorname{cosec} x - 2\cos^2 x \operatorname{cosec} x$$

$$= \left(\frac{3}{2}\right)\operatorname{cosec} x - 2(1 - \sin^2 x)\operatorname{cosec} x$$

$$= \left(\frac{3}{2}\right)\operatorname{cosec} x - 2\operatorname{cosec} x + 2\sin x$$

$$= 2\sin x - \left(\frac{1}{2}\right)\operatorname{cosec} x$$

$$= 2\sin x - \frac{1}{2}\operatorname{cosec} x.$$

Worked Example 22

Prove that $\sin 2x \cos x - \cos 2x \sin x = \sin x$.

Solution 21

L.H.S $\sin 2x \cos x - \cos 2x \sin x$

$$= 2\sin x \cos^2 x - (1 - 2\sin^2 x)\sin x$$

$$= 2\sin x \cos^2 x - \sin x + 2\sin^3 x$$

$$= 2\sin x(1 - \sin^2 x) - \sin x + 2\sin^3 x$$

$$= 2\sin x - 2\sin^3 x - \sin x + 2\sin^3 x = \sin x.$$

Therefore the L.H.S. = R.H.S.

Worked Example 22

If $\tan A = \frac{1}{5}$ and $\tan B = \frac{1}{8}$, find the value of $\tan(2B + A)$.

Solution 22

$$\tan(A + 2B) = \frac{\tan A + \tan 2B}{1 - \tan A \tan 2B}$$

$$= \frac{\tan A + \dfrac{2\tan B}{1 - \tan^2 B}}{1 - \tan A \cdot \dfrac{2\tan B}{1 - \tan^2 B}}$$

$$= \frac{\dfrac{1}{5} + \dfrac{\frac{2}{8}}{\left(1 - \frac{1}{64}\right)}}{1 - \dfrac{1}{5}\dfrac{\left(\frac{2}{8}\right)}{\left(1 - \frac{1}{64}\right)}}$$

$$= \frac{\dfrac{1}{5} + \dfrac{64}{4 \times 63}}{1 - \dfrac{64}{20 \times 63}} = \frac{\dfrac{4 \times 63 + 64 \times 5}{4 \times 5 \times 63}}{\dfrac{63 \times 20 - 64}{20 \times 63}}$$

$$= \frac{252 + 230}{1260 - 64} = \frac{572}{1196} = \frac{143}{299}.$$

Worked Example 23

If $\sin x = 0.6$, find $\sin 2x$ and $\sin 3x$.

Solution 23

$$\sin 2x = 2\sin x \cos x = \pm 2\sin x\sqrt{1 - \sin^2 x}$$

$$= \pm 2 \times 0.6 \times \sqrt{1 - 0.36}$$

$$= \pm 2 \times 0.6 \times 0.8 = \pm 0.96$$

$$\boxed{\sin 2x = \pm 0.96}$$

$$\sin 3x = 3\sin x - 4\sin^3 x = 3 \times 0.6 - 4 \times 0.6^3$$

$$= 1.8 - 0.864 = 0.936$$

$$\boxed{\sin 3x = 0.936}$$

Worked Example 24

If $\tan x = 4$, $\tan y = 2$, $\tan z = 3$, determine the value of $\tan(x + y + z)$.

Solution 24

$\tan(x+y+z) = \tan\{x+(y+z)\}$

$$= \frac{\tan x + \tan(y+z)}{1-\tan x.\tan(y+z)}$$

$$= \frac{\tan x + \dfrac{\tan y + \tan z}{1-\tan y \tan z}}{1-\tan x \dfrac{\tan y + \tan z}{1-\tan y \tan z}}$$

$$= \frac{4 + \dfrac{2+3}{1-2\times 3}}{1-4\times\dfrac{2+3}{1-2\times 3}}$$

$$= \frac{4+\dfrac{5}{-5}}{1-4\left(\dfrac{5}{-5}\right)} = \frac{3}{5}$$

$$\boxed{\tan(x+y+z) = \frac{3}{5}}$$

Exercises 5

1. Express the following sums into products:

   (i) $\sin A + \sin B$

   (ii) $\cos A + \cos B$

   Hence find the ratios (a) (i) to (ii) and (b) (ii) to (i).

2. Express the following differences into products:

   (i) $\sin P - \sin Q$

   (ii) $\cos P - \cos Q$

   Hence find the ratios (a) (i) to (ii) and (b) (ii) to (i).

3. Find the quotients in a simplified form:

   (i) $\dfrac{\sin\Theta - \sin\Phi}{\sin\Theta + \sin\Phi}$

   (ii) $\dfrac{\sin\Theta + \sin\Phi}{\sin\Theta - \sin\Phi}$

   (iii) $\dfrac{\cos\Theta + \cos\Phi}{\sin\Theta - \sin\Phi}$

   (iv) $\dfrac{\cos\Theta - \cos\Phi}{\sin\Theta + \sin\Phi}$.

4. If $\tan(x-y) = a$ and $\cot(x+y) = \frac{1}{b}$, find the simplified expressions in terms of a and b:

   (i) $\dfrac{\sin 2x + \sin 2y}{\sin 2x - \sin 2y}$

   (ii) $\dfrac{\cos 2x + \cos 2y}{\sin 2x + \sin 2y}$

   (iii) $\dfrac{\cos 2x - \cos 2y}{\cos 2x + \cos 2y}$

   (iv) $\dfrac{\sin 4x + \sin 4y}{\sin 4x - \sin 4y}$.

5. Express $\sin x + \sin 2x + \sin 3x + \sin 4x$ as a product.

6. Express $\cos x + \cos 2x + \cos 3x + \cos 4x$ as a product.

7. Express the following sums or differences:

   (i) $\sin 2x + \sin 6x$

   (ii) $\sin 3x - \sin 7x$

   (iii) $\cos 5x - \cos 3x$

   (iv) $\cos 7x + \cos 9x$

   (v) $\sin 7x + \sin 9x$ as products.

6

Products into Sums or Differences

We have proved that:

$$\sin\Theta + \sin\Phi = 2\sin\frac{\Theta+\Phi}{2}\cos\frac{\Theta-\Phi}{2}$$

$$\sin\Theta - \sin\Phi = 2\sin\frac{\Theta-\Phi}{2}\cos\frac{\Theta+\Phi}{2}$$

$$\cos\Theta + \cos\Phi = 2\cos\frac{\Theta+\Phi}{2}\cos\frac{\Theta-\Phi}{2}$$

$$\cos\Theta - \cos\Phi = -2\sin\frac{\Theta+\Phi}{2}\sin\frac{\Theta-\Phi}{2}.$$

If $\frac{\Theta+\Phi}{2} = A$ and $\frac{\Theta-\Phi}{2} = B$ then $\Theta = A + B$ and $\Phi = A - B$.

Therefore:

$$2\sin A\cos B = \sin(A+B) + \sin(A-B)$$

$$2\sin B\cos A = \sin(A+B) - \sin(A-B)$$

$$2\cos A\cos B = \cos(A+B) + \cos(A-B)$$

$$-2\sin A\sin B = \cos(A+B) - \cos(A-B).$$

The products into the sums or differences are:

$$\sin A\cos B = \frac{1}{2}\{\sin(A+B) + \sin(A-B)\}$$

$$\sin B\cos A = \frac{1}{2}\{\sin(A+B) - \sin(A-B)\}$$

$$\cos A\cos B = \frac{1}{2}\{\cos(A+B) + \cos(A-B)\}$$

$$\sin A\sin B = \frac{1}{2}\{\cos(A-B) - \cos(A+B)\}.$$

These formulae are useful when integration of products is required.

WORKED EXAMPLE 25

Express $\cos A\cos B\cos C$ as the sum of four cosines.

Solution 25

$\cos A\cos B\cos C$

$$= \cos A\left\{\left(\frac{1}{2}\right)\cos(B+C) + \left(\frac{1}{2}\right)\cos(B-C)\right\}$$

$$= \left(\frac{1}{2}\right)\cos A\cos(B+C) + \left(\frac{1}{2}\right)\cos A\cos(B-C)$$

$$= \left(\frac{1}{2}\right)\left\{\left(\frac{1}{2}\right)\cos(A+B+C) + \left(\frac{1}{2}\right)\cos(A-B-C)\right\}$$

$$+ \left(\frac{1}{2}\right)\left\{\left(\frac{1}{2}\right)\cos(A+B-C) + \left(\frac{1}{2}\right)\cos(A-B+C)\right\}.$$

Therefore:

$\cos A\cos B\cos C$

$$= \left(\frac{1}{4}\right)\cos(A+B+C) + \left(\frac{1}{4}\right)\cos(A-B-C) + \left(\frac{1}{4}\right)\cos(A+B-C) + \left(\frac{1}{4}\right)\cos(A-B+C).$$

Worked Example 26

Prove that $\cos^2 3x - \cos^2 x = -\sin 4x \sin 2x$.

Solution 26

$$
\begin{aligned}
(\cos^2 3x - \cos^2 x) \\
&= (\cos 3x - \cos x)(\cos 3x + \cos x) \\
&= (-2\sin 2x \sin x)(2\cos 2x \cos x) \\
&= -4\sin 2x \cos 2x \sin x \cos x \\
&= (-2\sin 2x \cos 2x)(2\sin x \cos x) \\
&= -\sin 4x \sin 2x.
\end{aligned}
$$

Worked Example 27

Express the following products into the sums or differences, and hence evaluate:

(i) $2\sin 70° \cos 50°$
(ii) $2\sin 90° \cos 60°$
(iii) $2\sin 45° \sin 75°$
(iv) $2\sin 30° \sin 40°$.

Solution 27

(i) $$\begin{aligned} 2\sin 70° \cos 50° &= \sin(50° + 70°) \\ &\quad - \sin(50° - 70°) \\ &= \sin 120° - \sin(-20°) \\ &= \sin 120° + \sin 20° \\ &= 0.866 + 0.342 = 1.21 \end{aligned}$$

since $\sin(-20°) = -\sin 20°$.

(ii) $$\begin{aligned} 2\sin 90° \cos 60° &= \sin(60° + 90°) \\ &\quad - \sin(60° - 90°) \\ &= \sin 150° - \sin(-30°) \\ &= \sin 150° + \sin 30° \\ &= 0.5 + 0.5 = 1. \end{aligned}$$

(iii) $$\begin{aligned} 2\sin 45° \sin 75° &= \cos(45° - 75°) \\ &\quad - \cos(45° + 75°) \\ &= \cos(-30°) - \cos 120° \\ &= \cos 30° - \cos 120° \\ &= 0.866 + 0.5 = 1.366. \end{aligned}$$

(iv) $$\begin{aligned} 2\sin 30° \sin 40° &= \cos(30° - 40°) \\ &\quad - \cos(30° + 40°) \\ &= \cos(-10°) - \cos 70° \\ &= \cos 10° - \cos 70° \\ &= 0.9848077 - 0.3420201 \\ &= 0.643. \end{aligned}$$

Worked Example 28

Express $2\cos 75° \cos 45°$ into a sum or difference, and hence evaluate $\cos 75°$ in surd form.

Solution 28

$$\begin{aligned} 2\cos 75° \cos 45° &= \cos(75° + 45°) + \cos(75° - 45°) \\ &= \cos 120° + \cos 30° = -\frac{1}{2} + \frac{\sqrt{3}}{2}, \end{aligned}$$

$$2\cos 75° \frac{1}{\sqrt{2}} = \frac{-1 + \sqrt{3}}{2},\ \cos 75° = \frac{-1 + \sqrt{3}}{2 \times 2} \times \sqrt{2}$$

$$= \frac{-\sqrt{2} + \sqrt{6}}{4} = \frac{\sqrt{6} - \sqrt{2}}{4}.$$

$$\boxed{\cos 75° = \frac{\sqrt{6} - \sqrt{2}}{4}}$$

Worked Example 29

Express $2\sin 22\frac{1}{2}° \cos 45°$ into a sum or difference, and hence express $\sin 67.5°$ in terms of $\sin 22.5°$.

Solution 29

$$\begin{aligned} 2\sin 22.5° \cos 45° &= \sin(22.5° + 45°) \\ &\quad + \sin(22.5° - 45°) \\ &= \sin 67.5° + \sin(-22.5°) \\ &= \sin 67.5° - \sin 22.5° \end{aligned}$$

$$2\sin 22.5° \cos 45° + \sin 22.5° = \sin 67.5°$$

$$\left(2\frac{1}{\sqrt{2}} + 1\right)\sin 22.5° = \sin 67.5°,$$

$$\boxed{\sin 67° = (\sqrt{2} + 1)\sin 22.5°}$$

Exercises 6

Express the following as sums or differences:

1. $\sin 25° \sin 35°$
2. $\sin 30° \sin 60°$
3. $\sin 40° \sin 50°$
4. $\cos 70° \cos 20°$
5. $\cos \alpha \cos 4\alpha$
6. $\cos y \cos 3y$
7. $\cos (x + y) \sin (x - y)$
8. $2 \cos 5x \cos 7x$
9. $2 \sin 3x \sin 5x$
10. $2 \sin t \sin 6t$
11. $2 \cos (x + 30°) \sin (x - 30°)$
12. $2 \cos (A + B) \sin (A - B)$
13. $2 \cos 75° \sin 75°$
14. $2 \sin 35° \cos 55°$
15. $2 \cos 45° \sin 35°$
16. $2 \sin 23° \cos 33°$
17. $2 \sin 5° \cos (-3°)$
18. $2 \sin 5x \sin 8x$
19. $10 \cos 7y \cos 3y$
20. $20 \cos 9y \sin 5y$.

7

Double Angle Formulae

$\sin 2A = 2\sin A\cos A$.

Consider $\sin(\Theta + \Phi) = \sin\Theta\cos\Phi + \sin\Phi\cos\Theta$

If $\Theta = \Phi = A \Rightarrow \sin(\Theta + \Phi) = \sin(A + A) = \sin 2A = \sin A\cos A + \sin A\cos A$

$$\boxed{\sin 2A = 2\sin A\cos A}$$

Consider $\cos(\Theta + \Phi) = \cos\Theta\cos\Phi - \sin\Theta\sin\Phi$.

If $\Theta = \Phi = A$

$\cos 2A = \cos A\cos A - \sin A\sin A$

$\cos 2A = \cos^2 A - \sin^2 A$

$$\boxed{\cos 2A = \cos^2 A - \sin^2 A}$$

$$= (1 - \sin^2 A) - \sin^2 A$$

$$\boxed{\cos 2A = 1 - 2\sin^2 A}$$

$\cos 2A = \cos^2 A - (1 - \cos^2 A)$

$$\boxed{\cos 2A = 2\cos^2 A - 1}$$

Consider $\tan(\Theta + \Phi) = \dfrac{\tan\Theta + \tan\Phi}{1 - \tan\Theta\tan\Phi}$

If $\Theta = \Phi = A \Rightarrow \tan 2A = \dfrac{\tan A + \tan A}{1 - \tan A\tan A} = \dfrac{2\tan A}{1 - \tan^2 A}$

$$\boxed{\tan 2A = \frac{2\tan A}{1 - \tan^2 A}}$$

WORKED EXAMPLE 30

Determine the formulae for $\sin 3x$ and $\cos 3x$ in terms of $\sin x$ and $\cos x$ respectively, using the formulae $\sin(A + B)$ and $\cos(A + B)$.

Hence show that $\sin 3x - \cos 3x = (\sin x + \cos x)(2\sin 2x - 1)$.

Solution 30

$$\begin{aligned}
\sin 3x &= \sin(2x + x) = \sin 2x\cos x + \sin x\cos 2x \\
&= 2\sin x\cos x\cos x + \sin x(1 - 2\sin^2 x) \\
&= 2\sin x\cos^2 x + \sin x - 2\sin^3 x \\
&= 2\sin x(1 - \sin^2 x) + \sin x - 2\sin^3 x \\
&= 2\sin x - 2\sin^3 x + \sin x - 2\sin^3 x
\end{aligned}$$

$$\boxed{\sin 3x = 3\sin x - 4\sin^3 x}$$

$$\begin{aligned}
\cos 3x &= \cos(2x + x) = \cos 2x\cos x - \sin 2x\sin x \\
&= (2\cos^2 x - 1)\cos x - 2\sin x\cos x\sin x \\
&= 2\cos^3 x - \cos x - 2\sin^2 x\cos x \\
&= 2\cos^3 x - \cos x - 2(1 - \cos^2 x)\cos x \\
&= 2\cos^3 x - \cos x - 2\cos x + 2\cos^3 x
\end{aligned}$$

$$\boxed{\cos 3x = 4\cos^3 x - 3\cos x}$$

$$\begin{aligned}
&\sin 3x - \cos 3x \\
&= 3\sin x - 4\sin^3 x - 4\cos^3 x + 3\cos x \\
&= 3(\sin x + \cos x) - 4(\sin^3 x + \cos^3 x) \\
&= 3(\sin x + \cos x) - 4(\sin x + \cos x)\times \\
&\qquad (\sin^2 x + \cos^2 x - \sin x\cos x) \\
&= (\sin x + \cos x)(3 - 4 + 4\sin x\cos x) \\
&= (\sin x + \cos x)(2\sin 2x - 1).
\end{aligned}$$

Worked Example 31

Show that $\tan 3x = \dfrac{3\tan x - \tan^3 x}{1 - 3\tan^2 x}$.

Solution 31

$$\tan 3x = \tan(x + 2x) = \frac{\tan x + \tan 2x}{1 - \tan x \tan 2x}$$

$$= \frac{\tan x + \dfrac{2\tan x}{1-\tan^2 x}}{1 - \tan x\left(\dfrac{2\tan x}{1-\tan^2 x}\right)}$$

$$= \frac{\tan x - \tan^3 x + 2\tan x}{1 - \tan^2 x - 2\tan^2 x}$$

$$= \frac{3\tan x - \tan^3 x}{1 - 3\tan^2 x}.$$

Worked Example 32

Simplify the following trigonometric expressions:

(i) $\dfrac{2\tan 15°}{1-\tan^2 15°}$

(ii) $\dfrac{2\tan x}{1-\tan^2 x}$

(iii) $\dfrac{2\tan\frac{x}{2}}{1-\tan^2\frac{x}{2}}$.

Solution 32

(i) $\dfrac{2\tan 15°}{1-\tan^2 15°} = \tan 30° = \dfrac{1}{\sqrt{3}}$

(ii) $\dfrac{2\tan x}{1-\tan^2 x} = \tan 2x$

(iii) $\dfrac{2\tan\frac{x}{2}}{1-\tan^2\frac{x}{2}} = \tan x$.

Worked Example 33

Simplify the following:

(i) $2\cos^2 15° - 1$

(ii) $1 - 2\sin^2 15°$

(iii) $\cos^2 30° - \sin^2 30°$

(iv) $2\sin 30°\cos 30°$

(v) $2\sin 15°\cos 15°$.

Solution 33

(i) $2\cos^2 15° - 1 = \cos 30° = \frac{\sqrt{3}}{2}$

(ii) $1 - 2\sin^2 15° = \cos 30° = \frac{\sqrt{3}}{2}$

(iii) $\cos^2 30° - \sin^2 30° = \cos 60° = \frac{1}{2}$

(iv) $2\sin 30°\cos 30° = \sin 60° = \frac{\sqrt{3}}{2}$

(v) $2\sin 15°\cos 15° = \sin 30° = \frac{1}{2}$.

Exercises 7

1. Write down the formula for the sine of a double angle in terms of single angles.
2. Write down the formula for the cosine of a double angle in terms of single angles.
3. Write down the formula for the tangent of a double angle in terms of single angles.
4. Prove the following formulae:

   (i) $\sin 4A = 2\sin 2A\cos 2A$

   (ii) $\cos 4A = \cos^2 2A - \sin^2 2A$
   $= 2\cos^2 2A - 1 = 1 - 2\sin^2 2A$

   (iii) $\tan 4A = \dfrac{2\tan 2A}{1-\tan^2 2A}$.

5. Simplify the following expressions:

   (i) $\dfrac{2\tan 60°}{1-\tan^2 60°}$

   (ii) $2\sin 6x\cos 6x$

   (iii) $\cos^2 3x - \sin^2 3x$

   (iv) $\dfrac{2\tan 120°}{1-\tan^2 120°}$

   (v) $1 - 2\sin^2 4x$

   (vi) $\dfrac{2\tan\left(\frac{x}{4}\right)}{1-\tan^2\left(\frac{x}{4}\right)}$

   (vii) $\dfrac{\cos^2 x + \sin^2 x}{\cos^2 x - \sin^2 x}$

   (viii) $2\cos^2 30° - 1$

   (ix) $\cos^2 300° - \sin^2 300°$

   (x) $2\sin\dfrac{1}{2}x\cos\dfrac{1}{2}x$.

8

Half Angle Formulae

$\sin 2A = 2\sin A\cos A$

If $2A = \Theta$, then $A = \frac{\Theta}{2}$, $\sin\Theta = 2\sin\frac{\Theta}{2}\cos\frac{\Theta}{2}$.

Similarly for $\cos 2A = \cos^2 A - \sin^2 A = 2\cos^2 A - 1 = 1 - 2\sin^2 A$

$\cos\Theta = \cos^2\frac{\Theta}{2} - \sin^2\frac{\Theta}{2} = 2\cos^2\frac{\Theta}{2} - 1 = 1 - 2\sin^2\frac{\Theta}{2}$, and for $\tan 2A = \frac{2\tan A}{1-\tan^2 A}$

$$\tan\Theta = \frac{2\tan\frac{\Theta}{2}}{1-\tan^2\frac{\Theta}{2}}$$

Worked Example 34

Write down the half angle formulae for:

(i) $\sin\frac{x}{2}$ (ii) $\cos\frac{x}{2}$

(iii) $\tan\frac{x}{2}$.

Solution 34

(i) $\sin\frac{x}{2} = 2\sin\frac{x}{4}\cos\frac{x}{4}$

(ii) $\cos\frac{x}{2} = \cos^2\frac{x}{4} - \sin^2\frac{x}{4}$

$= 1 - 2\sin^2\frac{x}{4} = 2\cos^2\frac{x}{4} - 1$

(iii) $\tan\frac{x}{2} = \frac{2\tan\frac{x}{4}}{1-\tan^2\frac{x}{4}}$.

Worked Example 35

Simplify the following trigonometric expressions:

(i) $2\sin\frac{3x}{2}\cos\frac{3x}{2}$

(ii) $\cos^2\frac{7x}{2} - \sin^2\frac{7x}{2}$

(iii) $\frac{2\tan\frac{3x}{4}}{1-\tan^2\frac{3x}{4}}$.

Solution 35

(i) $2\sin\frac{3x}{2}\cos\frac{3x}{2} = \sin 3x$

(ii) $\cos^2\frac{7x}{2} - \sin^2\frac{7x}{2} = \cos 7x$

(iii) $\frac{2\tan\frac{3x}{4}}{1-\tan^2\frac{3x}{4}} = \tan\frac{3x}{2}$.

Exercises 8

1. Express

   (i) $\sqrt{\frac{1-\sin x}{1+\sin x}}$

   (ii) $\sqrt{\frac{1-\cos x}{1+\cos x}}$ in terms of $\tan\frac{x}{2}$.

2. Simplify $\frac{1+\cos 2x}{1-\cos 2x}$.

3. Find the values of
   (i) $\sin 2x$
   (ii) $\tan 2x$
   (iii) $\cos 2x$, given that $\sec x = -\frac{2}{\sqrt{3}}$.

4. Write down the half angle formulae for:
   (i) $\sin 4x$
   (ii) $\cos 4x$ and
   (iii) $\tan 4x$.

5. Write down the half angle formulae for:
   (i) $\sin 16x$
   (ii) $\cos 16x$ and
   (iii) $\tan 16x$.

9

The t-Formulae

$$\sin\Theta = 2\sin\frac{\Theta}{2}\cos\frac{\Theta}{2} = \frac{2\sin\frac{\Theta}{2}\cos\frac{\Theta}{2}}{1}$$

$$= \frac{2\sin\frac{\Theta}{2}\cos\frac{\Theta}{2}}{\sin^2\frac{\Theta}{2}+\cos^2\frac{\Theta}{2}}$$

$$\sin\Theta = \frac{\frac{2\sin\frac{\Theta}{2}\cos\frac{\Theta}{2}}{\cos^2\frac{\Theta}{2}}}{\frac{\sin^2\frac{\Theta}{2}}{\cos^2\frac{\Theta}{2}}+\frac{\cos^2\frac{\Theta}{2}}{\cos^2\frac{\Theta}{2}}} = \frac{2\tan\frac{\Theta}{2}}{1+\tan^2\frac{\Theta}{2}}$$

$$\sin\Theta = \frac{2\tan\frac{\Theta}{2}}{1+\tan^2\frac{\Theta}{2}} = \frac{2t}{1+t^2}$$

where $t = \tan\frac{\Theta}{2}$ and since Θ is less than 90°, $\tan\frac{\Theta}{2} < 1$ and hence $1 - t^2$ is positive.

Constructing a right-angled triangle as shown, using the definition of $\sin\Theta = \frac{2t}{1+t^2}$ where the opposite side to Θ is $2t$ and the hypotenuse $1+t^2$, then the adjacent side using Pythagoras theorem is $1-t^2$.

From the triangle:

$$\sin\Theta = \frac{2t}{1+t^2}$$

$$\operatorname{cosec}\Theta = \frac{(1+t^2)}{2t} = \frac{1}{\sin\Theta}$$

$$\cos\Theta = \frac{(1-t^2)}{1+t^2}$$

$$\sec\Theta = \frac{(1+t^2)}{(1-t^2)} = \frac{1}{\cos\Theta}$$

$$\tan\Theta = \frac{2t}{1-t^2}$$

$$\cot\Theta = \frac{(1-t^2)}{2t} = \frac{1}{\tan\Theta}.$$

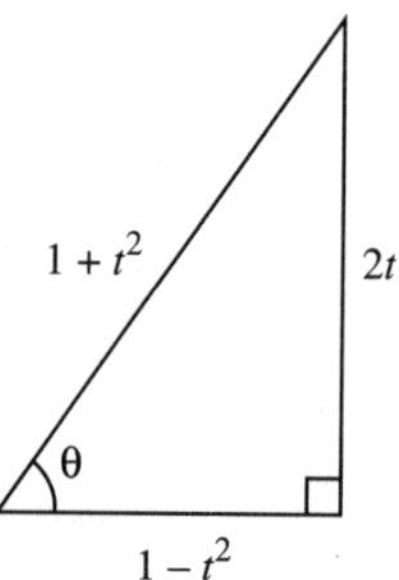

Fig. 2-I/39 t-formulae

Worked Example 36

Write down the formulae for the following trigonometric functions in terms of t:

(i) $\sin 6x$
(ii) $\cos 4x$
(iii) $\cos x$
(iv) $\tan 3x$
(v) $\sec 8x$.

State in each case the value for t.

Solution 36

(i) $\sin 6x = \frac{2t}{1+t^2}$ where $t = \tan 3x$

(ii) $\cos 4x = \frac{1-t^2}{1+t^2}$ where $t = \tan 2x$

(iii) $\cos x = \frac{1-t^2}{1+t^2}$ where $t = \tan\frac{x}{2}$

(iv) $\tan 3x = \frac{2t}{1-t^2}$ where $t = \tan\frac{3x}{2}$

(v) $\sec 8x = \frac{1+t^2}{1-t^2}$ where $t = \tan 4x$.

Worked Example 37

Express the following in terms of t:

(i) $\dfrac{1}{1+\sin x}$

(ii) $\dfrac{1}{1-\cos x}$

(iii) $\dfrac{1}{\sin x - 1}$

(iv) $\dfrac{1}{1+\cos x}$.

Solution 37

(i) $$\frac{1}{1+\sin x} = \frac{1}{1+\dfrac{2t}{1+t^2}} = \frac{1+t^2}{1+t^2+2t} = \frac{1+t^2}{(1+t)^2}$$

(ii) $$\frac{1}{1-\cos x} = \frac{1}{1-\dfrac{(1-t^2)}{1+t^2}} = \frac{1+t^2}{1+t^2-1+t^2} = \frac{1+t^2}{2t^2} = \frac{1}{2t^2}+\frac{1}{2}$$

(iii) $$\frac{1}{\sin x - 1} = \frac{1}{\dfrac{2t}{1+t^2}-1} = \frac{1+t^2}{2t-1-t^2}$$

(iv) $$\frac{1}{1+\cos x} = \frac{1}{1+\dfrac{1-t^2}{1+t^2}} = \frac{1+t^2}{1+t^2+1-t^2} = \frac{1+t^2}{2} = \frac{1}{2}(1+t^2)$$

where $t = \tan\dfrac{x}{2}$.

Worked Example 38

Solve the trigonometric equation $3\sin x - 4\cos x = 1$ using the t-formulae and $0° \le x \le 360°$.

Solution 38

$$3\sin x - 4\cos x = 1 \Rightarrow 3\frac{2t}{1+t^2} - 4\frac{1-t^2}{1+t^2} = 1$$

using Fig. 2-I/39, $6t - 4 + 4t^2 = 1 + t^2$

$$3t^2 + 6t - 5 = 0$$

$$t = \frac{-6 \pm \sqrt{36+60}}{6} = \frac{-6 \pm \sqrt{96}}{6}$$

$t = 0.633$ or $t = -2.633$

$\tan\dfrac{x}{2} = 0.633 = \tan 32.33353069$ $\quad \boxed{x = 64.67°}$

$\tan\dfrac{x}{2} = -2.633 = \tan 110.7965717°$ $\quad \boxed{x = 221.60°}$

Exercises 9

1. Express the following in terms of t where $t = \tan\frac{x}{2}$:

   (i) $\dfrac{1}{1-2\sin x}$

   (ii) $\sec x$

   (iii) $\dfrac{1}{\sin x}$

   (iv) $\dfrac{1}{2-\cos x}$.

2. Express the following in terms of t where $t = \tan x$:

   (i) $\sqrt{\dfrac{1+\sin 2x}{1-\sin 2x}}$

   (ii) $\sqrt{\dfrac{1+\cos 2x}{1-\cos 2x}}$.

3. Solve the trigonometric equation $\sin 2x - \cos 2x = 1$ using the t-formulae where $0° \le x \le 360°$.

4. Solve the trigonometric equation $7\sin x + 12\cos x = 5$ using the t-formulae, when $0° \le x \le 360°$.

5. Express $\dfrac{7+12\cos x}{7-12\cos x}$ in terms of t, where $t = \tan\frac{x}{2}$.

6. Show that $\dfrac{1+\cos 2x}{1-\cos 2x} = \cot^2 x$.

7. Show that $\dfrac{\sin x}{1+\cos x} = \tan\dfrac{1}{2}x$.

10

Expression of $a \cos \Theta + b \sin \Theta$ in the form $r \cos (\Theta \pm \alpha)$ or $r \sin (\Theta \pm \alpha)$

$a \cos \Theta + b \sin \Theta = r \cos (\Theta - \alpha)$

$a \cos \Theta + b \sin \Theta = r \cos \Theta \cos \alpha + r \sin \Theta \sin \alpha.$

Equating the coefficients of $\cos \Theta$ and $\sin \Theta$

$a = r \cos \alpha \quad (1) \qquad b = r \sin \alpha \quad (2)$

From these two expressions, the triangle may be constructed by using the definition $\cos \alpha = \frac{a}{r}$, $\sin \alpha = \frac{b}{r}$.

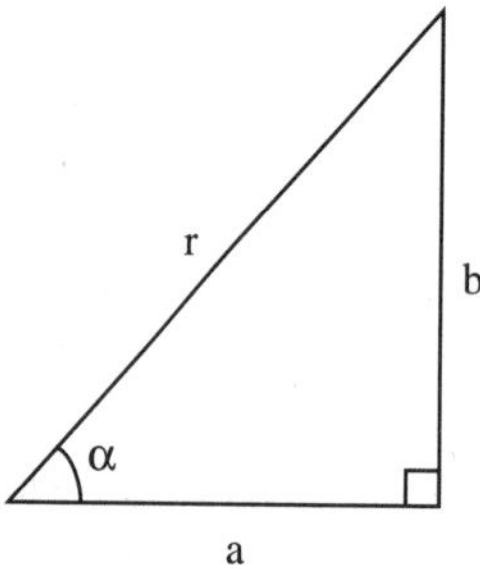

Fig. 2-I/40 $a \cos \Theta + b \sin \Theta = r \cos (\Theta - \alpha)$

$r^2 = a^2 + b^2$ and $\tan \alpha = \frac{b}{a}$, therefore,

$$a \cos \Theta + b \sin \Theta = \sqrt{a^2 + b^2} \cos \left(\Theta - \tan^{-1} \frac{b}{a} \right)$$

where $r = \sqrt{a^2 + b^2}$ and $\alpha = \tan^{-1} \left(\frac{b}{a} \right)$.

Alternatively squaring both sides of equations (1) and (2) and adding

$a^2 = r^2 \cos^2 \alpha$, $b^2 = r^2 \sin^2 \alpha$, $r^2 = a^2 + b^2$, dividing (2) by (1) $\tan \alpha = \frac{b}{a}$.

WORKED EXAMPLE 39

Express $3 \cos \Theta + 4 \sin \Theta$ in the form $r \cos (\Theta - \alpha)$.

Solution 39

$3 \cos \Theta + 4 \sin \Theta = r \cos (\Theta - \alpha)$

$3 \cos \Theta + 4 \sin \Theta = r \cos \Theta \cos \alpha + r \sin \Theta \sin \alpha.$

Equating the coefficients of $\cos \Theta$ and $\sin \Theta$

$r \cos \alpha = 3$, $r \sin \alpha = 4$, constructing the triangle.

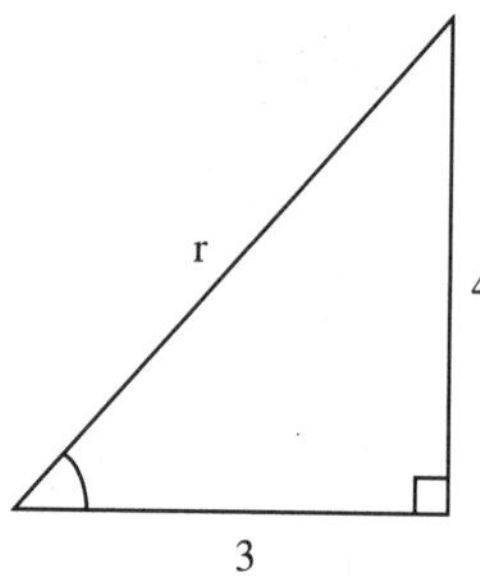

Fig. 2-I/41 $3 \cos \Theta + 4 \sin \Theta = 5 \cos (\Theta - 53° 8')$

$r = \sqrt{3^2 + 4^2} = 5$

$\tan \alpha = \frac{4}{3}$, $\alpha = \tan^{-1} \frac{4}{3} = 53° 8'$

therefore $3 \cos \Theta + 4 \sin \Theta = 5 \cos (\Theta - 53° 8')$.

WORKED EXAMPLE 40

Express $\sqrt{3} \cos \Theta - \sin \Theta$ in the form $r \cos (\Theta + \alpha)$.

Solution 40

$\sqrt{3} \cos \Theta - \sin \Theta = r \cos (\Theta + \alpha)$

$\sqrt{3} \cos \Theta - \sin \Theta = r \cos \Theta \cos \alpha - r \sin \Theta \sin \alpha.$

Equating the coefficients of $\cos \Theta$ and $\sin \Theta$

$\sqrt{3} = r \cos \alpha$ (1)

$-1 = -r \sin \alpha$ (2)

constructing the triangle.

From the triangle $r = \sqrt{1+3} = 2$, $\tan \alpha = \frac{1}{\sqrt{3}}$ or $\alpha = \frac{\pi^c}{6}$.

Therefore $\sqrt{3} \cos \Theta - \sin \Theta = 2 \cos\left(\Theta + \frac{\pi^c}{6}\right)$.

Alternatively squaring both sides of equation (1) and (2)

$$3 = r^2 \cos^2 \alpha \qquad \frac{3}{r^2} + \frac{1}{r^2} = 1$$

$$1 = r^2 \sin^2 \alpha$$

or $r^2 = 4$ $\qquad r = 2$

dividing equation (2) by equation (1) $\tan \alpha = \frac{1}{\sqrt{3}}$ or $\alpha = \frac{\pi^c}{6}$.

This second method, although it is more straightforward, involves more calculations.

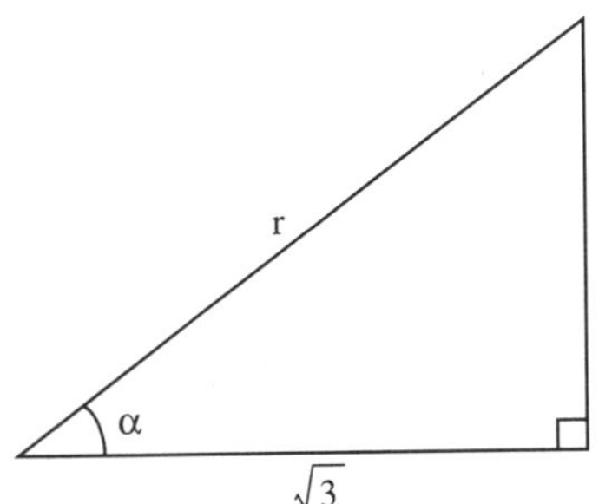

Fig. 2-I/42 $\sqrt{3} \cos \Theta - \sin \Theta = 2 \cos\left(\Theta + \frac{\pi}{6}\right)$.

Worked Example 41

Express $\sin \Theta + 2 \cos \Theta$ in the form $r \sin(\Theta + \alpha)$.

Solution 41

$\sin \Theta + 2 \cos \Theta = r \sin(\Theta + \alpha) \Rightarrow \sin \Theta + 2 \cos \Theta$

$$= r \sin \Theta \cos \alpha + r \sin \alpha \cos \Theta.$$

Equating the coefficients of $\sin \Theta$ and $\cos \Theta$, $1 = r \cos \alpha$ or $\cos \alpha = \frac{1}{r}$, $2 = r \sin \alpha$ or $\sin \alpha = \frac{2}{r}$ and constructing the right angled triangle from the definitions

$\cos \alpha = \frac{1}{r}$ and $\sin \alpha = \frac{2}{r}$, $r = \sqrt{2^2 + 1} = \sqrt{5}$ and $\tan \alpha = \frac{2}{1}$ or $\alpha = 63° 26'$, therefore, $\sin \Theta + 2 \cos \Theta = \sqrt{5} \sin(\Theta + 63° 26')$.

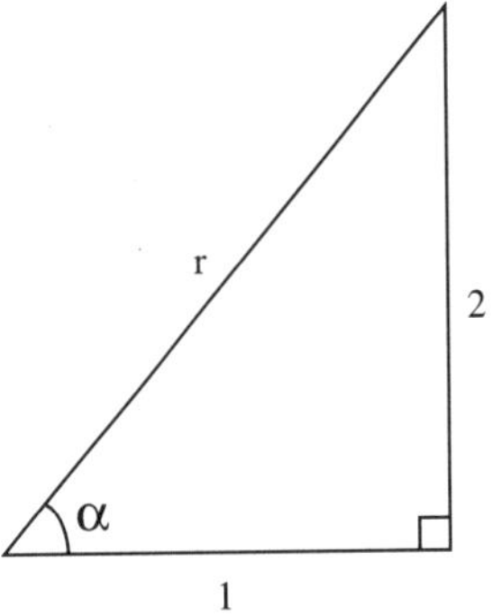

Fig. 2-I/43 $\sin \Theta + 2 \cos \Theta = \sqrt{5} \sin(\Theta + 63° 26')$

Worked Example 42

Express $\sqrt{5} \sin \Theta - \cos \Theta$ in the form $r \sin(\Theta - \alpha)$.

Solution 42

Let $\sqrt{5} \sin \Theta - \cos \Theta = r \sin(\Theta - \alpha) = r \sin \Theta \cos \alpha - r \sin \alpha \cos \Theta$.

Equating the coefficients of $\sin \Theta$ and $\cos \Theta$, $\sqrt{5} = r \cos a$ and $1 = r \sin \alpha$, $\cos \alpha = \frac{\sqrt{5}}{r}$ and $\sin \alpha = \frac{1}{r}$.

Constructing the triangle $r^2 = 5 + 1$ or $r = \sqrt{6}$, $\tan \alpha = \frac{1}{\sqrt{5}}$ or $\alpha = \tan^{-1}\left(\frac{1}{\sqrt{5}}\right) = 24° 6'$ therefore

$$\boxed{\sqrt{5} \sin \Theta - \cos \Theta = \sqrt{6} \sin(\Theta - 24° 6')}$$

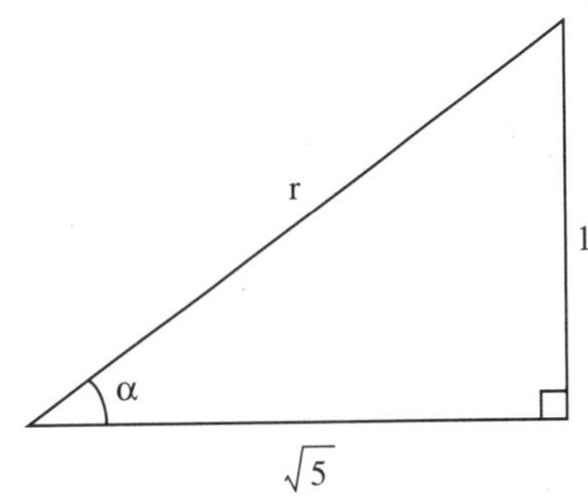

Fig.2-I/44

$\sqrt{5} \sin \Theta - \cos \Theta = \sqrt{6} \sin(\Theta - 24° 6')$

Worked Example 43

Express $3 \sin 2\Theta - 4 \cos 2\Theta$ in the form $R \sin(2\Theta - \alpha)$ where $R > 0$ and α is acute.

Solution 43

$3\sin 2\Theta - 4\cos 2\Theta = R\sin(2\Theta - \alpha) = R\sin 2\Theta\cos\alpha - R\sin\alpha\cos 2\Theta$.

Equating the coefficients of $\sin 2\Theta$ and $\cos 2\Theta$, $3 = R\cos\alpha$ or $\cos\alpha = \frac{3}{R}$, $4 = R\sin\alpha$ or $\sin\alpha = \frac{4}{R}$.

Constructing the right angled triangle using the definitions of $\cos\alpha$ and $\sin\alpha$

$R = \sqrt{3^2 + 4^2} = 5$ and $\tan\alpha = \frac{4}{3}$ or $\alpha = 53°\,8'$ therefore

$3\sin 2\Theta - 4\cos 2\Theta = 5\sin(2\Theta - 53°\,8')$.

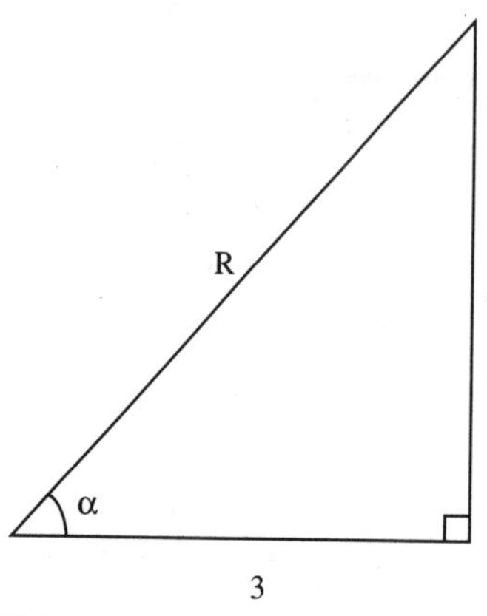

Fig. 2-I/45 $3\sin 2\Theta - 4\cos 2\Theta = 5\sin(2\Theta - 53°\,8')$

Worked Example 44

Given that $a\cos\Theta + b\sin\Theta = 5\cos\left(\Theta - \frac{\pi}{3}\right)$, find the constants a and b.

Solution 44

$a\cos\Theta + b\sin\Theta = 5\cos\left(\Theta - \frac{\pi}{3}\right) = 5\cos\Theta\cos\frac{\pi}{3} + 5\sin\Theta\sin\frac{\pi}{3}$.

Equating the coefficients of $\cos\Theta$ and $\sin\Theta$,

$$a = 5\cos\frac{\pi}{3} = \frac{5}{2}, b = 5\sin\frac{\pi}{3} = \frac{5\sqrt{3}}{2}.$$

Worked Example 45

Given that $a\sin\Theta - b\cos\Theta = \sqrt{3}\sin\left(\Theta - \frac{\pi}{6}\right)$,find the constants a and b.

Solution 45

$$a\sin\Theta - b\cos\Theta = \sqrt{3}\sin\left(\Theta - \frac{\pi}{6}\right)$$
$$= \sqrt{3}\sin\Theta\cos\frac{\pi}{6}$$
$$- \sqrt{3}\cos\Theta\sin\frac{\pi}{6}.$$

Equating the coefficients of $\sin\Theta$ and $\cos\Theta$

$$a = \sqrt{3}\cos\frac{\pi}{6} = \sqrt{3}\frac{\sqrt{3}}{2} = \frac{3}{2},$$

$$b = \sqrt{3}\sin\frac{\pi}{6} = \sqrt{3}\frac{1}{2} = \frac{\sqrt{3}}{2}.$$

Exercises 10

1. Express $3\sin x + 4\cos x$ in the form $R\sin(x + \alpha)$.
2. Express $\sin x - \cos x$ in the form $R\sin(x - \alpha)$.
3. Express $2\sin x - \cos x$ in the form $R\sin(x - \alpha)$.
4. Express $\sqrt{3}\cos x + \sqrt{2}\sin x$ in the form $R\cos(x - \alpha)$.
5. Find the maximum value of $\sqrt{5}\sin x + 3\cos x$.
6. Find the maximum value of $3\sin 2x + 4\cos 2x$.
7. Given that $a\sin x + b\cos x = 13\sin\left(x + \frac{\pi}{6}\right)$, find the constants a and b.
8. Given that a $\cos x - b\sin x = 15\cos\left(x + \frac{\pi}{4}\right)$, find the constants a and b.

11

Identities of Circular or Trigonometric Functions and Their Applications

$$\boxed{\sin^2 x + \cos^2 x \equiv 1} \quad (1)$$

This expression states that the sum of the squares of the sine and cosine of an angle is identically equal to unity. Identically *equal* means that it is true for any value of x, that is, when $x = 0°$, $x = 30°$, $x = 60°$, $x = 90°$, or any other value.

$$\sin^2 0° + \cos^2 0° \equiv 1 \text{ or } 0 + 1 \equiv 1$$

$$\sin^2 30° + \cos^2 30° \equiv 1 \text{ or } \tfrac{1}{4} + \tfrac{3}{4} \equiv 1$$

$$\sin^2 60° + \cos^2 60° \equiv 1 \text{ or } \tfrac{3}{4} + \tfrac{1}{4} \equiv 1$$

$$\sin^2 90° + \cos^2 90° \equiv 1 \text{ or } 1 + 0 \equiv 1.$$

Dividing each term of (1) by $\cos^2 x$, results in $\frac{\sin^2 x}{\cos^2 x} + \frac{\cos^2 x}{\cos^2 x} \equiv \frac{1}{\cos^2 x}$

$$\boxed{\tan^2 x + 1 \equiv \sec^2 x} \ldots (2)$$

Dividing each term of (1) by $\sin^2 x$, results in $\frac{\sin^2 x}{\sin^2 x} + \frac{\cos^2 x}{\sin^2 x} \equiv \frac{1}{\sin^2 x}$

$$\boxed{1 + \cot^2 x \equiv \operatorname{cosec}^2 x} \ldots (3)$$

The identities proved above are useful in eliminating an unknown between two trigonometrical equations.

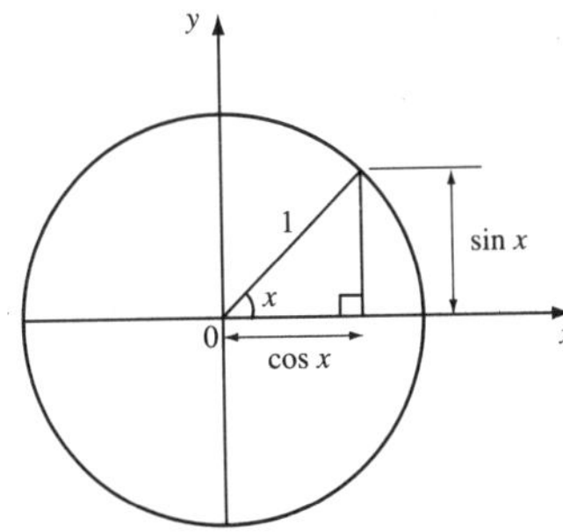

Fig. 2-I/46 $\sin^2 x + \cos^2 x \equiv 1$

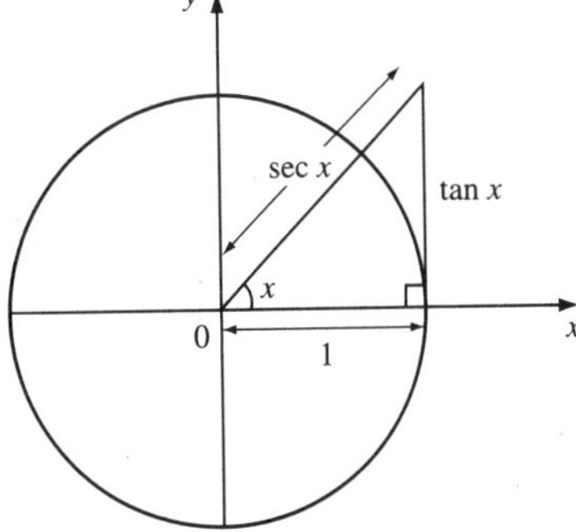

Fig. 2-I/47 $1 + \tan^2 x \equiv \sec^2 x$

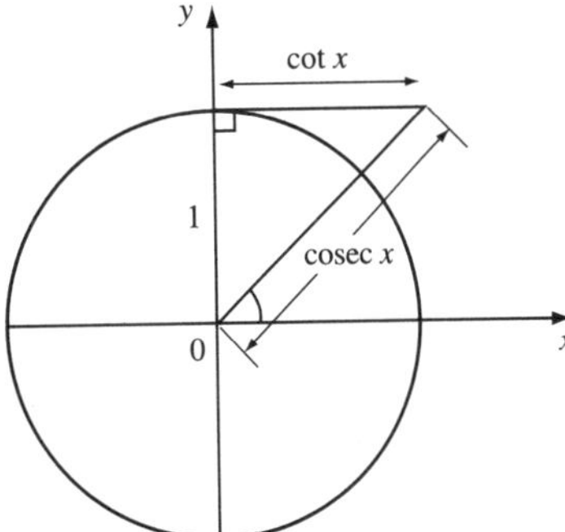

Fig. 2-I/48 $1 + \cot^2 x \equiv \operatorname{cosec}^2 x$

WORKED EXAMPLE 46

Simplify the following expressions:

(i) $\dfrac{1}{1 + \sin x} + \dfrac{1}{1 - \sin x}$

(ii) $\dfrac{1}{1 + \cos x} + \dfrac{1}{1 - \cos x}$

(iii) $\dfrac{1}{\sec x + \tan x} + \dfrac{1}{\sec x - \tan x}$

(iv) $\dfrac{1}{\operatorname{cosec} x + \cot x} + \dfrac{1}{\operatorname{cosec} x - \cot x}$

(v) $\dfrac{1}{1 + \sec x} + \dfrac{1}{1 - \sec x}$

(vi) $\dfrac{1}{1 + \operatorname{cosec} x} + \dfrac{1}{1 - \operatorname{cosec} x}$

(vii) $\dfrac{1}{\sec x + \operatorname{cosec} x} + \dfrac{1}{\operatorname{cosec} x - \sec x}$

(viii) $\dfrac{1}{\cot x - \operatorname{cosec} x} + \dfrac{1}{\cot x + \operatorname{cosec} x}$

(ix) $\dfrac{1}{\sin x + \cos x} + \dfrac{1}{\sin x - \cos x}$

(x) $\dfrac{1}{\sec x + \tan x} + \dfrac{1}{\sec x - \tan x}$.

Solution 46

(i) $\dfrac{1}{1 + \sin x} + \dfrac{1}{1 - \sin x}$

$$= \frac{1 - \sin x + 1 + \sin x}{1 - \sin^2 x} = \frac{2}{\cos^2 x} = 2\sec^2 x$$

(ii) $\dfrac{1}{1 + \cos x} + \dfrac{1}{1 - \cos x}$

$$= \frac{1 - \cos x + 1 + \cos x}{1 - \cos^2 x} = \frac{2}{\sin^2 x} = 2\operatorname{cosec}^2 x$$

(iii) $\dfrac{1}{\sec x + \tan x} + \dfrac{1}{\sec x - \tan x}$

$$= \frac{\sec x - \tan x + \sec x + \tan x}{1} = 2\sec x$$

(iv) $\dfrac{1}{\operatorname{cosec} x + \cot x} + \dfrac{1}{\operatorname{cosec} x - \cot x}$

$$= \frac{\operatorname{cosec} x - \cot x + \operatorname{cosec} x + \cot x}{\operatorname{cosec}^2 x - \cot^2 x}$$

$$= 2\operatorname{cosec} x$$

(v) $\dfrac{1}{1 + \sec x} + \dfrac{1}{1 - \sec x}$

$$= \frac{1 - \sec x + 1 + \sec x}{1 - \sec^2 x} = \frac{2}{-\tan^2 x}$$

$$= -2\cot^2 x$$

(vi) $\dfrac{1}{1 + \operatorname{cosec} x} + \dfrac{1}{1 - \operatorname{cosec} x}$

$$= \frac{1 - \operatorname{cosec} x + 1 + \operatorname{cosec} x}{1 - \operatorname{cosec}^2 x} = \frac{2}{-\cot^2 x}$$

$$= -2\tan^2 x$$

(vii) $\dfrac{1}{\sec x + \operatorname{cosec} x} + \dfrac{1}{\operatorname{cosec} x - \sec x}$

$$= \frac{\operatorname{cosec} x - \sec x + \sec x + \operatorname{cosec} x}{\operatorname{cosec}^2 x - \sec^2 x}$$

$$= \frac{2\operatorname{cosec} x}{\dfrac{1}{\sin^2 x} - \dfrac{1}{\cos^2 x}} = \frac{2\operatorname{cosec} x \sin^2 x \cos^2 x}{\cos^2 x - \sin^2 x}$$

$$= \frac{2\sin x \cos^2 x}{\cos 2x}$$

(viii) $\dfrac{1}{\cot x - \operatorname{cosec} x} + \dfrac{1}{\cot x + \operatorname{cosec} x}$

$$= \frac{\cot x + \operatorname{cosec} x + \cot x - \operatorname{cosec} x}{\cot^2 x - \operatorname{cosec}^2 x}$$

$$= \frac{2\cot x}{-1} = -2\cot x$$

(ix) $\dfrac{1}{\sin x + \cos x} + \dfrac{1}{\sin x - \cos x}$

$$= \frac{\sin x - \cos x + \sin x + \cos x}{\sin^2 x - \cos^2 x}$$

$$= \frac{2\sin x}{-\cos 2x} = \frac{-2\sin x}{\cos 2x} = -2\sin x \sec 2x$$

(x) $\dfrac{1}{\sec x + \tan x} + \dfrac{1}{\sec x - \tan x}$

$$= \frac{\sec x - \tan x + \sec x + \tan x}{\sec^2 x - \tan^2 x} = 2\sec x.$$

Exercises 11

1. Show that $(\operatorname{cosec}\Theta - \sin\Theta)(\sec\Theta - \cos\Theta)$ $(\tan\Theta + \cot\Theta) = 1$.

2. Show that $\dfrac{\operatorname{cosec}\alpha}{\operatorname{cosec}\alpha - 1} + \dfrac{\operatorname{cosec}\alpha}{\operatorname{cosec}\alpha + 1} = 2\sec^2\alpha$.

3. Show that $(1 + \cot\Theta - \operatorname{cosec}\Theta)$ $(1 + \tan\Theta + \sec\Theta) = 2$.

4. Show that $\dfrac{\tan\alpha + \sec\alpha - 1}{\tan\alpha - \sec\alpha + 1} = \dfrac{1 + \sin\alpha}{\cos\alpha}$.

5. Show that $\dfrac{1-\cos\alpha}{1+\cos\alpha} = (\cot\alpha - \operatorname{cosec}\alpha)^2$.

6. If $\tan\Theta + \sin\Theta = x$, $\tan\Theta - \sin\Theta = y$, where $0 < \Theta < \frac{\pi}{2}$, show that $x^2 - y^2 = 4\sqrt{xy}$.

7. Prove the following identities:

(i) $(\cos x + \sin x)^2 + (\cos x - \sin x)^2 = 2$

(ii) $(\cos x - \sin x)^3 - (\cos x + \sin x)^3$

$= -2\sin x - 4\sin x\cos^2 x$

(iii) $\cos^4 x - \sin^4 x = \cos 2x$

(iv) $\cos^6 x + \sin^6 x$

$= \cos^4 x - \cos^2 x\sin^2 x + \sin^4 x$

(v) $\cos^3 x - \sin^3 x$

$= (\cos x - \sin x)(1 + \sin x\cos x)$.

8. Show that:

(i) $\tan\left(\dfrac{\pi}{4} - \alpha\right)\tan\left(\dfrac{\pi}{4} + \alpha\right) = 1$

(ii) $\cos x + \cos\left(x + 2\dfrac{\pi}{3}\right) + \cos\left(x + 4\dfrac{\pi}{3}\right) = 0$

(iii) $\sin x + \sin\left(x + 2\dfrac{\pi}{3}\right) + \sin\left(x + 4\dfrac{\pi}{3}\right) = 0$

(iv) $\tan(A + B + C)$

$$= \frac{\tan A + \tan B + \tan C - \tan A\tan B\tan C}{1 - (\tan A\tan B + \tan B\tan C + \tan A\tan C)}.$$

9. Determine $\cos 5x$ in terms of $\cos x$

(**Ans.** $16\cos^5 x - 20\cos^3 x + 5\cos x$).

10. Determine $\sin 5x$ in terms of $\sin x$

(**Ans.** $16\sin^5 x - 20\sin^3 x + 5\sin x$).

12

Eliminate x between Circular Functions (LOCI)

Worked Example 47

Eliminate x between:

(i) $\sin x = a$
$\cos x = b$

(ii) $\tan x = a$
$\sec x = b$

(iii) $\sec x = a$
$\operatorname{cosec} x = b$

(iv) $\cot x = a$
$\cos x = b$

(v) $\operatorname{cosec} x = a$
$\cot x = b$

(vi) $\sin x + \cos x = a$
$\sin x - \cos x = b$

(vii) $\tan x + \cot x = a$
$\tan x - \cot x = b$

(viii) $\operatorname{cosec} x + \cot x = a$
$\operatorname{cosec} x - \cot x = b$

(ix) $\tan x + \cos x = a$
$\tan x - \cos x = b$

(x) $1 + \sin x = a$
$1 + \cos x = b$.

Solution 47

(i) $\sin x = a$ and $\cos x = b$.
Squaring up both sides of these equations, $\sin^2 x = a^2$, $\cos^2 x = b^2$ and adding $\sin^2 x + \cos^2 x = a^2 + b^2 = 1$, the relationship that exists between the two trigonometrical equations for all values of x:

$$\boxed{a^2 + b^2 = 1}$$

(ii) $\tan x = a$, and $\sec x = b$.
Squaring up both sides of these equations, $\tan^2 x = a^2$, $\sec^2 x = b^2$, $1 + \tan^2 x = \sec^2 x$.
For all values of x:

$$\boxed{1 + a^2 = b^2}$$

(iii) $\sec x = a$ and $\operatorname{cosec} x = b$.

$$\frac{\sec x}{\operatorname{cosec} x} = \frac{a}{b} = \frac{\dfrac{1}{\cos x}}{\dfrac{1}{\sin x}} = \frac{\sin x}{\cos x} = \tan x,$$

$$\left(\frac{\sec x}{\operatorname{cosec} x}\right)^2 + 1 = \sec^2 x$$

$$\boxed{\left(\frac{a}{b}\right)^2 + 1 = a^2}$$

(iv) $\cot x = a$ and $\cos x = b$,

$$\frac{\cot x}{\cos x} = \frac{\cos x}{\sin x \cos x} = \frac{1}{\sin x} = \operatorname{cosec} x = \frac{a}{b}$$

$$\left(\frac{\cot x}{\cos x}\right)^2 = 1 + \cot^2 x$$

$$\boxed{\left(\frac{a}{b}\right)^2 - 1 = a^2}$$

(v) $\operatorname{cosec} x = a$ and $\cot x = b$,

$$\operatorname{cosec}^2 x = 1 + \cot^2 x$$

$$\boxed{a^2 = 1 + b^2}$$

(vi) $\sin x + \cos x = a \qquad \ldots (1)$

$\sin x - \cos x = b \qquad \ldots (2)$

Adding both (1) and (2)

$$2\sin x = a + b \text{ or } \sin x = \frac{(a+b)}{2} \qquad \ldots(3)$$

Subtracting (2) from (1)

$$2\cos x = a - b, \cos x = \frac{(a-b)}{2} \qquad \ldots(4)$$

Squaring both (3) and (4) and adding

$$\sin^2 x + \cos^2 x = \left(\frac{a+b}{2}\right)^2 + \left(\frac{a-b}{2}\right)^2 = 1$$

$$(a+b)^2 + (a-b)^2 = 4$$

$$a^2 + 2ab + b^2 + a^2 - 2ab + b^2 = 4$$

$$\boxed{a^2 + b^2 = 2}$$

(vii) $\tan x + \cot x = a \qquad \ldots(1)$

$\tan x - \cot x = b \qquad \ldots(2)$

Adding (1) and (2)

$$2\tan x = a + b \text{ or } \tan x = \frac{(a+b)}{2}$$

Subtracting (2) from (1)

$$2\cot x = a - b \text{ or } \cot x = \frac{(a-b)}{2}$$

$$\tan x \cot x = \left(\frac{a+b}{2}\right)\left(\frac{a-b}{2}\right) = 1$$

$$\boxed{a^2 - b^2 = 4}$$

(viii) $\operatorname{cosec} x + \cot x = a \qquad \ldots(1)$

$\operatorname{cosec} x - \cot x = b \qquad \ldots(2)$

Adding (1) and (2)

$$\operatorname{cosec} x = \left(\frac{a+b}{2}\right) \qquad \ldots(3)$$

Subtracting (2) from (1)

$$\cot x = \left(\frac{a-b}{2}\right) \qquad \ldots(4)$$

Squaring up both sides of (3) and (4), and apply $\operatorname{cosec}^2 x = 1 + \cot^2 x$

$$\left(\frac{a+b}{2}\right)^2 = 1 + \left(\frac{a-b}{2}\right)^2,$$

$$(a+b)^2 = 4 + (a-b)^2$$

$$a^2 + 2ab + b^2 = 4 + a^2 - 2ab + b^2$$

$$\boxed{ab = 1}$$

(ix) $\tan x + \cos x = a \qquad \ldots(1)$

$\tan x - \cos x = b \qquad \ldots(2)$

Adding (1) and (2)

$2\tan x = a + b \qquad \ldots(3)$

Subtracting (2) from (1)

$2\cos x = a - b \qquad \ldots(4)$

Using $\tan^2 x = \sec^2 x - 1$

$$\boxed{\frac{(a+b)^2}{4} = \frac{4}{(a-b)^2} - 1}$$

(x) $1 + \sin x = a \qquad \ldots(1)$

$1 + \cos x = b \qquad \ldots(2)$

From (1) $\sin x = a - 1$, and squaring up $\sin^2 x = (a-1)^2$

From (2) $\cos x = b - 1$, and squaring up $\cos^2 x = (b-1)^2$

$$\boxed{(a-1)^2 + (b-1)^2 = 1}$$

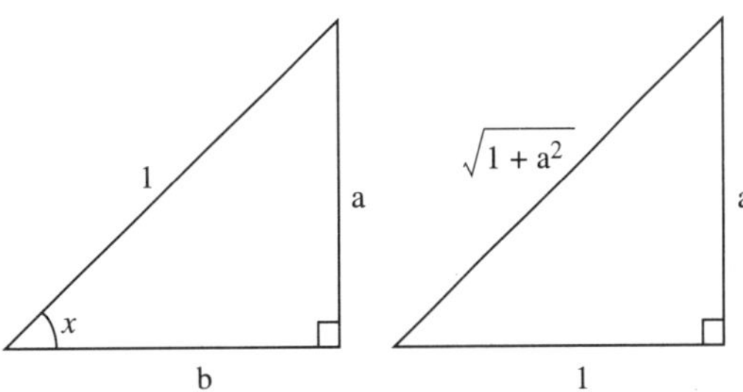

Fig. 2-I/49 $a^2 + b^2 = 1$

WORKED EXAMPLE 48

Given that $x = 3\sin\left(Kt - \frac{\pi}{3}\right)$, and $y = 4\sin\left(Kt + \frac{\pi}{6}\right)$, find the cartesian equation of the locus of the point (x, y) as t varies.

Solution 48

$$x = 3\sin\left(Kt - \frac{\pi}{3}\right)$$

$$x = 3\sin Kt\cos\frac{\pi}{3} - 3\sin\frac{\pi}{3}\cos Kt$$

$$y = 4\sin\left(Kt + \frac{\pi}{6}\right)$$

$$y = 4\sin Kt\cos\frac{\pi}{6} + 4\sin\frac{\pi}{6}\cos Kt$$

$$x = \frac{3}{2}\sin Kt - \frac{3\sqrt{3}}{2}\cos Kt \qquad \ldots(1)$$

$$y = 2\sqrt{3}\sin Kt + 2\cos Kt \qquad \ldots(2)$$

Multiplying equations (1) by 2, and (2) by $\frac{3\sqrt{3}}{2}$

$$2x = 3\sin Kt - 3\sqrt{3}\cos Kt \qquad \ldots(3)$$

$$\frac{3\sqrt{3}}{2}y = 9\sin Kt + 3\sqrt{3}\cos Kt \qquad \ldots(4)$$

Adding (3) and (4)

$$12\sin Kt = 2x + \frac{3\sqrt{3}}{2}y \text{ or}$$

$$\boxed{\sin Kt = \frac{1}{6}x + \frac{\sqrt{3}}{8}y} \qquad (7)$$

Multiplying equations (1) by $2\sqrt{3}$ and (2) by $\frac{3}{2}$

$$2\sqrt{3}x = \frac{3}{2}2\sqrt{3}\sin Kt - \frac{3\sqrt{3}}{2}2\sqrt{3}\cos Kt \qquad \ldots(5)$$

$$\frac{3}{2}y = \frac{3}{2}2\sqrt{3}\sin Kt + \frac{6}{2}\cos Kt \qquad \ldots(6)$$

Subtracting equation (5) from (6)

$$\frac{3}{2}y - 2\sqrt{3}x = 3\cos Kt + 9\cos Kt,$$

$$12\cos Kt = \frac{3}{2}y - 2\sqrt{3}x$$

$$\boxed{\cos Kt = \frac{1}{8}y - \frac{\sqrt{3}}{6}x} \qquad (8)$$

Squaring up (7) and (8) and adding

$$\sin^2 Kt + \cos^2 Kt$$

$$= \left(\frac{1}{6}x + \frac{\sqrt{3}}{8}y\right)^2 + \left(\frac{1}{8}y - \frac{\sqrt{3}}{6}x\right)^2 = 1$$

$$\frac{1}{36}x^2 + \frac{3}{64}y^2 + \frac{\sqrt{3}}{24}xy + \frac{1}{64}y^2 + \frac{3}{36}x^2 - \frac{\sqrt{3}}{24}xy = 1$$

$$\frac{4}{64}y^2 + \frac{4}{36}x^2 = 1, \ \frac{x^2}{9} + \frac{y^2}{16} = 1$$

$$\boxed{\frac{y^2}{4^2} + \frac{x^2}{3^2} = 1}$$

This is an ellipse.

It can be seen that $\sin^2\left(Kt - \frac{\pi}{3}\right) + \sin^2\left(Kt + \frac{\pi}{6}\right) = 1$ where $\sin\left(Kt + \frac{\pi}{6}\right) = \cos\left(Kt + \frac{\pi}{6} - \frac{\pi}{2}\right) = \cos\left(Kt - \frac{\pi}{3}\right)$.

WORKED EXAMPLE 49

The coordinates of two points A and B are

$$\left[\frac{\tan\Theta}{1 - \sec\Theta + \tan\Theta}, \frac{\tan\Theta}{1 - \sec\Theta + \tan\Theta}\right] \text{ and}$$

$$\left[\frac{\tan\Theta}{\sec\Theta - \tan\Theta + 1}, \frac{\tan\Theta}{\sec\Theta - \tan\Theta + 1}\right]$$

respectively.

Show that these coordinates expressed as half angles are

$$\left[\frac{\cos\frac{\Theta}{2}}{\cos\frac{\Theta}{2} - \sin\frac{\Theta}{2}}, \frac{\cos\frac{\Theta}{2}}{\cos\frac{\Theta}{2} - \sin\frac{\Theta}{2}}\right] \text{ and}$$

$$\left[\frac{\sin\frac{\Theta}{2}}{\cos\frac{\Theta}{2} - \sin\frac{\Theta}{2}}, \frac{\sin\frac{\Theta}{2}}{\cos\frac{\Theta}{2} - \sin\frac{\Theta}{2}}\right]$$

and hence show that the length AB is independent of the parameter. Find its value.

Solution 49

$$A\left(\frac{\tan\Theta}{1-\sec\Theta+\tan\Theta}, \frac{\tan\Theta}{1-\sec\Theta+\tan\Theta}\right)$$

$$B\left(\frac{\tan\Theta}{\sec\Theta-\tan\Theta+1}, \frac{\tan\Theta}{\sec\Theta-\tan\Theta+1}\right)$$

$$\frac{\tan\Theta}{1-\sec\Theta+\tan\Theta}$$

$$=\frac{\tan\Theta}{1-\sec\Theta+\tan\Theta}\times\frac{\cos\Theta}{\cos\Theta}$$

$$=\frac{\sin\Theta}{\cos\Theta-1+\sin\Theta}$$

$$=\frac{2\sin\frac{\Theta}{2}\cos\frac{\Theta}{2}}{2\cos^2\frac{\Theta}{2}-1-1+2\sin\frac{\Theta}{2}\cos\frac{\Theta}{2}}$$

$$=\frac{\sin\frac{\Theta}{2}\cos\frac{\Theta}{2}}{\cos^2\frac{\Theta}{2}-1+\sin\frac{\Theta}{2}\cos\frac{\Theta}{2}}$$

$$=\frac{\sin\frac{\Theta}{2}\cos\frac{\Theta}{2}}{\sin\frac{\Theta}{2}\cos\frac{\Theta}{2}-\sin^2\frac{\Theta}{2}}$$

$$=\frac{\cos\frac{\Theta}{2}}{\cos\frac{\Theta}{2}-\sin\frac{\Theta}{2}}$$

$$\frac{\tan\Theta}{1+\sec\Theta-\tan\Theta}=\frac{\tan\Theta}{1+\sec\Theta-\tan\Theta}\times\frac{\cos\Theta}{\cos\Theta}$$

$$=\frac{\sin\Theta}{\cos\Theta+1-\sin\Theta}$$

$$=\frac{\sin\frac{\Theta}{2}}{\cos\frac{\Theta}{2}-\sin\frac{\Theta}{2}}$$

$$AB=\sqrt{\left(\frac{\tan\Theta}{1-\sec\Theta+\tan\Theta}-\frac{\tan\Theta}{\sec\Theta-\tan\Theta+1}\right)^2+\left(\frac{\tan\Theta}{1-\sec\Theta+\tan\Theta}-\frac{\tan\Theta}{\sec\Theta+1-\tan\Theta}\right)^2}$$

$$=\sqrt{\left(\frac{\cos\frac{\Theta}{2}}{\cos\frac{\Theta}{2}-\sin\frac{\Theta}{2}}-\frac{\sin\frac{\Theta}{2}}{\cos\frac{\Theta}{2}-\sin\frac{\Theta}{2}}\right)^2+\left(\frac{\cos\frac{\Theta}{2}-\sin\frac{\Theta}{2}}{\cos\frac{\Theta}{2}-\sin\frac{\Theta}{2}}\right)^2}$$

$$=\sqrt{\left(\frac{\cos\frac{\Theta}{2}-\sin\frac{\Theta}{2}}{\cos\frac{\Theta}{2}-\sin\frac{\Theta}{2}}\right)^2+(1)}=\sqrt{2}.$$

Exercises 12

1. Eliminate x between the following circular functions:

   $m\sin x=a$

   $n\cos x=b$

2. Eliminate x between the following circular functions:

   $\sin x=p$

   $\cos x=q$

3. Eliminate x between the following circular functions:

   $\operatorname{cosec} x+\cot x=m$

   $\operatorname{cosec} x-\cot x=n$

4. Eliminate x between the following circular functions:

   $\sin x+\cos x=2p$

   $\sin x-\cos x=3q$

5. Given that $x = 5\sin\left(\omega t+\frac{\pi}{4}\right)$ and $y = 7\sin\left(\omega t-\frac{\pi}{6}\right)$, find the cartesian equation of the locus of the point (x, y) as t varies.

6. Eliminate x between:

   $\cos x+\tan x=m$, and $\tan x-\cos x=n$

13

Trigonometric Equations

There are two types of solutions of trigonometric equations:

(a) The solution of an equation in a specified interval, and

(b) The general solution of an equation.

Solution in a Specified Interval

Let us consider the simple trigonometric equation $\sin x = \frac{1}{2}$, whose solution is required in the range $0° \le x \le 360°$.

Solution

$$\sin x = \frac{1}{2} = \sin 30° = \sin 150°.$$

There are two angles between 0° and 360° whose sine is equal to $\frac{1}{2}$, that is, sin 30° and sin 150°. The solutions in this range are: $x = 30°, 150°$.

The General Solution of sin *x*

The general solution of $\sin x = \frac{1}{2}$ is given by the formula $x = n\pi + (-1)^n \frac{\pi}{6}$, where $\sin \frac{\pi}{6} = \frac{1}{2}$, that is the first angle whose sine is equal to $\frac{1}{2}$.

By putting $n = -1, 0, 1, 2, 3, \ldots\ldots$ we obtain the following angles:

$$n = -1 \quad x = -\pi - \frac{\pi}{6} = -\frac{7\pi}{6}$$

$$n = 0 \quad x = \frac{\pi}{6}$$

$$n = 1 \quad x = \pi - \frac{\pi}{6} = \frac{5\pi}{6}$$

$$n = 2 \quad x = \frac{2}{\pi} + \frac{\pi}{6} = \frac{13\pi}{6}$$

$$n = 3 \quad x = 3\pi - \frac{\pi}{6} = \frac{17\pi}{6} \text{ and so on.}$$

Let us examine the meaning of these angles in the General Solution, by referring to the sine graph.

By drawing the line $y = \frac{1}{2}$ on the graph Fig. 2-I/50, it is observed that the line intersects the graph at the angles $x = -\frac{7\pi}{6}, \frac{\pi}{6}, \frac{5\pi}{6}, \frac{13\pi}{6}, \frac{17\pi}{6}$ and so on indefinitely.

If in general $\sin x = a = \sin \alpha$ the general solution is

$$\boxed{x = n\pi + (-1)^n \alpha}$$

where $n = 0, \pm 1, \pm 2, \pm 3$, etc.

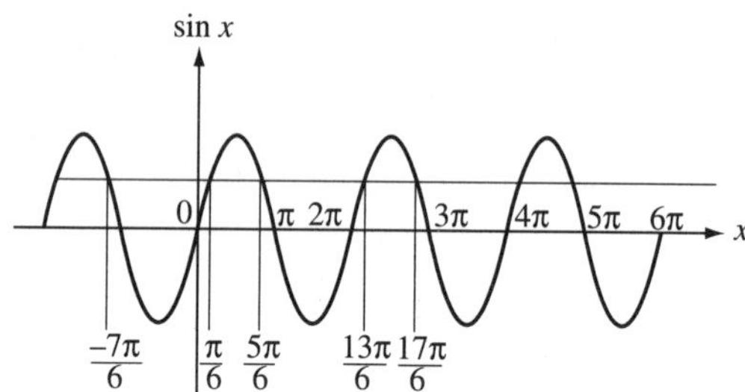

Fig. 2-I/50 The general solution of $\sin x = \frac{1}{2}$

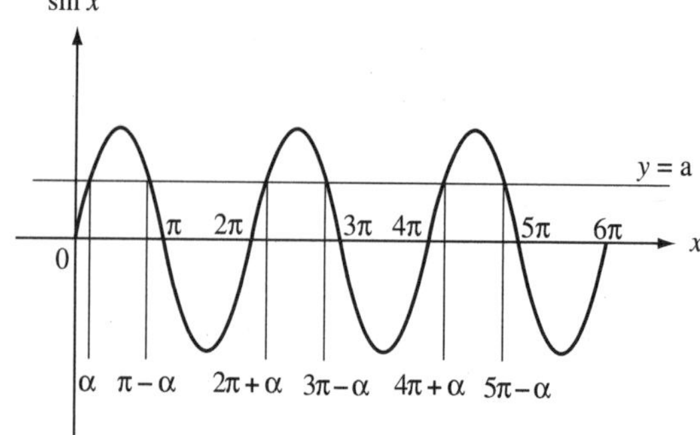

Fig. 2-I/51 The general solution $x = n\pi + (-1)^n\alpha$ where $n = 0, \pm 1, \pm 2, \pm 3$, etc.

Show that the general solutions of $x = \sin \alpha$ are $x = 2n\pi + \alpha$ or $x = (2n + 1)\pi - \alpha$ and hence show that the general solution is

$$\boxed{x = n\pi + (-1)^n\alpha}$$

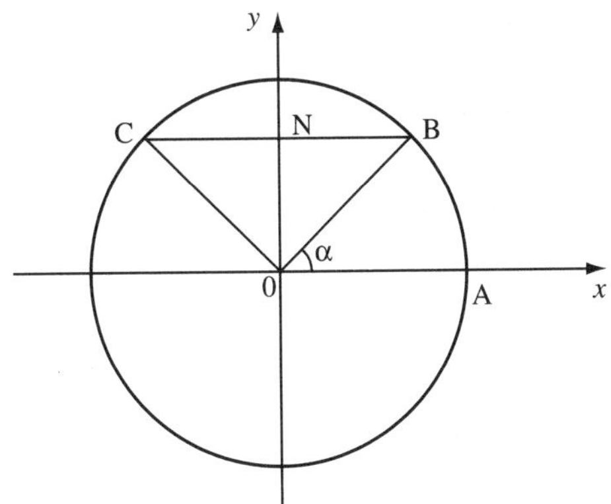

Fig. 2-I/52 The proof of $x = n\pi + (-1)^n\alpha$

Let the arc AB subtend an angle α where $\sin\alpha = ON$ and AC subtends an angle $\pi - \alpha$ where $\sin\alpha = \sin(\pi - \alpha) = ON$ then

$$\boxed{x = 2n\pi + \alpha} \qquad \ldots(1)$$

where $n = 0, 1, 2, 3,$ - - - - - - - or

$$\boxed{x = (2n+1)\pi - \alpha} \qquad \ldots(2)$$

where $n = 0, 1, 2, 3$ - - - - - - - then the general solution will be

$$\boxed{x = n\pi + (-1)^n\alpha} \qquad \ldots(3)$$

Since when $n = 2k$ in (3), it gives (1) $x = 2k\pi + (-1)^{2k}\alpha = 2k\pi + \alpha$, when $n = 2k+1$, $x = (2k+1)\pi + (-1)^{2k+1}\alpha$ it gives (2) $x = (2k+1)\pi - \alpha$.

Worked Example 50

Find all the solutions between 0° and 360° of the following equations:

(i) $6(1 - \cos^2 x) = \sin x + 1$

(ii) $2\sin^2 x - \sin x - 1 = 0$

(iii) $\left(\sin x + \frac{\sqrt{3}}{2}\right)\left(\sin x - \frac{1}{\sqrt{2}}\right) = 0$

Solution 50

(i) $6(1 - \cos^2 x) = \sin x + 1$

$$6\sin^2 x - \sin x - 1 = 0$$

$$\sin x = \frac{1 \pm \sqrt{1+24}}{12} = \frac{1 \pm 5}{12} = \frac{1}{2} \text{ or } -\frac{1}{3}$$

$$\sin x = \frac{1}{2} = \sin 30° = \sin 150°, x = 30°, 150°$$

$$\sin x = -\frac{1}{3} = \sin 199° 28' = \sin 340° 31'$$

$$x = 199° 28', 340° 31'.$$

Therefore $x = 30°, 150°, 199° 28', 340° 31'$.

(ii) $2\sin^2 x - \sin x - 1 = 0$

$$\sin x = \frac{1 \pm \sqrt{1+8}}{4} = \frac{1 \pm 3}{4} = 1 \text{ or } -\frac{1}{2},$$

$$\sin x = 1 = \sin\frac{\pi}{2} = \sin 90°$$

$$\sin x = -\frac{1}{2} = \sin 210° = \sin 330°$$

$$x = 90°, 210°, 330°.$$

(iii) $\left(\sin x + \frac{\sqrt{3}}{2}\right)\left(\sin x - \frac{1}{\sqrt{2}}\right) = 0$

$$\sin x + \frac{\sqrt{3}}{2} = 0 \text{ or } \sin x - \frac{1}{\sqrt{2}} = 0$$

$$\sin x = -\frac{\sqrt{3}}{2} = \sin 240° = \sin 300°$$

$$\sin x = \frac{1}{\sqrt{2}} = 45° = \sin 135°$$

$$x = 45°, 135°, 240°, 300°.$$

Worked Example 51

Solve the equation $\sin\left(3x - \frac{\pi}{4}\right) = -\frac{1}{2}$ when $0 < x < 2\pi$.

Solution 51

$$\sin\left(3x - \frac{\pi}{4}\right) = -\frac{1}{2} = \sin\frac{7\pi}{6} = \sin\frac{11\pi}{6} = \sin\left(-\frac{\pi}{6}\right)$$

$$= \sin\frac{19\pi}{6} = \sin\frac{23\pi}{6} = \sin\frac{31\pi}{6}$$

$$3x - \frac{\pi}{4} = -\frac{\pi}{6} \text{ or } 3x = \frac{2\pi}{24} = \frac{\pi}{12} \text{ or } x = \frac{\pi}{36}$$

$$3x - \frac{\pi}{4} = \frac{7\pi}{6} \text{ or } 3x = \frac{17\pi}{12} \text{ or } x = \frac{17\pi}{36}$$

$$3x - \frac{\pi}{4} = \frac{11\pi}{6} \text{ or } 3x = \frac{25\pi}{12} \text{ or } x = \frac{25\pi}{36}$$

$$3x - \frac{\pi}{4} = \frac{19\pi}{6} \text{ or } 3x = \frac{41\pi}{12} \text{ or } x = \frac{41\pi}{36}$$

$$3x - \frac{\pi}{4} = \frac{23\pi}{6} \text{ or } 3x = \frac{49\pi}{12} \text{ or } x = \frac{49\pi}{36}$$

$$3x - \frac{\pi}{4} = \frac{31\pi}{6} \text{ or } 3x = \frac{65\pi}{12} \text{ or } x = \frac{65\pi}{36}.$$

WORKED EXAMPLE 52

Show that $\sin 3x = 3\sin x - 4\sin^3 x$, and hence solve the equation $6\sin x - 8\sin^3 x = 1$ for $0° < x < 360°$.

Solution 52

See proof in text:

$$6\sin x - 8\sin^3 x = 1$$

$$2(3\sin x - 4\sin^3 x) = 1$$

$$2\sin 3x = 1$$

$$\sin 3x = \frac{1}{2} = \sin 30° = \sin 150° = \sin 390°$$

$$= \sin 510° = \sin 750° = \sin 870°$$

$$x = 10°, 50°, 130°, 170°, 250°, 290°.$$

WORKED EXAMPLE 53

Solve the equation $4 + \sin 2x = 10\cos^2 x$ for $0° \leq x \leq 360°$.

Solution 53

$$4 + \sin 2x = 10\cos^2 x \qquad \ldots(1)$$

$\cos 2x = 2\cos^2 x - 1$ or $\cos 2x + 1 = 2\cos^2 x$ and substituting this in equation (1)

$$4 + \sin 2x = 5(\cos 2x + 1)$$

$$\sin 2x - 5\cos 2x = 1 \qquad \ldots(2)$$

There are three methods by which this equation can be solved:

(a) The graphical method which is rather tedious.

(b) Employing the t-formulae, or

(c) Employing the $R\sin(2x - \alpha)$ form.

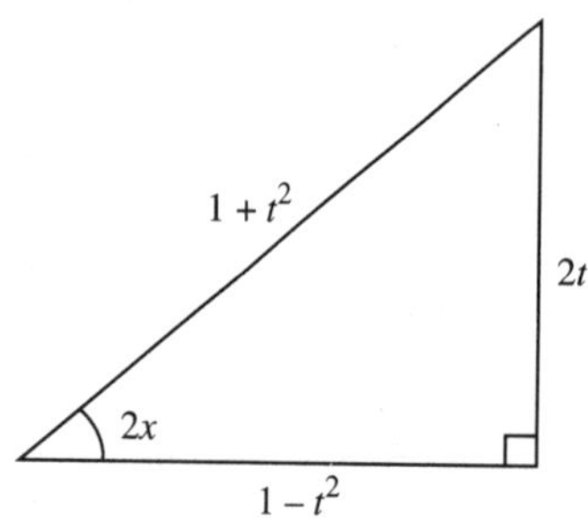

Fig. 2-I/53 t-formulae

(b) t - Formulae Method

Where $t = \tan x$, $\sin 2x = \dfrac{2t}{1+t^2}$

$$\cos 2x = \frac{1-t^2}{1+t^2}.$$

Substituting these equations in (2)

$$\frac{2t}{1+t^2} - 5\left(\frac{1-t^2}{1+t^2}\right) = 1$$

$$2t - 5 + 5t^2 = 1 + t^2$$

$$4t^2 + 2t - 6 = 0$$

$$2t^2 + t - 3 = 0$$

$$t = \frac{-1 \pm \sqrt{1+24}}{4} = \frac{-1 \pm 5}{4} = -\frac{3}{2} \text{ or } 1$$

$$\tan x = -\frac{3}{2} = \tan 123° 41' = \tan 303° 41',$$

$$x = 123° 41' \text{ or } 303° 41'$$

$$\tan x = 1 = \tan 45° = \tan 225°.$$

The solutions of x are:

$$x = 45°, 123° 41', 225°, 303° 41'.$$

(c) *ALTERNATIVELY*

$$\sin 2x - 5\cos 2x = R\sin(2x - \alpha)$$

$$= R\sin 2x\cos\alpha - R\sin\alpha\cos 2x.$$

Equating the coefficients of $\sin 2x$ and $\cos 2x$, $R\cos\alpha = 1$, $R\sin\alpha = 5$.

$$R = \sqrt{5^2 + 1} = \sqrt{26}, \tan\alpha = 5, \alpha = 78° 41'.$$

$$\sin(2x - 78° 41) = \frac{1}{\sqrt{26}} = \sin 11° 19'$$

$$= \sin 168° 41' = \sin 371° 19' = \sin 528° 41'$$

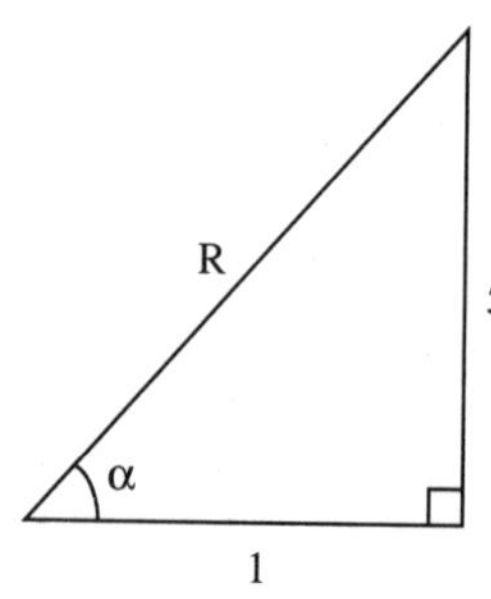

Fig. 2-I/54 $\alpha = 78° 41'$ $\quad R = \sqrt{26}$

$2x - 78° 41' = 11° 19'$, $2x = 90°$ or $x = 45°$, $2x - 78° 41' = 168° 41'$ or

$2x = 247° 22'$ or $x = 123° 41'$, $2x - 78° 41' = 371° 19'$ or $x = 225°$,

$2x - 78° 41' = 528° 41'$ or $x = 303° 41'$.

Therefore $x = 45°, 123° 41', 225°, 303° 41'$.

WORKED EXAMPLE 54

Solve $\sin 5x = -0.866$ when $0 \le x \le 180°$.

Solution 54

$\sin 5x = -0.866 = \sin 240° = \sin 300° = \sin 600° = \sin 660°$

$$5x = 240°, x = 48°$$

$$5x = 300°, x = 60°$$

$$5x = 600°, x = 120°$$

$$5x = 660°, x = 132°.$$

WORKED EXAMPLE 55

Show that, for all values of Θ and α,

$$\sin\Theta + \sin(\Theta + \alpha) + \sin(\Theta + 2\alpha) = (1 + 2\cos\alpha)\sin(\Theta + \alpha).$$

Hence solve the equation:

$\sin\Theta + \sin(\Theta + \alpha) + \sin(\Theta + 2\alpha) = 0$ for values of α and Θ in the interval $0 < \Theta < 2\pi, 0 < \alpha < 2\pi$.

Solution 55

To show that $\sin\Theta + \sin(\Theta + \alpha) + \sin(\Theta + 2\alpha) = (1 + 2\cos\alpha)\sin(\Theta + \alpha)$

L.H.S. $\sin(\Theta+\alpha) + \{\sin\Theta + \sin(\Theta + 2\alpha)\} = \sin(\Theta + \alpha) + 2\sin(\Theta + \alpha)\cos\alpha = \sin(\Theta + \alpha)(1 + 2\cos\alpha) =$ R.H.S.

$$\sin(\Theta + \alpha)(1 + 2\cos\alpha) = 0$$

Either $\sin(\Theta + \alpha) = 0$.(1)

or $1 + 2\cos\alpha = 0$. (2)

From (1) $\sin(\Theta + \alpha) = 0 = \sin\pi = \sin 2\pi = \sin 3\pi$, $\Theta + \alpha = \pi$ *or*

$\Theta + \alpha = 2\pi$ or $\Theta + \alpha = 3\pi$.

From (2) $1 + 2\cos\alpha = 0$, $2\cos\alpha = -1$,

$$\cos\alpha = -\frac{1}{2} = \cos 120° = \cos 240°,$$

$$\alpha = 120° \text{ or } 240°.$$

GENERAL SOLUTION of $\cos x = a$

If $\cos x = a = \cos\alpha$, then $x = 2n\pi \pm \alpha$ is the general solution.

WORKED EXAMPLE 56

Find the general solution of $\cos x = -\dfrac{1}{2}$.

Solution 56

$$\cos x = -\frac{1}{2} = \cos\frac{2\pi}{3}$$

The first angle from the reference that gives the cosine equal to $-\frac{1}{2}$ is $\frac{2\pi}{3}$.

$$x = \frac{2n}{\pi} \pm \frac{2\pi}{3}.$$

For $n = 0$ $\quad x = \dfrac{2\pi}{3}$ or $x = -\dfrac{2\pi}{3}$.

For $n = 1$ $\quad x = 2\pi + \dfrac{2\pi}{3} = \dfrac{8\pi}{3}$ or

$$x = 2\pi - \frac{2\pi}{3} = \frac{4\pi}{3}.$$

GENERAL SOLUTION of $\tan x = a$

The general solution of $\tan x = a$ is $\boxed{x = n\pi + \alpha}$ where $\tan\alpha = a$.

Find the general solution of $\tan x = 2 = \tan 63° 26'$.

The general solution is $x = n\,180° + 63° 26'$.

WORKED EXAMPLE 57

Find the solutions of $3\tan 2x = \cot x$ for which $0° < x < 360°$.

Solution 57

$3\tan 2x = \cot x \quad 3\left(\dfrac{2\tan x}{1 - \tan^2 x}\right) = \dfrac{1}{\tan x}$

$6\tan^2 x = 1 - \tan^2 x \Rightarrow 7\tan^2 x = 1$

$$\Rightarrow \tan x = \pm\frac{1}{\sqrt{7}}$$

$$\tan x = \frac{1}{\sqrt{7}} = \tan 20^\circ 42'$$

$$x = 20^\circ 42' \text{ or } 200^\circ 42'$$

$$\tan x = -\frac{1}{\sqrt{7}} = \tan 159^\circ 17'$$

$$x = 159^\circ 17' \text{ or } 339^\circ 17'.$$

Therefore, the solutions of x in the specified range are:

$$x = 20^\circ 42', 159^\circ 17', 200^\circ 42', 339^\circ 17'.$$

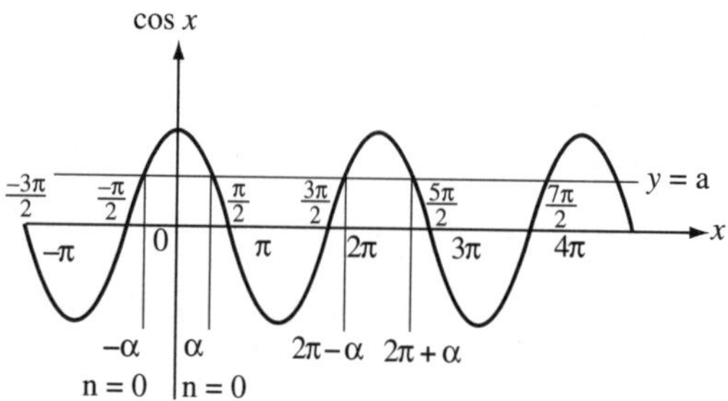

Fig. 2-I/55 The general solution of $\cos x = \cos \alpha$ is $x = 2n\pi \pm \alpha$

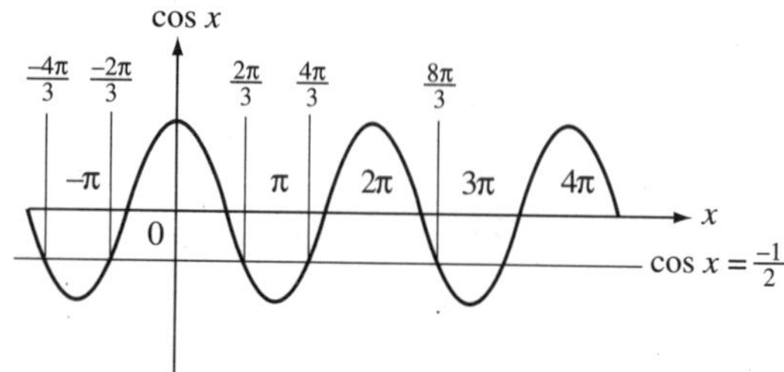

Fig. 2-I/56 The general solution of $\cos x = -\frac{1}{2}$

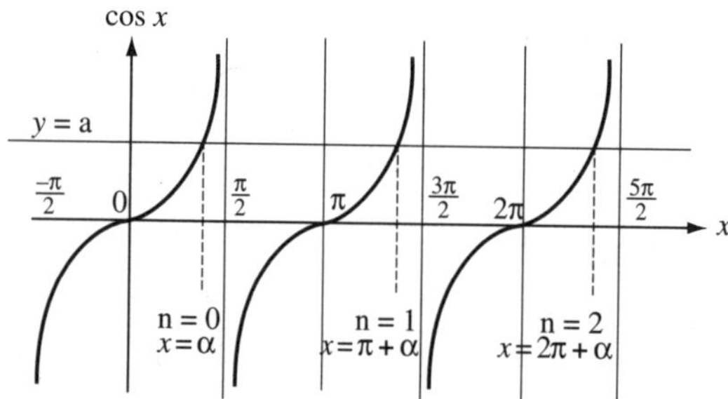

Fig. 2-I/57 The general solution of $\tan x = a = \tan \alpha$, $x = \alpha + n\pi$

Worked Example 58

Find all the solutions between 0° and 360° of the following equations:

(i) $\tan^2 x - 3\tan x + 2 = 0$

(ii) $(\tan x - 1)(\tan x - 3) = 0$.

Solution 58

(i) $\tan^2 x - 3\tan x + 2 = 0$

$$\tan x = \frac{3 \pm \sqrt{9-8}}{2} = \frac{3 \pm 1}{2} = 2 \text{ or } 1,$$

$$\tan x = 2, x = 63^\circ 26' \text{ and } x = 243^\circ 26',$$

$$\tan x = 1, x = 45^\circ \text{ and } x = 225^\circ,$$

$$x = 45^\circ, 63^\circ 26', 225^\circ, 243^\circ 26'.$$

(ii) $(\tan x - 1)(\tan x - 3) = 0$

$$\tan x = 1, x = 45^\circ \text{ and } 225^\circ$$

$$\tan x = 3, x = 71^\circ 34' \text{ and } 251^\circ 34', \; x = 45^\circ, 71^\circ 34', 225^\circ, 251^\circ 34'.$$

Worked Example 59

Show that:

(i) $\operatorname{cosec} 2x + \cot 2x = \cot x$

(ii) $\operatorname{cosec} 2x - \cot 2x = \tan x$.

Hence prove that $\operatorname{cosec}^2 2x = 1 + \cot^2 2x$, and deduce the values of $\tan 22\frac{1}{2}^\circ$, $\cot 22\frac{1}{2}^\circ$, $\tan 75^\circ$, and $\cot 75^\circ$ in surd form.

Solution 59

(i) $$\operatorname{cosec} 2x + \cot 2x = \frac{1 + \tan^2 x}{2\tan x} - \frac{1 - \tan^2 x}{2\tan x}$$

$$= \frac{2}{2\tan x} = \cot x$$

$$\operatorname{cosec} 2x + \cot 2x = \cot x.$$

(ii) $$\operatorname{cosec} 2x - \cot 2x = \frac{1 + \tan^2 x}{2\tan x} - \frac{1 - \tan^2 x}{2\tan x}$$

$$= \frac{2\tan^2 x}{2\tan x} = \tan x$$

$(\text{cosec}2x + \cot 2x)(\text{cosec}2x - \cot 2x)$

$= \cot x \tan x; \text{cosec}^2 2x - \cot^2 2x = 1.$

Therefore $\text{cosec}^2 2x = 1 + \cot^2 2x$.

$\tan 22\frac{1}{2}^\circ = \text{cosec}\, 45^\circ - \cot 45^\circ = \sqrt{2} - 1$

$\cot 22\frac{1}{2}^\circ = \text{cosec}\, 45^\circ + \cot 45^\circ = \sqrt{2} + 1$

$\tan 75^\circ = \text{cosec}\, 150^\circ - \cot 150^\circ = 2 + \sqrt{3}.$

$\cot 75^\circ = \text{cosec}\, 150^\circ + \cot 150^\circ = 2 - \sqrt{3}.$

Worked Example 60

Find the general solution of $\cos x = \sin 4x$.

Solution 60

$$\cos x = \sin 4x = 2 \sin 2x \cos 2x$$

$$\cos x = 2(2 \sin x \cos x)(2 \cos^2 x - 1)$$

$$\cos x = 8 \sin x \cos^3 x - 4 \sin x \cos x$$

$$\cos x(1 - 8 \sin x \cos^2 x + 4 \sin x) = 0$$

$$\cos x(1 - 8 \sin x\{1 - \sin^2 x\} + 4 \sin x) = 0$$

$$\cos x(8 \sin^3 x - 4 \sin x + 1) = 0.$$

Either $\cos x = 0, x = 2n\pi \pm \frac{\pi}{2}$ general solution or $8 \sin^3 x - 4 \sin x + 1 = 0$.

Let $\sin x = \frac{1}{2}, 8\left(\frac{1}{8}\right) - 4\left(\frac{1}{2}\right) + 1 = 0$, therefore $\sin x - \frac{1}{2}$ is a factor,

$$\begin{array}{r|l} & 8 \sin^2 x + 4 \sin x - 2 \\ \hline \sin x - \frac{1}{2} & 8 \sin^3 x - 4 \sin x + 1 \\ & 8 \sin^3 x - 4 \sin^2 x \\ \hline & 4 \sin^2 x - 4 \sin x + 1 \\ & 4 \sin^2 x - 2 \sin x \\ \hline & -2 \sin x + 1 \\ & -2 \sin x + 1 \\ \hline & 0 \end{array}$$

$$\left(\sin x - \frac{1}{2}\right)(8 \sin^2 x + 4 \sin x - 2) = 0$$

$$\sin x = \frac{1}{2}, \quad \boxed{x = n\pi + (-1)^n \frac{\pi}{6}}$$

$8 \sin^2 x + 4 \sin x - 2 = 0$ or $4 \sin^2 x + 2 \sin x - 1 = 0$

$$\sin x = \frac{-2 \pm \sqrt{4 + 16}}{8} = \frac{-2 \pm \sqrt{20}}{8} = \frac{-1 \pm \sqrt{5}}{4}$$

$$\sin x = \frac{-1 + \sqrt{5}}{4} = 0.3090169$$

$$x = 18^\circ \quad \boxed{x = n\pi + (-1)^n 18^\circ}$$

$$\sin x = \frac{-1 - \sqrt{5}}{4} = -0.8090169$$

$$x = -54^\circ \quad \boxed{x = n\pi + (-1)^n (-54^\circ)}$$

Worked Example 61

Solve the equation $\sin x = \cos 4x$ for values of x between 0° and 180°.

Solution 61

$$\sin x = \cos 4x = 2 \cos^2 2x - 1 = 1 - 2 \sin^2 2x$$

$$\sin x = 1 - 2(2 \sin x \cos x)^2 = 1 - 8 \sin^2 x \cos^2 x$$

$$\sin x = 1 - 8 \sin^2 x(1 - \sin^2 x)$$

$$\sin x = 1 - 8 \sin^2 x + 8 \sin^4 x$$

$$8 \sin^4 x - 8 \sin^2 x - \sin x + 1 = 0.$$

Let $\sin x = 1, 8 - 8 - 1 + 1 = 0$, then $(\sin x - 1)$ is a factor

$$\begin{array}{r|l} & 8 \sin^3 x + 8 \sin^2 x - 1 \\ \hline \sin x - 1 & 8 \sin^4 x - 8 \sin^2 x - \sin x + 1 \\ & 8 \sin^4 x - 8 \sin^3 x \\ \hline & 8 \sin^3 x - 8 \sin^2 x - \sin x + 1 \\ & 8 \sin^3 x - 8 \sin^2 x \\ \hline & -\sin x + 1 \\ & -\sin x + 1 \\ \hline & 0 \end{array}$$

$$(\sin x - 1)(8 \sin^3 x + 8 \sin^2 x - 1) = 0.$$

Either $\sin x - 1 = 0, \sin x = 1, x = \frac{\pi}{2}$ or $8 \sin^3 x + 8 \sin^2 x - 1 = 0$.

Let $\sin x = -\frac{1}{2}$

$$8\left(-\frac{1}{2}\right)^3 + 8\left(-\frac{1}{2}\right)^2 - 1 = 0 \Rightarrow \sin x + \frac{1}{2} = 0.$$

Dividing $8 \sin^3 x + 8 \sin^2 x - 1$ by $\sin x + \frac{1}{2}$ gives $8 \sin^2 x + 4 \sin x - 2$.

Either $\sin x + \frac{1}{2} = 0$ or $8 \sin^2 x + 4 \sin x - 2 = 0$

$\sin x = -\frac{1}{2}$ no solution

$$\sin x = \frac{-4 \pm \sqrt{16+64}}{16} = \frac{-1 \pm \sqrt{5}}{4}$$

$$\sin x = \frac{-1+\sqrt{5}}{4} = 0.3090169, \quad x = 18°, \quad x = 162°.$$

Worked Example 62

Find the general solutions: $\cos 2x + \cos 4x - \cos 3x = 0$.

Solution 62

$\cos 2x + \cos 4x = 2\cos 3x \cos x$

$\cos 2x + \cos 4x - \cos 3x$

$\quad = 2\cos 3x \cos x - \cos 3x = 0$

$\cos 3x(2\cos x - 1) = 0.$

Either $\cos 3x = 0 \Rightarrow \cos \frac{\pi}{2} = 0$ or $2\cos x - 1$

$\quad = 0, \cos x = \frac{1}{2}, x = 2n\pi \pm \frac{\pi}{3}.$

The general solution: $3x = 2n\pi \pm \frac{\pi}{2}, x = \frac{2n\pi}{3} \pm \frac{\pi}{6}.$

Worked Example 63

Find the general solutions:
$\tan x - \tan 2x - \tan 3x + \tan 4x = 0.$

Solution 63

$\tan x + \tan 4x = \tan 2x + \tan 3x$

L.H.S. $\frac{\sin x}{\cos x} + \frac{\sin 4x}{\cos 4x} = \frac{\sin x \cos 4x + \sin 4x \cos x}{\cos x \cos 4x}$

$$= \frac{\sin 5x}{\cos x \cos 4x}$$

R.H.S. $\tan 2x + \tan 3x = \frac{\sin 2x}{\cos 2x} + \frac{\sin 3x}{\cos 3x}$

$$= \frac{\sin 2x \cos 3x + \sin 3x \cos 2x}{\cos 2x \cos 3x}$$

$$= \frac{\sin 5x}{\cos 2x \cos 3x} \Rightarrow \frac{\sin 5x}{\cos x \cos 4x} = \frac{\sin 5x}{\cos 2x \cos 3x}$$

$$\frac{\sin 5x(\cos 2x \cos 3x - \cos x \cos 4x)}{\cos x \cos 2x \cos 3x \cos 4x} = 0.$$

Either $\sin 5x = 0$ or $\cos 2x \cos 3x - \cos x \cos 4x$

$\quad = 0, \sin 5x = \sin 0, 5x = n\pi$ or

$$\boxed{x = \frac{n\pi}{5}}$$

$\cos 2x \cos 3x - \cos x \cos 4x = 0,$

where $x, 2x, 3x, 4x, \neq K\pi + \frac{\pi}{2}$

$$\frac{\cos 5x + \cos x}{2} - \frac{\cos 5x + \cos 3x}{2} = 0,$$

$\cos 5x + \cos x - \cos 5x - \cos 3x = 0$

or $\cos 3x = \cos x.$

$4\cos^3 x - 3\cos x = \cos x$

$4\cos^3 x - 4\cos x = 0$

$4\cos x(\cos^2 x - 1) = 0$

$\cos x = 0$

$x = 2n\pi \pm \frac{\pi}{2}$ not valid

$\cos^2 x - 1 = 0$

$\cos x = \pm 1$

$\cos x = 1 \qquad \boxed{x = 2n\pi}$

$\cos x = -1 \qquad \boxed{x = 2n\pi + \pi}$

Worked Example 64

Find the general solution of $\sin 3x + \cos 2x - \sin 2x + \cos 3x = 0$.

Solution 64

$-\sin 3x + \sin 2x = \cos 2x + \cos 3x$

$(\sin 2x - \sin 3x) - (\cos 2x + \cos 3x) = 0$

$$\left(-2\sin\frac{x}{2}\cos\frac{5x}{2}\right) - \left(2\cos\frac{5x}{2}\cos\frac{x}{2}\right) = 0$$

$$-2\cos\frac{5x}{2}\left(\sin\frac{x}{2} + \cos\frac{x}{2}\right) = 0$$

$$\cos\frac{5x}{2} = 0 = \cos\frac{\pi}{2}$$

$$\frac{5x}{2} = 2n\pi \pm \frac{\pi}{2} \text{ or } \boxed{x = \frac{4n\pi}{5} \pm \frac{\pi}{5}}$$

$\sin\frac{x}{2} + \cos\frac{x}{2} = 0,$

$$\tan\frac{x}{2} = -1 = \tan\frac{3\pi}{4}$$

$$\frac{x}{2} = n\pi + \frac{3\pi}{4}$$

$$\boxed{x = 2n\pi + \frac{3\pi}{2}}$$

Worked Example 65

Find the general solution:

$5\sin^2 x - 2\cos^2 x = 3\sin x\cos x.$

Solution 65

$$5\sin^2 x - 2\cos^2 x = 3\sin x\cos x.$$

Dividing each term by $\cos^2 x$

$$\frac{5\sin^2 x}{\cos^2 x} - \frac{2\cos^2 x}{\cos^2 x} - \frac{3\sin x\cos x}{\cos^2 x}$$

$5\tan^2 x - 2 = 3\tan x,\ 5t^2 - 3t - 2 = 0$

where $\tan x = t,\ t = \dfrac{3 \pm \sqrt{9+40}}{10} = \dfrac{3 \pm 7}{10} = 1$

or $-\dfrac{2}{5}$, $\tan x = 1$ or $\Rightarrow$ $\boxed{x = n\pi + \dfrac{\pi}{4}}$

$\tan x = -\dfrac{2}{5} = \tan 158°\,11'$ $\boxed{x = n\pi + 158°\,11'}$

Worked Example 66

Find the general solution:

$3\sin^2 x - 5\cos^2 x = 2\sqrt{3}\sin x\cos x.$

Solution 66

$$3\sin^2 x - 5\cos^2 x = 2\sqrt{3}\sin x\cos x,$$

$$\frac{3\sin^2 x}{\cos^2 x} - \frac{5\cos^2 x}{\cos^2 x} = \frac{2\sqrt{3}\sin x\cos x}{\cos^2 x}$$

$$3\tan^2 x - 5 = 2\sqrt{3}\tan x$$

$3\tan^2 x - 2\sqrt{3}\tan x - 5 = 0$

$\tan x = t = \dfrac{2\sqrt{3} \pm \sqrt{12+60}}{6},$

$t = \dfrac{2\sqrt{3} \pm \sqrt{72}}{6} = \dfrac{\sqrt{3}}{3} \pm \dfrac{3\sqrt{2}}{3} = \dfrac{1}{\sqrt{3}} \pm \sqrt{2},$

$\tan x = \dfrac{1}{\sqrt{3}} + \sqrt{2} = 1.9915638 = \tan 63°\,20'$

$\boxed{x = n\pi + 63°\,20'}$

$\tan x = \dfrac{1}{\sqrt{3}} - \sqrt{2} = -0.836863 = \tan 140°\,5'$

$\boxed{x = n\pi + 140°\,5'}$

Exercises 13

Solve the following equations for values of x from 0° to 360° inclusive:

(i) $\operatorname{cosec} x = -2.8$

(ii) $\operatorname{cosec} x = -3.2$

(iii) $\sec x = 5$

(iv) $\cot x = -3$

(v) $\tan x = 0.1$

(vi) $\sin x = -0.7$

(vii) $\cos x = 0.3$

(viii) $\sec x = -2$

(ix) $2\sin 3x - \sin 2x + 2\sin x = 0$

(x) $2\sin 2x = \sin x$

(xi) $\cos(x + 40°) = -0.6$

(xii) $\sec\dfrac{x}{2} = -2.4$

(xiii) $2\cos 2x - \sin x = 1$

(xiv) $\tan x = -\dfrac{1}{\sqrt{3}}$

(xv) $\sec 3x = -1$

(xvi) $\sin x = \sin\dfrac{3\pi}{4} - \sin\dfrac{\pi}{6}$

(xvii) $2\sin 2x = 3\cos 2x$

(xviii) $\tan x + \tan 2x = 0$

(xix) $\tan 2x = \cot x$

(xx) $3\tan x = \tan 2x$

(xxi) $\sin x = \sqrt{3}\cos x$

(xxii) $\sin 2x = 1$

(xxiii) $\operatorname{cosec}\left(x + \dfrac{3\pi}{2}\right) = \sec\dfrac{\pi}{4}$

(xxiv) $\sin 2x = -\dfrac{1}{2}$

(xxv) $\cos\left(2x - \dfrac{3\pi}{4}\right) = \cos\dfrac{\pi}{4}$

(xxvi) $\operatorname{cosec} 2x = \operatorname{cosec}(x - 30°)$

(xxvii) $\operatorname{cosec}^2 x - 11\cot x \operatorname{cosec} x + 3 = 0$

(xxviii) $3\sin x - 4\sin^3 x - 4\sin^2 x = 0$

(xxix) $\sec\left(2x - \dfrac{\pi}{3}\right) = \operatorname{cosec}\left(x + \dfrac{\pi}{6}\right)$

(xxx) $3\sin x - 4\cos x = 1.$

14

Simultaneous Trigonometric Eqations

WORKED EXAMPLE 67

Solve the simultaneous equations:
$x - y = \frac{\pi}{12}$, $\tan x = \sqrt{3} \tan y$

Solution 67

$$\frac{\tan x}{\tan y} = \sqrt{3} \qquad \frac{\tan x}{\tan y} - 1 = \sqrt{3} - 1$$

$$\frac{\tan x - \tan y}{\tan y} = \sqrt{3} - 1$$

$$\frac{\tan x}{\tan y} + 1 = \sqrt{3} + 1$$

$$\frac{\tan x + \tan y}{\tan y} = \sqrt{3} + 1$$

$$\frac{\tan x - \tan y}{\tan x + \tan y} = \frac{\sqrt{3} - 1}{\sqrt{3} + 1}$$

$$\frac{\frac{\sin x}{\cos x} - \frac{\sin y}{\cos y}}{\frac{\sin x}{\cos x} + \frac{\sin y}{\cos y}} = \frac{\sqrt{3} - 1}{\sqrt{3} + 1}$$

$$\frac{\sin x \cos y - \sin y \cos x}{\sin x \cos y + \sin y \cos x} = \frac{\sin (x - y)}{\sin (x + y)} = \frac{\sqrt{3} - 1}{\sqrt{3} + 1}$$

$$\sin (x + y) = \frac{\sqrt{3} + 1}{\sqrt{3} - 1} \times \sin (x - y)$$

$$= \frac{\sqrt{3} + 1}{\sqrt{3} - 1} \times \sin \frac{\pi}{12}$$

$$= \frac{\sqrt{3} + 1}{\sqrt{3} - 1} \frac{\sqrt{6} - \sqrt{2}}{4}$$

where $\sin \frac{\pi}{12} = \sin \left(\frac{\pi}{4} - \frac{\pi}{6} \right)$

$$= \sin \frac{\pi}{4} \cos \frac{\pi}{6} - \sin \frac{\pi}{6} \cos \frac{\pi}{4}$$

$$= \frac{\sqrt{2}}{2} \left(\frac{\sqrt{3}}{2} - \frac{1}{2} \right) = \frac{\sqrt{6} - \sqrt{2}}{4}$$

$$\sin (x + y) = \frac{\sqrt{3} + 1}{\sqrt{3} - 1} \frac{\sqrt{6} - \sqrt{2}}{4}$$

$$= \frac{\sqrt{6} + \sqrt{2}}{4} = \sin \frac{5\pi}{12}$$

where $\frac{\sqrt{3} + 1}{\sqrt{3} - 1} \times \frac{\sqrt{6} - \sqrt{2}}{4}$

$$= \frac{\left(\sqrt{3} + 1 \right)^2}{2} \cdot \frac{\sqrt{6} - \sqrt{2}}{4}$$

$$= \frac{3 + 2\sqrt{3} + 1}{8} \left(\sqrt{6} - \sqrt{2} \right)$$

$$= \frac{4\sqrt{6} - 4\sqrt{2} + 6\sqrt{2} - 2\sqrt{6}}{8}$$

$$= \frac{2\sqrt{6} + 2\sqrt{2}}{8} = \frac{\sqrt{6} + \sqrt{2}}{4}$$

$$\sin \frac{5\pi}{12} = \sin \left(\frac{\pi}{4} + \frac{\pi}{6} \right)$$

$$= \sin \frac{\pi}{4} \cos \frac{\pi}{6} + \sin \frac{\pi}{6} \cos \frac{\pi}{4}$$

$$= \frac{\sqrt{2}}{2} \left(\frac{\sqrt{3}}{2} + \frac{1}{2} \right) = \frac{\sqrt{6} + \sqrt{2}}{4}$$

$$x + y = \frac{5\pi}{2} \qquad x + y = n\pi + (-1)^n \frac{5\pi}{24} \qquad . (1)$$

$$x - y = \frac{\pi}{2} \qquad . (2)$$

ADDING (1) and (2)

$$2x = n\pi + (-1)^n \frac{5\pi}{12} + \frac{\pi}{12}$$

$$x = \frac{n\pi}{2} + (-1)^n \frac{5\pi}{24} + \frac{\pi}{24}.$$

SUBTRACTING (2) from (1)

$$2y = n\pi + (-1)^n \frac{5\pi}{12} - \frac{\pi}{12}$$

$$y = \frac{n\pi}{2} + (-1)^n \frac{5\pi}{24} - \frac{\pi}{24}.$$

WORKED EXAMPLE 68

Solve the simultaneous equations:

$$\cos x + \cos y = \frac{1}{5}, \cos x \cos y = -\frac{1}{2}$$

when $0 < x < 360°$ and $0 < y < 360°$.

Solution 68

It is observed that if the sum of two roots and the product of two roots are given, a quadratic equation may be formed, that is, if $\alpha + \beta$ and $\alpha\beta$ are given, then

$$X^2 - (\alpha + \beta)X + \alpha\beta = 0, \cos x = \alpha \text{ and } \cos y = \beta,$$

$$X^2 - \frac{1}{5}X - \frac{1}{2} = 0, 10X^2 - 2X - 5 = 0,$$

$$X = \frac{2 \pm \sqrt{4 + 200}}{20}$$

$X = 0.814$ hence $\cos x = 0.814$ or $X = -0.614$ hence $\cos y = -0.614$, $x = 35° 31'$ or $324° 29'$, $y = 127° 52'$ or $233° 8'$, or *vice versa*.

Exercises 14

Solve the following simultaneous equations:

(i) $\cos x + \cos y = 2$
$\cos x \cos y = 1$

(ii) $\cos x + \cos y = \sqrt{2}$
$\cos x \cos y = \frac{1}{2}$

(iii) $\cos x + \cos y = \sqrt{3}$
$\cos x \cos y = \frac{3}{4}$

(iv) $\cos x + \cos y = 1$
$\cos x \cos y = \frac{1}{4}$

(v) $\cos x + \cos y = -1$
$\cos x \cos y = \frac{1}{4}$

(vi) $\cos x + \cos y = \frac{1 + \sqrt{3}}{2}$
$\cos x \cos y = \frac{\sqrt{3}}{4}$

(vii) $\sin x + \cos y = \sqrt{2}$
$\sin x \cos y = \frac{1}{2}$

(viii) $\cot x + \cot y = \frac{4\sqrt{3}}{3}$
$\cot x \cot y = 1$

(ix) $\sec x + \operatorname{cosec} y = 5$
$\sec x \operatorname{cosec} y = 6$

(x) $\cot x + \tan y = 3$
$\cot x \cdot \tan y = 2$
when $0 \le x \le 2\pi$ and $0 \le y \le 2\pi$.

15

The Application of the Sine and Cosine Rules in Solving Triangles

Any triangle has three sides and three angles. The sides are a, b, and c, and correspond opposite the angles A, B, and C respectively.

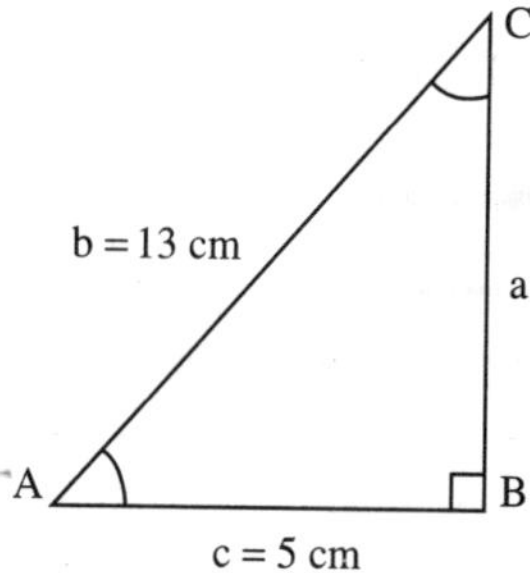

Fig. 2-I/58 A right angled triangle

The Right Angled Triangle

WORKED EXAMPLE 69

The right angled triangle shown has the following components known, the side $AB = c = 5$ cm and $AC = b = 13$ cm. Calculate all the other components.

Solution 69

$$\sin A = \frac{a}{b},$$

$$\cos A = \frac{c}{b} = \frac{5}{13},$$

$$\tan A = \frac{a}{c}.$$

Using Pythagoras theorem: $a^2 + c^2 = b^2$ from which

$$a = \sqrt{b^2 - c^2} = \sqrt{13^2 - 5^2} = \sqrt{169 - 25} = 12$$

$$\sin A = \frac{a}{b} = \frac{12}{13},$$

$A = 67° 23'$, $C = 90° - 67° 23' = 22° 37'$.

Therefore $a = 12$ cm, $b = 13$ cm, $c = 5$ cm.

$$A = 67° 23', C = 22° 37', \text{ and } B = 90°.$$

THE SINE RULE

Let ABC be any triangle with sides a, b, c, and opposite angles A, B, and C respectively.

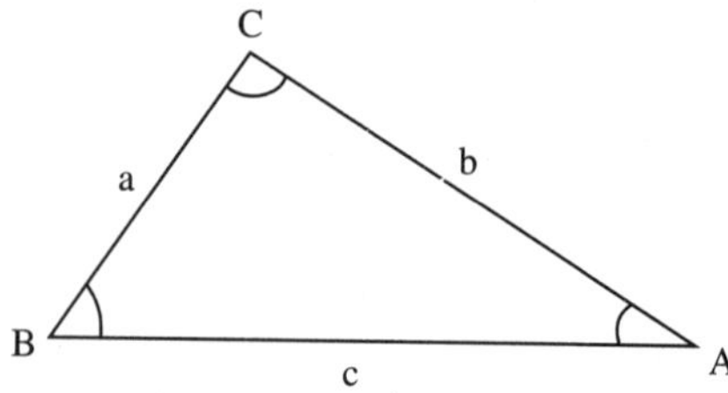

Fig. 2-I/59 Triangle with sides a, b, c, corresponding to angles A, B, C respectively.

The sine formula is given by:

$$\frac{a}{\sin A} = \frac{b}{\sin B} = \frac{c}{\sin C} = 2R \qquad \ldots\ldots (1)$$

where R is the radius of the circumcircle of the triangle ABC.

It is required to prove equation (1).

Let BOD be the diameter of the circle with centre O, in which $BCD = 90°$, since BOD is a diameter. Then $B´C = B\hat{D}C = ´$ since the angles $B´C$ and BDC are subtending the same arc BC.

In the triangle BDC,

$$\sin A = \frac{BC}{BD} = \frac{a}{2R} \text{ or } \frac{a}{\sin A} = 2R.$$

Similarly, by constructing the diameters AOE and COF, we have that in the triangle ABE.

$A°B = A\hat{C}B = \hat{C}, ABE = 90°$, then

$$\sin \hat{C} = \frac{AB}{AE} = \frac{c}{2R} \text{ and in the triangle, } FAC$$

$A\hat{F}C = A\hat{B}C = \hat{B}, F´C = 90°$, then

$$\sin B = \frac{AC}{FC} = \frac{b}{2R} \text{ therefore}$$

$$\frac{a}{\sin A} = \frac{b}{\sin B} = \frac{c}{\sin C} = 2R.$$

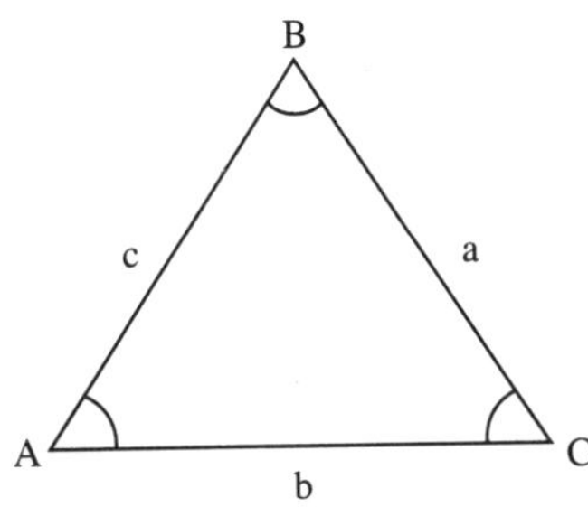

Fig. 2-I/60 $\dfrac{a}{\sin A} = \dfrac{b}{\sin B} = \dfrac{c}{\sin C} = 2R$

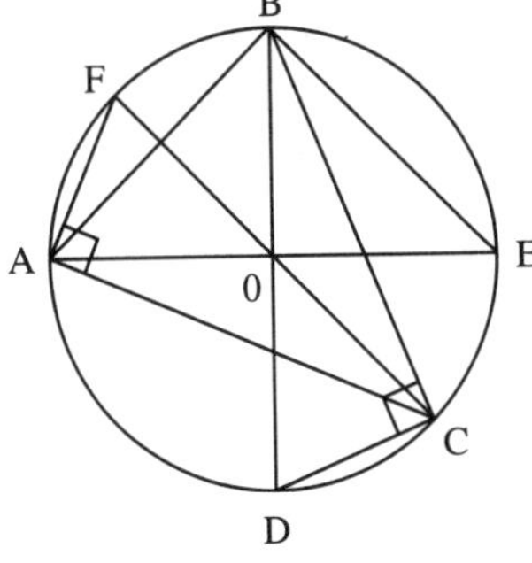

Fig. 2-I/61 R is the radius of the circumcircle of the triangle ABC.

The Area of a Triangle

Let Δ be the area of a triangle ABC as shown in Fig. 2-I/62:

Let BD be the height of the triangle.

From the triangle ADB,

$$\sin A = \frac{h}{AB} \text{ or } h = AB \sin A = c \sin A.$$

$$\Delta = \frac{1}{2} \text{ height} \times \text{base} = \frac{1}{2} b(c \sin A),$$

$$\Delta = \frac{1}{2} bc \sin A.$$

From the triangle BDC:

$$\sin C = \frac{h}{BC} = \frac{h}{a}, h = a \sin C$$

$$\Delta = \frac{1}{2} \text{ height} \times \text{base} = \frac{1}{2}\, hb = \frac{1}{2} ba \sin C.$$

Similarly:

$$\Delta = \frac{1}{2}(AE)(BC) = \frac{1}{2} ab \sin C$$

$$\sin C = \frac{AE}{AC} = \frac{AE}{b} \Rightarrow AE = b \sin C$$

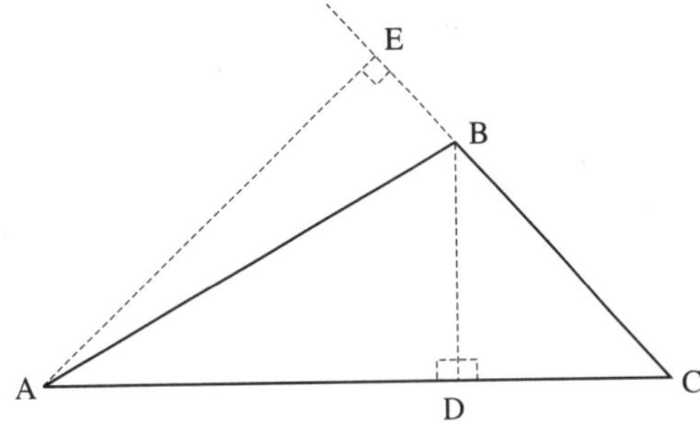

Fig. 2-I/62 Proof of the area of triangle $ABC = \frac{1}{2} ab \sin C$ or $AE = b \sin C$.

The Cosine Rule

$$a^2 = b^2 + c^2 - 2bc \cos A$$

$$b^2 = a^2 + c^2 - 2ac \cos B$$

$$c^2 = a^2 + b^2 - 2ab \cos C$$

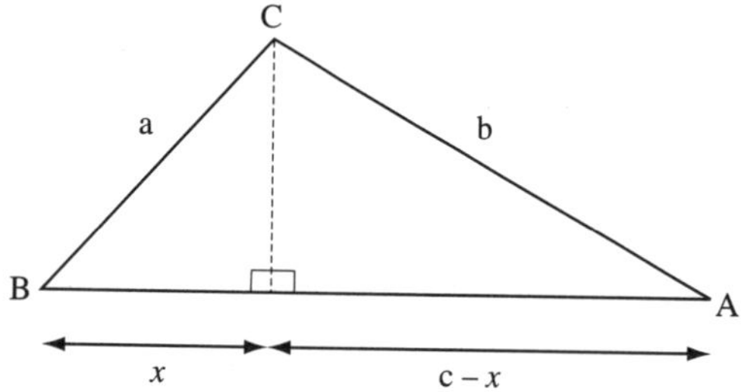

Fig. 2-I/63 Proof of the cosine rule $a^2 = b^2 + c^2 - 2bc \cos A$.

The Cosine Rule

$$a^2 = b^2 + c^2 - 2bc \cos A$$
$$b^2 = a^2 + c^2 - 2ac \cos B$$
$$c^2 = a^2 + b^2 - 2ab \cos C$$

Knowing the three sides of a triangle, we can determine the angles of the triangle from the above formulae.

To prove the above formulae:

$$h^2 = a^2 - x^2 = b^2 - (c - x)^2$$
$$a^2 - x^2 = b^2 - c^2 - x^2 + 2cx$$
$$a^2 + c^2 - b^2 = 2cx$$
$$\cos B = \frac{x}{a}$$
$$a^2 + c^2 - b^2 = 2ca \cos B$$
$$\boxed{b^2 = a^2 + c^2 - 2ac \cos B}$$

Similarly the other two formulae can be proved

$$\boxed{a^2 = b^2 + c^2 - 2bc \cos A}$$
$$\boxed{c^2 = a^2 + b^2 - 2ab \cos C}$$

WORKED EXAMPLE 70

In the triangle ABC, it is given that $AB = 7$ cm, $BC = 6$ cm and $AC = 5$ cm.

Determine the angles of the triangle and the sine of the smallest angle and the area of the triangle.

Solution 70

$$a^2 = b^2 + c^2 - 2bc \cos A$$
$$\cos A = \frac{b^2 + c^2 - a^2}{2bc} = \frac{5^2 + 7^2 - 6^2}{2(5)(7)} = 0.543$$
$$b^2 = a^2 + c^2 - 2ac \cos B$$
$$\cos B = \frac{a^2 + c^2 - b^2}{2ac} = \frac{6^2 + 7^2 - 5^2}{2(6)(7)} = 0.714$$
$$\cos A = 0.5428571 \quad \text{or} \quad A = 57^\circ\, 7'$$
$$\cos B = 0.7142857 \quad \text{or} \quad B = 44^\circ\, 25'$$

$C = 180^\circ - (A + B) = 180^\circ - (57^\circ\, 7' + 44^\circ\, 25') = 78^\circ\, 28'$.

The angles are $57^\circ\, 7'$, $44^\circ\, 25'$, and $78^\circ\, 28'$.

The smallest angle is B, the angle opposite the smallest side, $\sin B = \sin 44^\circ\, 25' = 0.7$,

$$\Delta = \frac{1}{2} ac \sin B = \frac{1}{2}(6)(7)(0.7) = 14.7 \text{ cm}^2.$$

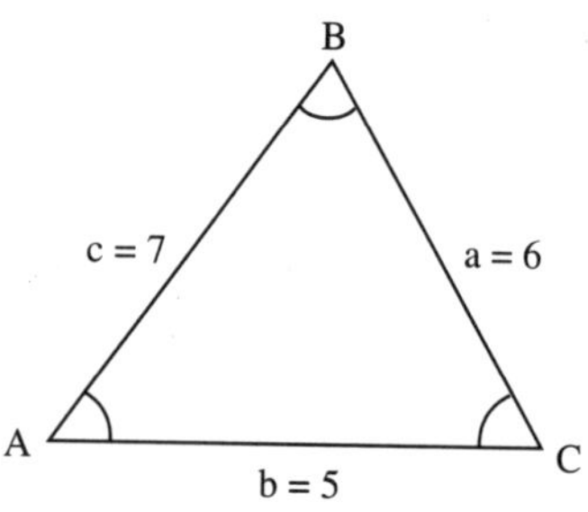

Fig. 2-I/64 To determine the angles A, B and C.

EXPRESSIONS OF SINE, COSINE AND TANGENT OF HALF ANGLES in terms of the sides a, b and c.

To prove that $\sin \frac{1}{2} A = \sqrt{\frac{(s - b)(s - c)}{bc}}$

where $s = \frac{a + b + c}{2}$, substitute

$\cos A = 1 - 2 \sin^2 \frac{1}{2} A$ in the equation

$$2bc \cos A = b^2 + c^2 - a^2$$
$$1 - 2 \sin^2 \frac{1}{2} A = \frac{b^2 + c^2 - a^2}{2bc}$$
$$2 \sin^2 \frac{1}{2} A = 1 - \frac{b^2 + c^2 - a^2}{2bc}$$
$$= \frac{2bc - b^2 - c^2 + a^2}{2bc}$$

$$\sin^2 \frac{1}{2}A = \frac{a^2 - (b^2 + c^2 - 2bc)}{4bc}$$

$$= \frac{a^2 - (b-c)^2}{4bc}$$

$$= \frac{(a-b+c)(a+b-c)}{4bc}$$

$$= \frac{(2s-b-b)(2s-c-c)}{4bc}$$

$$= \frac{(s-b)(s-c)}{bc}.$$

THE POSITIVE SOLUTION IS

$$\boxed{\sin \frac{1}{2}A = \sqrt{\frac{(s-b)(s-c)}{bc}}.}$$

Similarly, it can be proved that

$$\boxed{\sin \frac{1}{2}B = \sqrt{\frac{(s-a)(s-c)}{ac}},}$$

$$\boxed{\sin \frac{1}{2}C = \sqrt{\frac{(s-a)(s-b)}{ab}},}$$

To prove that $\cos \frac{1}{2}A = \sqrt{\frac{s(s-a)}{bc}}$

$$a^2 = b^2 + c^2 - 2bc \cos A$$

$$2bc \cos A = b^2 + c^2 - a^2$$

$$\cos A = \frac{b^2 + c^2 - a^2}{2bc} = 2\cos^2 \frac{1}{2}A - 1$$

$$b^2 + c^2 - a^2 = 4bc \cos^2 \frac{1}{2}A - 2bc$$

$$4bc \cos^2 \frac{1}{2}A = b^2 + c^2 + 2bc - a^2 = (b+c)^2 - a^2$$

$$= (b+c-a)(b+c+a)$$

but $2s$ is the perimeter, $a + b + c = 2s$

$$4bc \cos^2 \frac{1}{2}A = (2s-a-a)2s,$$

$$\cos^2 \frac{1}{2}A = \frac{4(s-a)s}{4bc},$$

$$\boxed{\cos \frac{1}{2}A = \sqrt{\frac{s(s-a)}{bc}}}$$

The formulae for $\cos \frac{1}{2}B$ and $\cos \frac{1}{2}C$ are proved similarly

$$\boxed{\cos \frac{1}{2}B = \sqrt{\frac{s(s-b)}{ac}}} \text{ and } \boxed{\cos \frac{1}{2}C = \sqrt{\frac{s(s-c)}{ab}}}.$$

To prove that $\tan \frac{A}{2} = \sqrt{\frac{(s-b)(s-c)}{s(s-a)}}$

$$\tan \frac{A}{2} = \frac{\sin \frac{A}{2}}{\cos \frac{A}{2}} = \frac{\sqrt{\frac{(s-b)(s-c)}{bc}}}{\sqrt{\frac{s(s-a)}{bc}}}$$

$$\boxed{\tan \frac{A}{2} = \sqrt{\frac{(s-b)(s-c)}{s(s-a)}}.}$$

Similarly, it can be proved that

$$\boxed{\tan \frac{B}{2} = \sqrt{\frac{(s-a)(s-c)}{s(s-b)}}}$$

$$\boxed{\tan \frac{C}{2} = \sqrt{\frac{(s-b)(s-a)}{s(s-c)}}.}$$

WORKED EXAMPLE 71

In the triangle ABC, the sides are given $a = 5$ m, $b = 6$ m, $c = 7$ m.

Determine the smallest and greatest angles.

Solution 71

The smallest angle is A and the greatest angle is C.

$$\sin \frac{1}{2}A = \frac{\sqrt{(s-b)(s-c)}}{\sqrt{bc}}$$

$$= \frac{\sqrt{(9-6)(9-7)}}{\sqrt{(6)(7)}} = \frac{1}{\sqrt{7}}$$

where $2s = 5 + 6 + 7 = 18$ or $s = 9$

$$\sin \frac{1}{2}A = \frac{1}{\sqrt{7}} = \sin 22° \, 12' \, 27''$$

$A = 44^\circ\, 25'$

$$\sin\frac{C}{2} = \frac{\sqrt{(s-a)(s-b)}}{\sqrt{ab}} = \frac{\sqrt{(9-5)(9-6)}}{\sqrt{(5)(6)}}$$

$$= \sqrt{\frac{(4)(3)}{(5)(6)}} = \frac{\sqrt{2}}{\sqrt{5}}$$

$$= \sin 39^\circ\, 13'53'' \quad C = 78^\circ\, 28'.$$

HERON'S FORMULA

To prove that the area of a triangle

$$\boxed{\Delta = \sqrt{s(s-a)(s-b)(s-c)}} \text{ where}$$

$$s = \frac{a+b+c}{2} \text{ – Heron's Formula}$$

$$s = \frac{1}{2}ab\sin C = \frac{1}{2}ab\, 2\sin\frac{C}{2}\cos\frac{C}{2}$$

$$= ab\frac{\sqrt{(s-b)(s-a)}}{\sqrt{ab}}\,\frac{\sqrt{s(s-c)}}{\sqrt{ab}}$$

$$= \sqrt{s(s-a)(s-b)(s-c)}.$$

MOLLWEIDE'S RELATION

$$\frac{a}{\sin A} = \frac{b}{\sin B} = \frac{c}{\sin C}$$

$$\frac{a}{\sin A} = \frac{b+c}{\sin B + \sin C} = \frac{b-c}{\sin B - \sin C} \text{ since}$$

$$\frac{b}{\sin B} = \frac{c}{\sin C} \Rightarrow \frac{b}{c}$$

$$= \frac{\sin B}{\sin C} \Rightarrow \frac{b}{c} + 1 = \frac{\sin B}{\sin C} + 1$$

$$\frac{b+c}{c} = \frac{\sin B + \sin C}{\sin C} \Rightarrow \frac{b+c}{\sin B + \sin C} = \frac{c}{\sin C}$$

$$\frac{b}{c} = \frac{\sin B}{\sin C} \Rightarrow \frac{b}{c} - 1 = \frac{\sin B}{\sin C} - 1$$

$$\frac{b-c}{c} = \frac{\sin B - \sin C}{\sin C}$$

$$\frac{b-c}{\sin B - \sin C} = \frac{c}{\sin C}$$

$$\frac{b+c}{\sin B + \sin C} = \frac{b-c}{\sin B - \sin C} = \frac{c}{\sin C}$$

$$\frac{a}{2\sin\frac{A}{2}\cos\frac{A}{2}}$$

$$= \frac{b+c}{2\sin\frac{B+C}{2}\cos\frac{B-C}{2}}$$

$$= \frac{b-c}{2\sin\frac{B-C}{2}\cos\frac{B+C}{2}} \text{ from which}$$

$$\frac{b-c}{a} = \frac{2\sin\frac{B-C}{2}\cos\frac{B+C}{2}}{2\sin\frac{A}{2}\cos\frac{A}{2}}$$

$$= \frac{\sin\frac{B-C}{2}}{\cos\frac{A}{2}} \text{ since } \sin\frac{A}{2} = \cos\frac{B+C}{2}$$

$$\boxed{\sin\frac{B-C}{2} = \frac{b-c}{a}\cos\frac{A}{2}} \quad \ldots(1)$$

$$\frac{b+c}{a} = \frac{2\sin\frac{B+C}{2}\cos\frac{B-C}{2}}{2\sin\frac{A}{2}\cos\frac{A}{2}} = \frac{\cos\frac{B-C}{2}}{\sin\frac{A}{2}}$$

$$\boxed{\cos\frac{B-C}{2} = \frac{b+c}{a}\sin\frac{A}{2}} \quad \ldots(2)$$

Dividing (1) by (2)

$$\boxed{\tan\frac{B-C}{2} = \frac{b-c}{b+c}\cot\frac{A}{2}}$$ .. this is Mollweide's relation.

WORKED EXAMPLE 72

Find the value of $\sin 18^\circ$ and $\cos 36^\circ$ in surd form.

Solution 72

$2\Theta = 90^\circ - 3\Theta$ where $\Theta = 18^\circ$ $\quad \sin 2\Theta = \cos 3\Theta$
$2\sin\Theta\cos\Theta = 4\cos^3\Theta - 3\cos\Theta$

$$2\sin\Theta = 4\cos^2\Theta - 3, \text{ since } \cos\Theta \neq 0$$

$$= 4(1-\sin^2\Theta) - 3$$

$$4\sin^2\Theta + 2\sin\Theta - 1 = 0$$

$$\sin\Theta = \frac{-2 \pm \sqrt{4+16}}{8}$$

$$= \frac{-2 \pm 2\sqrt{5}}{8} = \frac{-1+\sqrt{5}}{4}$$

or $\dfrac{-1-\sqrt{5}}{4}$ which is disregarded

$$\boxed{\sin 18^\circ = \frac{-1+\sqrt{5}}{4}}$$

$$\cos 36^\circ = 1 - 2\sin^2 18^\circ = 1 - 2\left(\frac{-1+\sqrt{5}}{4}\right)^2$$

$$= 1 - 2\left(\frac{1+5-2\sqrt{5}}{16}\right) = 1 - \left(\frac{3-\sqrt{5}}{4}\right)$$

$$= 1 - \frac{3}{4} + \frac{\sqrt{5}}{4} = \frac{1}{4} + \frac{\sqrt{5}}{4}$$

$$\boxed{\cos 36^\circ = \frac{1+\sqrt{5}}{4}}$$

WORKED EXAMPLE 73

Find the values of $\sin 22\frac{1}{2}^\circ$, $\cos 22\frac{1}{2}^\circ$, $\tan 22\frac{1}{2}^\circ$, $\tan 7\frac{1}{2}^\circ$ in surd form.

Solution 73

$$\sin\frac{x}{2} = \sqrt{\frac{1-\cos x}{2}} \text{ since } \cos x = 1 - 2\sin^2\frac{x}{2}$$

If $x = 45^\circ$, then

$$\cos 45^\circ = \frac{1}{\sqrt{2}}, \sin 22\frac{1}{2}^\circ = \sqrt{\frac{1-\frac{1}{\sqrt{2}}}{2}}$$

$$\cos\frac{x}{2} = \sqrt{\frac{\cos x + 1}{2}}, \text{ then } \cos 22\frac{1}{2}^\circ = \sqrt{\frac{1+\frac{1}{\sqrt{2}}}{2}}$$

$$\tan\frac{x}{2} = \sqrt{\frac{1-\cos x}{1+\cos x}}$$

$$\text{then } \tan 22\tfrac{1}{2}^\circ = \sqrt{\frac{1-\frac{1}{\sqrt{2}}}{1+\frac{1}{\sqrt{2}}}} = \sqrt{\frac{\sqrt{2}-1}{\sqrt{2}+1}}.$$

$$\tan(45^\circ - 30^\circ) = \tan 15^\circ = \frac{\tan 45^\circ - \tan 30^\circ}{1 + \tan 45^\circ \tan 30^\circ}$$

$$= \frac{1-\frac{1}{\sqrt{3}}}{1+\frac{1}{\sqrt{3}}} = \frac{\sqrt{3}-1}{\sqrt{3}+1}$$

$$\tan x = \frac{2t}{1-t^2} = \frac{2\tan\frac{x}{2}}{1-\tan^2\frac{x}{2}}. \text{ from the } t\text{-formulae.}$$

$$\tan 15^\circ = \frac{2\tan 7.5^\circ}{1-\tan^2 7.5^\circ} = \frac{\sqrt{3}-1}{\sqrt{3}+1} = 0.26794$$

$$2t\left(\sqrt{3}+1\right) = \left(\sqrt{3}-1\right)\left(1-t^2\right).$$

$$\left(\sqrt{3}-1\right)t^2 + \left(2\sqrt{3}+2\right)t - \left(\sqrt{3}-1\right) = 0$$

$$t = \frac{-\left(2\sqrt{3}+2\right) \pm \sqrt{\left(2\sqrt{3}+2\right)^2 + 4\left(\sqrt{3}-1\right)\left(\sqrt{3}-1\right)}}{2\left(\sqrt{3}-1\right)}$$

$$= \frac{-\left(2\sqrt{3}+2\right) \pm \sqrt{12+4+8\sqrt{3}+12+4-8\sqrt{3}}}{2\left(\sqrt{3}-1\right)}$$

$$t = \frac{-\left(\sqrt{3}+1\right) \pm 2\sqrt{2}}{\sqrt{3}-1}, \quad t = \frac{-\sqrt{3}-1+2\sqrt{2}}{\sqrt{3}-1} \text{ or}$$

$$t = \frac{-\sqrt{3}-1-2\sqrt{2}}{\sqrt{3}-1} \text{ which is disregarded therefore}$$

$$t = \frac{2\sqrt{2}-\sqrt{3}-1}{\sqrt{3}-1}$$

$$\boxed{\tan 7^\circ 30' = \frac{2\sqrt{2}-\sqrt{3}-1}{\sqrt{3}-1}}$$

WORKED EXAMPLE 74

Show that in a non right angled triangle ABC, $\tan A \tan B \tan C = \tan A + \tan B + \tan C$.

Solution 74

$A+B+C=\pi, \qquad A+B=\pi-C$

$\tan(A+B)=\tan(\pi-C)$

$$=\frac{\tan\pi-\tan C}{1+\tan\pi\tan C}=-\tan C$$

$$\frac{\tan A+\tan B}{1-\tan A\tan B}=-\tan C$$

$\tan A+\tan B=-\tan C+\tan A\tan B\tan C$

$\tan A\tan B\tan C=\tan A+\tan B+\tan C.$

WORKED EXAMPLE 75

To show that in a triangle ABC, $\cot A\cot B+\cot B\cot C+\cot C\cot A=1$.

Solution 75

Dividing each side by $\cot A\cot B\cot C$, we have

$$\frac{\cot A\cot B+\cot B\cot C+\cot C\cot A}{\cot A\cot B\cot C}=\frac{1}{\cot A\cot B\cot C}$$

$$\frac{1}{\cot C}+\frac{1}{\cot A}+\frac{1}{\cot B}=\frac{1}{\cot A\cot B\cot C}$$

$$=\tan A\tan B\tan C$$

$\tan C+\tan A+\tan B=\tan A\tan B\tan C$, therefore, $\cot A\cot B+\cot B\cot C+\cot C\cot A=1$.

In the case of a right-angled triangle, if $A=90°$, then $\cot A=\cot 90°=0$, $\cot B\cot C=1$, $\cot C=\tan B$ which is valid since B and C are complementary angles.

SOLUTION OF TRIANGLES

FORMULAE

The sine rule: $\dfrac{a}{\sin A}=\dfrac{b}{\sin B}=\dfrac{c}{\sin C}=2R.$

The cosine rule:

$$a^2=b^2+c^2-2bc\cos A$$
$$b^2=a^2+c^2-2ac\cos B$$
$$c^2=a^2+b^2-2ab\cos C$$

$$\sin\frac{1}{2}A=\sqrt{\frac{(s-b)(s-c)}{bc}} \qquad \cos\frac{1}{2}A=\sqrt{\frac{s(s-a)}{bc}}$$

$$\sin\frac{1}{2}B=\sqrt{\frac{(s-a)(s-c)}{ac}} \qquad \cos\frac{1}{2}B=\sqrt{\frac{s(s-b)}{ac}}$$

$$\sin\frac{1}{2}C=\sqrt{\frac{(s-a)(s-b)}{ab}} \qquad \cos\frac{1}{2}C=\sqrt{\frac{s(s-c)}{ab}}$$

$$\tan\frac{1}{2}A=\sqrt{\frac{(s-b)(s-c)}{s(s-a)}} \qquad s=\frac{a+b+c}{2}$$

$$\tan\frac{1}{2}B=\sqrt{\frac{(s-a)(s-c)}{s(s-b)}} \qquad \Delta=\sqrt{s(s-a)(s-b)(s-c)}$$

$$\tan\frac{1}{2}C=\sqrt{\frac{(s-b)(s-a)}{s(s-c)}}$$

$$\sin\frac{B-C}{2}=\frac{b-c}{a}\cos\frac{A}{2}, \qquad \cos\frac{B-C}{2}=\frac{b+c}{a}\sin\frac{A}{2}$$

$$\tan\frac{B-C}{2}=\frac{b-c}{b+c}\cot\frac{A}{2}$$ *Mollweide's relations.*

Exercises 15

1. In a triangle, the sides are 4, 3 and $\sqrt{37}$ m respectively. Find the largest angle.
2. In a triangle, $a=\sqrt{57}$ m, $A=60°$, and $c=2\sqrt{3}$ m. Find the side b and the angle B.
3. In a triangle, the sides are proportional to $\sqrt{2}, \sqrt{3}, \sqrt{5}$.
   (i) Find $\sin A$, $\sin B$, $\sin C$, $\cos A$, $\cos B$, $\cos C$.
   (ii) Show that $A+B=90°$.
   (iii) Show that $\cos(B-A)=\dfrac{12}{5\sqrt{6}}$.
4. In a triangle, the sides are proportional to $\sqrt{3}, \sqrt{5}, \sqrt{6}$.
   (i) Find $\cos A$, $\cos B$, $\cos C$, $\sin A$, $\sin B$, $\sin C$.
   (ii) Show that $\sin(A+B)=\dfrac{2\sqrt{7}}{\sqrt{5}\sqrt{6}}$.
5. In a triangle, the sides are proportional to $\sqrt{1}, \sqrt{3}, \sqrt{6}$.
   (i) Find $\cos A$, $\cos B\cos C$, $\sin A$, $\sin B$, $\sin C$.
   (ii) Show that $\sin(A+B)=\dfrac{1}{3}\sqrt{6}$.
   (iii) Show that $\sin(B-A)=\dfrac{1}{9}\sqrt{6}$.

16

Graphs of Circular or Trigonometric Functions

WORKED EXAMPLE 76

Draw the graph $y = 2\sin\Theta + 3\cos\Theta$, where $0° < \Theta < 360°$.

Hence solve the equation $2\sin\Theta + 3\cos\Theta = 1$.

Verify the solution by employing two other methods.

Solution 76

The graph is plotted ($1\text{ cm} \equiv 30°$ on the x-axis, $2\text{ cm} \equiv 1$ on the y-axis).

The straight line $y = 1$ intersects the curve at two points $A(108°, 1)$ $B(319°, 1)$.

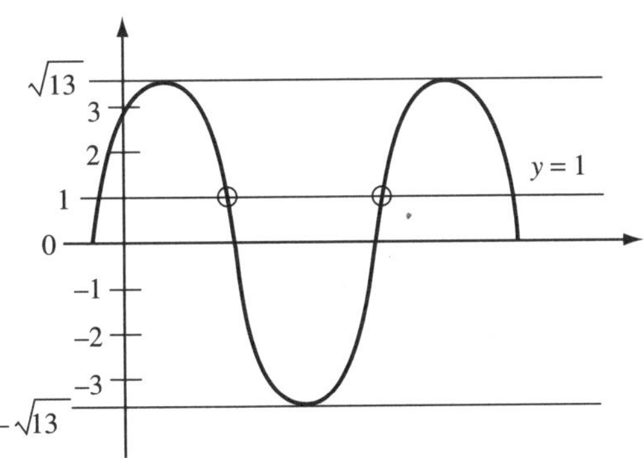

Fig. 2-I/65 $y = 2\sin\Theta + 3\cos\Theta$

Method 1

$R\sin(\Theta + \alpha)$

$= R\sin\Theta\cos\alpha + R\sin\alpha\cos\Theta = 2\sin\Theta + 3\cos\Theta$

$R\cos\alpha = 2$ $\quad R\sin\alpha = 3$ $\quad R = \sqrt{2^2 + 3^2} = \sqrt{13}$

$\tan\alpha = 1.5$ $\quad \alpha = 56.3°$

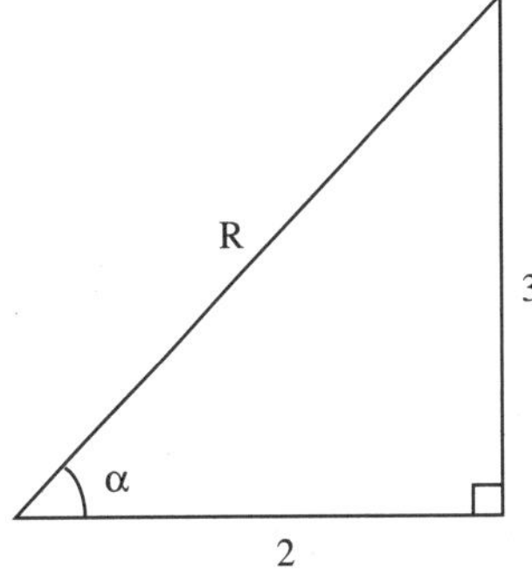

Fig. 2-I/66

$2\sin\Theta + 3\cos\Theta = \sqrt{13}\sin(\Theta + 56°\ 19') = 1$

$\sin(\Theta + 56°\ 19')$

$$= \frac{1}{\sqrt{13}} = \sin 16°\ 6' = \sin 163.9° = \sin 376.1°,$$

$\Theta = 107°\ 35'$ and $\Theta = 319°\ 45'$.

Method 2

$2\sin\Theta + 3\cos\Theta \equiv 1.$

Employing the t-formulae $2\dfrac{2t}{1+t^2} + 3\dfrac{1-t^2}{1+t^2} = 1.$

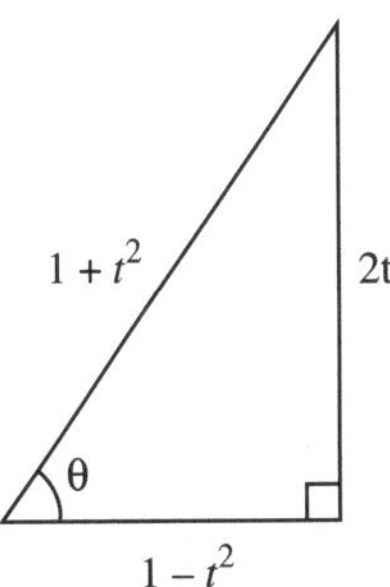

Fig. 2-I/67 t-formulae

$x°$	0	30	45	60	90	120	135	150
$\sin x$	0	0.5	0.707	0.866	1	0.866	0.707	0.5
$2\sin x$	0	1	1.414	1.732	2	1.732	1.414	1
$\cos x$	1	0.866	0.707	0.5	0	−0.5	−0.707	−0.866
$3\cos x$	3	2.598	2.121	1.5	0	−1.5	−2.121	−2.598
y	3	3.598	3.535	3.232	2	0.232	−0.707	−1.598
$x°$	180	210	225	240	270	300	330	360
$\sin x$	0	−0.5	−0.707	−0.866	−1	−0.866	−0.5	0
$2\sin x$	0	−1	−1.414	−1.732	−2	−1.732	−1	0
$\cos x$	−1	−0.866	−0.707	−0.5	0	0.5	0.866	1
$3\cos x$	−3	−2.598	−2.121	−1.5	0	1.5	2.598	3
y	−3	−3.598	−3.535	−3.232	−2	−0.232	1.598	3

$\Theta°$	0	30	45	60	90	120	135	150	180
$\sin\Theta$	0	0.5	0.707	0.866	1	0.866	0.707	0.5	0
$\sin\left(\Theta+\frac{\pi}{3}\right)$	0.866	1		0.866	0.5	0		−0.5	−0.866
$\Theta°$	210	225		240	270	300	315	330	360
$\sin\Theta$	−0.5	−0.707		−0.866	−1	−0.866	−0.707	−0.5	0
$\sin\left(\Theta+\frac{\pi}{3}\right)$	−1			−0.866	−0.5	0		0.5	0.866

$$4t + 3 - 3t^2 = 1 + t^2$$

$$4t^2 - 4t - 2 = 0 \text{ where } t = \tan\frac{\Theta}{2},\ 2t^2 - 2t - 1 = 0$$

$$t = \frac{2 \pm \sqrt{4+8}}{4} = \frac{2 \pm \sqrt{12}}{4} = \frac{1 \pm \sqrt{3}}{2}$$

$$t = \tan\frac{\Theta}{2} = \frac{1+\sqrt{3}}{2}$$

$$= 1.366 = \tan 53.79° \rightarrow \Theta = 107.6°$$

$$t = \tan\frac{\Theta}{2} = \frac{1-\sqrt{3}}{2} = -0.366$$

$$= \tan 159.897° \rightarrow \Theta = 319.8°.$$

Worked Example 77

Plot the graphs of $\sin\left(\Theta + \frac{\pi}{3}\right)$ and $\sin\Theta$ on the same axes in the range $0 \leq \Theta \leq 360°$.

Hence find the solution of the two curves $y = \sin\left(\Theta + \frac{\pi}{3}\right) = \sin\Theta$.

Verify the answers algebraically and by *two other methods*.

Solution 77

The graphs are plotted as shown with the y-axis representing $\sin\Theta$ and $\sin\left(\Theta + \frac{\pi}{3}\right)$ and the x-axis representing $\Theta°$. (The scales chosen are 1 cm $\equiv$ 30° on the x-axis, 10 cm $\equiv$ 1)

The two curves intersect at A and B. The coordinates of $A(60°, 0.866)$ and $B(240°, -0.866)$.

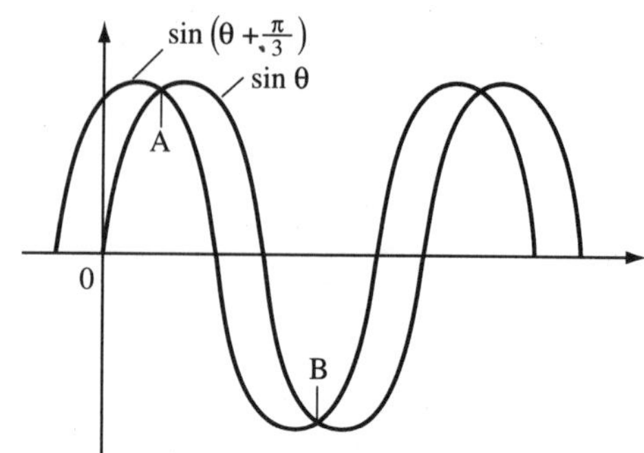

Fig. 2-I/68 $\Theta = 60°$, $\Theta = 240°$ graphical solution

Solving the simultaneous equations $y = \sin\Theta$, $y = \sin\left(\Theta + \frac{\pi}{3}\right)$, $\sin\Theta = \sin\left(\Theta + \frac{\pi}{3}\right) = \sin\Theta\cos\frac{\pi}{3} + \sin\frac{\pi}{3}\cos\Theta = \frac{1}{2}\sin\Theta + 0.866\cos\Theta$

$\frac{1}{2}\sin\Theta = 0.866\cos\Theta$, $\tan\Theta = 1.732$, $\Theta = 60°$ or $240°$, $y = \sin 60° = 0.866$

$$y = \sin\left(\Theta + \frac{\pi}{3}\right) = \sin\left(60 + \frac{\pi}{3}\right) = 0.866.$$

Therefore, $A(60°, 0.866)$ and $B(240°, -0.866)$.

<u>Method 1</u>

$\sin\Theta = \frac{1}{2}\sin\Theta + \frac{\sqrt{3}}{2}\cos\Theta$, $\sin\Theta - \frac{1}{2}\sin\Theta = \frac{\sqrt{3}}{2}\cos\Theta$

$\frac{1}{2}\sin\Theta = \frac{\sqrt{3}}{2}\cos\Theta$, $\sin\Theta - \sqrt{3}\cos\Theta = 0$ but

$$\sin\Theta - \sqrt{3}\cos\Theta \equiv R\sin(\Theta - \alpha)$$
$$\equiv R\sin\Theta\cos\alpha - R\sin\alpha\cos\Theta.$$

Equating the coefficients of $\sin\Theta$, $1 = R\cos\alpha$ (1)

Equating the coefficients of $\cos\Theta$, $\sqrt{3} = R\sin\alpha$ (2)

$$R = \sqrt{(\sqrt{3})^2 + 1^2} = 2,\ \tan\alpha = \sqrt{3},\ \alpha = \frac{\pi}{3}$$

Therefore, $\sin\theta - \sqrt{3}\cos\theta \equiv 2\sin\left(\theta - \frac{\pi}{3}\right) = 0$

$$\sin\left(\theta - \frac{\pi}{3}\right) = 0 \Rightarrow \theta - \frac{\pi}{3} = 0° \text{ or}$$
$$= 180° \Rightarrow \theta = 60°, 240°$$

When $\theta = 60°$, $y = \sin 60° = 0.866$.

$\theta = 240°$, $y = \sin 240° = -0.866$.

Therefore, $A\ (60°, 0.866)$, $B\ (240°, -0.866)$.

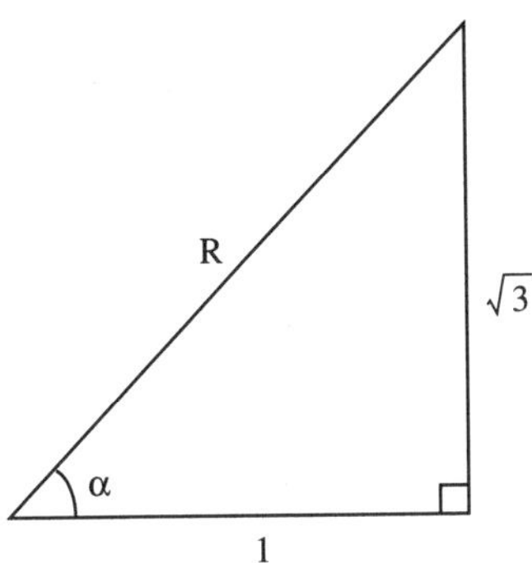

Fig. 2-I/69 $\tan\alpha = \frac{\sqrt{3}}{1}$, $R = 2$

<u>Method 2</u>

$\sin\theta = \sin\left(\theta + \frac{\pi}{3}\right)$, $\sin\theta - \sin\left(\theta + \frac{\pi}{3}\right) = 0$

Expressing the difference of sines as a product

$$\sin\theta - \sin\left(\theta + \frac{\pi}{3}\right)$$
$$= 2\cos\frac{1}{2}\left(\theta + \theta + \frac{\pi}{3}\right)\sin\frac{1}{2}\left(\theta - \theta - \frac{\pi}{3}\right)$$
$$= 2\cos\frac{1}{2}\left(2\theta + \frac{\pi}{3}\right)\sin\left(-\frac{\pi}{6}\right)$$
$$= -2\cos\frac{1}{2}\left(2\theta + \frac{\pi}{3}\right)\sin\frac{\pi}{6} = 0$$

therefore $\cos\frac{1}{2}\left(2\theta + \frac{\pi}{3}\right) = 0 = \cos 90° = \cos 270°$ from which we have $\theta = 60°, 240°$.

Exercises 16

1. Solve graphically the equation $x = 2\cos\left(2x - \frac{2\pi}{3}\right)$ in the range $0 < x < \frac{2\pi}{3}$.
2. Solve graphically $y = \sin x + \sin\frac{x}{2} = 1$ in the range $0 \le x \le \pi$.
3. Solve graphically:
   (i) $\frac{x}{-\frac{1}{2}} + \frac{y}{3} = 1$, and $y = \sin^{-1}x$ in the range $-\pi \le \sin^{-1}x \le \pi$.
   (ii) $\frac{x}{\frac{1}{2}} + \frac{y}{3} = 1$, and $y = \cos^{-1}x$ in the range $-\pi \le \cos^{-1}x \le \pi$.
   (iii) $\frac{x}{5} + \frac{y}{6} = 1$, and $y = \tan^{-1}x$ in the range $0 \le \tan^{-1}x \le \frac{3\pi}{2}$.
4. Solve graphically:
   (i) $\sin x = x - \frac{2\pi}{3}$
   (ii) $\sin x = x - \frac{2\pi}{4}$
   (iii) $\sin x = x - \frac{2\pi}{5}$

   in the range $0 \le x \le \pi$.
5. Calculate the length of the arcs of a circle of radius 1 m subtending an angle.
   (i) $\frac{\pi}{4}$
   (ii) $\frac{\pi}{3}$

(iii) $\frac{\pi}{2}$

(iv) π

(v) 2π.

6. Draw the graphs:

   (i) $y = \sin x$

   (ii) $y = \sin 2x$

   (iii) $y = \sin 3x$

   (iv) $y = \sin \frac{x}{2}$

   in the range $-2\pi \leq x \leq 2\pi$ on the same x-axis.

7. Draw the graphs:

   (i) $y = \cos \frac{x}{2}$

   (ii) $y = 2\cos x$

   in the range $-2\pi \leq x \leq 2\pi$ on the same x-axis.

8. Draw the graphs:

   (i) $y = \tan x$

   (ii) $y = \cot x$

   (iii) $y = \operatorname{cosec} x$

   (iv) $y = \sec x$

   in the range $0 \leq x \leq 2\pi$.

9. Using the same axes, draw the graphs $y = \tan\left(x + \frac{\pi}{3}\right)$ and $y = \sin 2x$ for $0° \leq x \leq 180°$.

10. Using the same axes, draw the graphs $y = \frac{1}{2} \operatorname{cosec} x$ and $y = 2\cos x$ for $-\pi \leq x \leq \pi$.
    Solve graphically the equation $\sec x \operatorname{cosec} x = 4$.

11. Solve graphically:

    (i) $3\sin x + 4\cos x = 1$

    (ii) $7\sin x + 24\cos x = 5$

    (iii) $\cos x + \sin x = 1$ in the range $0° \leq x \leq 360°$.

12. Draw the following graphs in the range $-180° \leq x \leq 180°$

    (i) $y = 3\sin\left(2x - \frac{\pi}{3}\right)$

    (ii) $y = 2\cos\left(x + \frac{2\pi}{3}\right)$

    (iii) $y = \cos\left(3x + \frac{5\pi}{6}\right)$.

13. Draw the graphs of **QUESTION 12** and state the coordinates of the minimum and maximum values and the points where the graphs intersect the y and x axes.

14. Express the following:

    (i) $f(x) = \sin x - \cos x$

    (ii) $f(x) = 3\sin x - 4\cos x$

    (iii) $f(x) = \cos 2x - 3\sin 2x$

    (iv) $f(x) = 4\sin 3x + 6\cos 3x$

    (v) $f(x) = 7\cos 2x + 12\sin 2x$

    (vi) $f(x) = 24\cos 2x + 7\sin 2x$

    (vii) $f(x) = 4\sin x + 7\cos x$

    (viii) $f(x) = 4\cos x + 3\sin x$

    in the form $R\sin(kx \pm \alpha)$ or $R\cos(kx \pm \alpha)$ where $k = 1, 2$ or 3 and hence sketch the curves.

17

The Inverse Trigonometric Functions for Sine, Cosine and Tangent

The sine of thirty degrees is equal to a half, **i.e.** $\sin 30° = \frac{1}{2}$; by definition of the inverse trigonometric function, the angle whose sine is equal to a half is 30°, and this is denoted by $\sin^{-1}\frac{1}{2} = 30°$ or $\arcsin\frac{1}{2} = 30°$.

In general: $y = \sin^{-1} x$ or $x = \sin y$

y is an angle and x is a number.

Similarly: $y = \cos^{-1} x$ or $x = \cos y$,

$\cos^{-1}\left(\frac{1}{2}\right) = \frac{\pi}{3}$

Similarly: $y = \tan^{-1} x$ or $x = \tan y$, $\frac{\pi}{4} = \tan^{-1} 1$.

The tangent of 45° or $\frac{\pi}{4}$ is equal to unity. The angle whose tangent is equal to 1 is 45° or $\frac{\pi}{4}$; $\sin^{-1} x$, $\cos^{-1} x$, $\tan^{-1} x$ or $\arcsin x$, $\arccos x$ and $\arctan x$ are angles.

Worked Example 78

Find the relationship between x and y if $\sin^{-1} x + \sin^{-1} y = \frac{\pi}{4}$ or $\Theta + \phi = \frac{\pi}{4}$ where $\Theta = \sin^{-1} x$ and $\Phi = \sin^{-1} y$.

Solution 78

Taking sines on both sides of this equation:

$$\sin(\sin^{-1} x + \sin^{-1} y) = \sin\frac{\pi}{4}$$

$$\sin(\sin^{-1} x)\cos(\sin^{-1} y) + \sin(\sin^{-1} y)\cos(\sin^{-1} x) = \frac{1}{\sqrt{2}}$$

$$x\cos(\sin^{-1} y) + y\cos(\sin^{-1} x) = \frac{1}{\sqrt{2}} \quad \ldots(1)$$

where $\sin(\sin^{-1} x) = x$ and $\sin(\sin^{-1} y) = y$; let $\sin^{-1} x = \Theta$, by definition $x = \sin\Theta$, therefore, $\sin(\Theta) = x$ similarly for $\sin(\sin^{-1} y) = y$.

In general: $\cos(\cos^{-1} x) = x \quad \tan(\tan^{-1} x) = x$

$\sin(\sin^{-1} x) = x$.

From *equation* (1) $x\cos\phi + y\cos\Theta = \frac{1}{\sqrt{2}}$,

$$x\sqrt{1-\sin^2\phi} + y\sqrt{1-\sin^2\Theta} = \frac{1}{\sqrt{2}},$$

$$\boxed{x\sqrt{1-y^2} + y\sqrt{1-x^2} = \frac{1}{\sqrt{2}}}$$

Inverse Trigonometric or Circular Function Defined Over Suitable Domain

The Inverse Sine

$$y = \sin x, \quad f(x) = \sin x \quad f\colon x \rightarrowtail \sin x$$

This function is a many-to-one mapping for the domain $x \epsilon \mathbb{R}$, $f\colon x \rightarrowtail \sin x$ is read that f is such that x is mapped onto $\sin x$.

When $x = \frac{\pi}{6}$, $\sin\frac{\pi}{6} = \frac{1}{2}$:

When $x = \frac{5\pi}{6}$, $\sin\frac{5\pi}{6} = \frac{1}{2}$.

Many values of x are mapped onto one value of y, **i.e.** a many-to-one mapping.

This function maps $\frac{\pi}{6}$ to $\frac{1}{2}$, $\frac{5\pi}{6}$ to $\frac{1}{2}$

$\frac{\pi}{6} \rightarrowtail \sin\frac{\pi}{6}$ or $\frac{\pi}{6} \rightarrow \frac{1}{2}$, $\frac{\pi}{6}$ is mapped onto $\frac{1}{2}$.

An inverse function does not exist unless a suitable domain is defined. The function $f: x \rightarrowtail \sin x$ is a one-one function if the domain is defined e.g.

$\left[-\frac{\pi}{2}, \frac{\pi}{2}\right]$ and the inverse function does exist.

The inverse sine function is denoted as arcsin or $\sin^{-1}$. The input of the function $f: x \rightarrowtail \sin x$ is an angle, and the output is a number.

The inverse function $f^{-1}: x \rightarrowtail \arcsin x$. The input is a number and the output is an angle. Arcsin x means "the angle whose sine is x".

$f: x \rightarrowtail \sin x$

$-\frac{\pi}{2} \le x \le \frac{\pi}{2}$, $\quad f^{-1}: x \rightarrowtail \arcsin x \quad -1 \le x \le 1.$

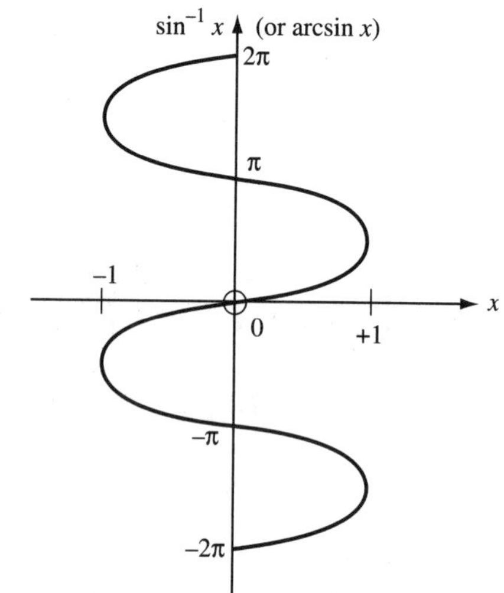

Fig. 2-I/71 Inverse sine

The Inverse Cosine

$f: x \rightarrowtail \cos x \quad 0 \le x \le \pi.$

The inverse function exists $f^{-1}: x \rightarrowtail \arccos x$ or $\cos^{-1}$ where $-1 \le x \le 1$. Arccos x means "the angle whose cosine is x".

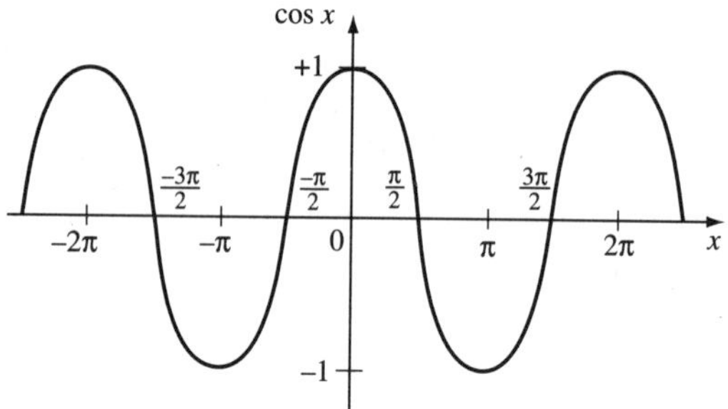

Fig. 2-I/72 Cosine

The Inverse Tangent

$f: x \rightarrow \tan x$ for $-\frac{\pi}{2} \le x \le \frac{\pi}{2}$.

The inverse function exists $f^{-1}: x \rightarrowtail \arctan x$. Arctan x or $\tan^{-1} x$ means "the angle whose tangent is x".

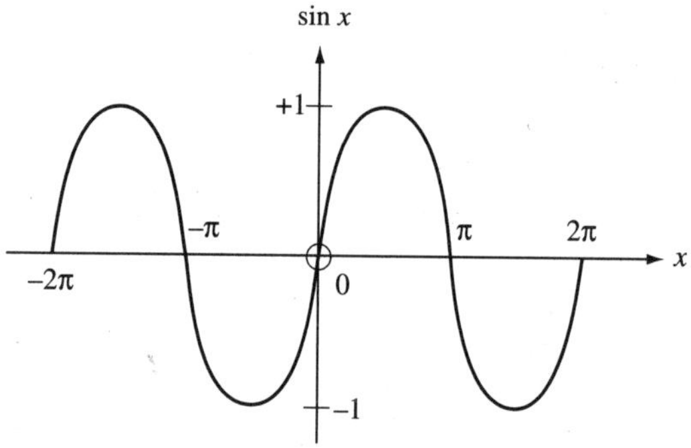

Fig. 2-I/70 sine wave

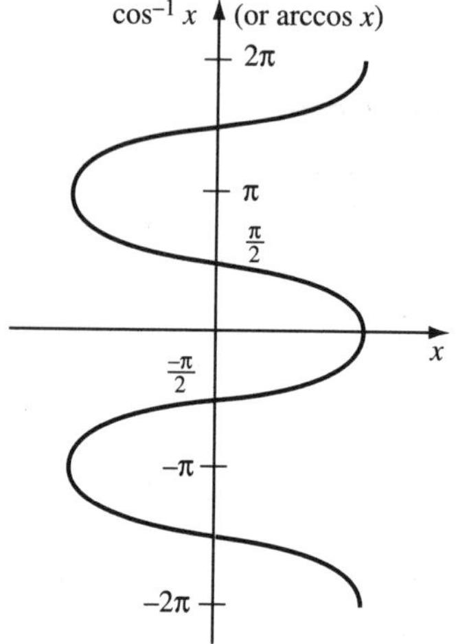

Fig. 2-I/73 Inverse cosine

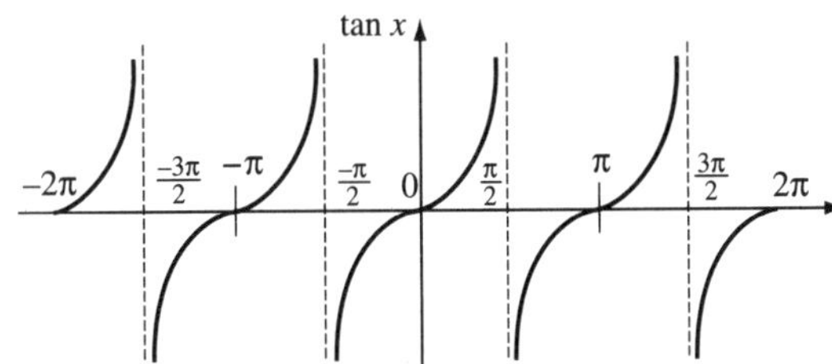

Fig. 2-I/74 Tangent

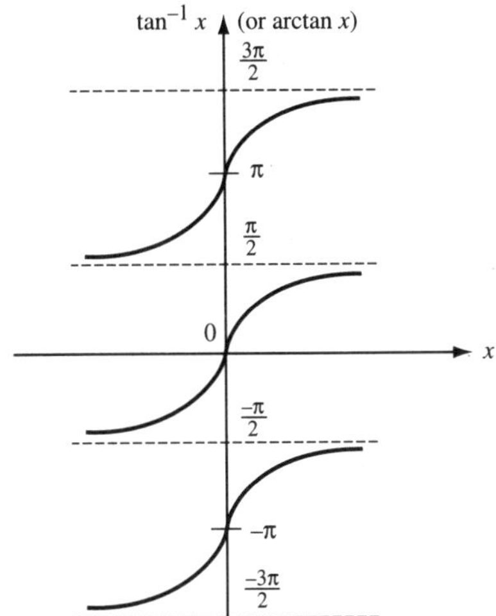

Fig. 2-I/75 Inverse tangent

WORKED EXAMPLE 79

Find, without using tables or calculators the values of x when:

(i) $\tan^{-1} 2 - \tan^{-1} 1 = \sin^{-1} x$

(ii) $\tan^{-1} \frac{1}{2} + \tan^{-1} \frac{1}{3} = \cos^{-1} x$

(iii) $\tan^{-1} 5 + \tan^{-1} 1 = \tan^{-1} x$.

Solution 79

(i) $\tan^{-1} 2 - \tan^{-1} 1 = \sin^{-1} x$ .... (1)

This equation states that the difference of two angles is equal to an angle.

If $\tan^{-1} 2 = \Theta$, $\tan^{-1} 1 = \Phi$, $\sin^{-1} x = \psi$ then $\Theta - \Phi = \psi$

Taking tangents on both sides of equation (1)

$\tan(\tan^{-1} 2 - \tan^{-1} 1)$

$$= \tan(\sin^{-1} x) = \frac{\tan(\tan^{-1} 2) - \tan(\tan^{-1} 1)}{1 + \tan(\tan^{-1} 2)\tan(\tan^{-1} 1)}$$

$$\frac{2-1}{1+2(1)} = \tan(\sin^{-1} x) = \frac{1}{3}.$$

Let $\psi = \sin^{-1} x$, $\tan \psi = \frac{1}{3}$,

$$\sin \psi = x = \frac{1}{\sqrt{10}}$$

$$\boxed{x = \frac{1}{\sqrt{10}}}$$

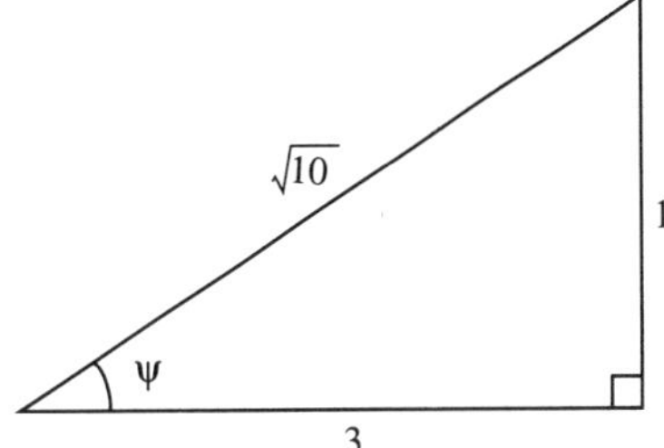

Fig. 2-I/76

(ii) $\tan^{-1} \frac{1}{2} + \tan^{-1} \frac{1}{3} = \cos^{-1} x$.

Taking tangents on both sides:

$$\tan\left(\tan^{-1} \frac{1}{2} + \tan^{-1} \frac{1}{3}\right) = \tan(\cos^{-1} x)$$

$$\frac{\tan\left(\tan^{-1} \frac{1}{2}\right) + \tan\left(\tan^{-1} \frac{1}{3}\right)}{1 - \tan\left(\tan^{-1} \frac{1}{2}\right)\tan\left(\tan^{-1} \frac{1}{3}\right)}$$

$$= \frac{\frac{1}{2} + \frac{1}{3}}{1 - \frac{1}{2} \cdot \frac{1}{3}} = \tan(\cos^{-1} x),$$

$$\frac{\frac{5}{6}}{\frac{5}{6}} = \tan(\cos^{-1} x) = 1$$

Let $\Theta = \cos^{-1} x$, $\tan \Theta = 1$,

$$\Theta = \frac{\pi}{4}, \frac{\pi}{4} = \cos^{-1} x \qquad \cos \frac{\pi}{4} = x = \frac{1}{\sqrt{2}}$$

$$\boxed{x = \frac{1}{\sqrt{2}}}$$

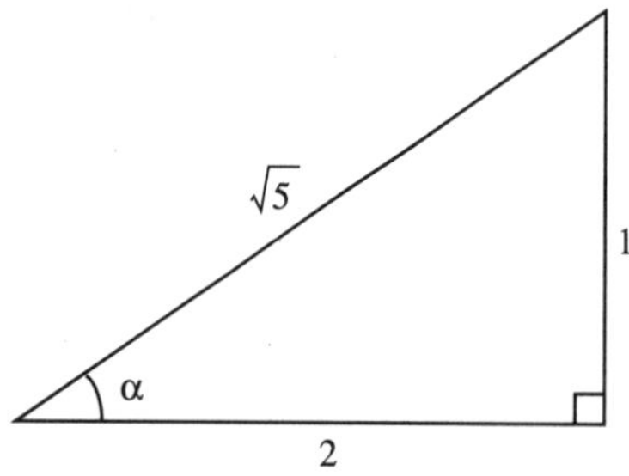

Fig. 2-I/77

(iii) $\tan^{-1} 5 + \tan^{-1} 1 = \tan^{-1} x.$

Taking tangents on both sides, $\tan(\tan^{-1} 5 + \tan^{-1} 1) = \tan(\tan^{-1} x)$

$$\frac{\tan(\tan^{-1} 5) + \tan(\tan^{-1} 1)}{1 - \tan(\tan^{-1} 5).\tan(\tan^{-1} 1)}$$

$$= \tan(\tan^{-1} x)$$

$$\frac{5+1}{1-5.1} = \frac{6}{-4} = x, \quad x = \frac{6}{-4} = -1.5$$

$$\boxed{x = -1.5}$$

Worked Example 80

(i) Show that $\tan^{-1}(1+x) + \tan^{-1}(1-x)$

$$= \tan^{-1} \frac{2}{x^2}.$$

(ii) Show that $\tan^{-1} x + \tan^{-1} y = \tan^{-1} \dfrac{x+y}{1-xy}.$

Solution 80

(i) $\tan^{-1}(1+x) + \tan^{-1}(1-x) = \tan^{-1} \dfrac{2}{x^2}.$

Taking tangents on both sides,

$$\tan\{\tan^{-1}(1+x) + \tan^{-1}(1-x)\}$$

$$= \tan\tan^{-1}\left(\frac{2}{x^2}\right)$$

$$\frac{\tan\tan^{-1}(1+x) + \tan\tan^{-1}(1-x)}{1 - \tan\tan^{-1}(1+x)\tan\tan^{-1}(1-x)}$$

$$= \frac{1+x+1-x}{1-(1+x)(1-x)}$$

$$= \frac{2}{1-(1-x^2)} = \frac{2}{x^2}, \text{ L.H.S.} = \text{R.H.S.}$$

(ii) $\tan^{-1} x + \tan^{-1} y = \tan^{-1} \dfrac{x+y}{1-xy}.$

Taking tangents on both sides,

$$\tan(\tan^{-1} x + \tan^{-1} y) = \tan\tan^{-1} \frac{x+y}{1-xy}$$

$$\text{L.H.S.} = \frac{\tan(\tan^{-1} x) + \tan(\tan^{-1} y)}{1 - \tan(\tan^{-1} x)\tan(\tan^{-1} y)}$$

$$= \frac{x+y}{1-xy}, \text{ R.H.S.} = \frac{x+y}{1-xy}.$$

Therefore, L.H.S. = R.H.S.

$$\boxed{\tan^{-1} x + \tan^{-1} y = \tan^{-1} \frac{x+y}{1-xy}}$$

Worked Example 81

Show that $4\tan^{-1} \dfrac{1}{5} - \tan^{-1} \dfrac{1}{239}$

$$= \frac{\pi}{4} = \tan^{-1} \frac{1}{2} + \tan^{-1} \frac{1}{3}$$

$$= \sin^{-1} \frac{1}{\sqrt{5}} + \cot^{-1} 3.$$

Solution 81

Let $\Theta = \tan^{-1} \dfrac{1}{5}$ and $\Phi = \tan^{-1} \dfrac{1}{239}$, $4\Theta - \Phi = \dfrac{\pi}{4}.$

Taking tangents on both sides

$$\tan(4\Theta - \Phi) = \tan \frac{\pi}{4} = 1$$

$$\frac{\tan 4\Theta - \tan\Phi}{1 + \tan 4\Theta \tan\Phi} = 1$$

where $\Theta = \tan^{-1} \dfrac{1}{5}, \dfrac{1}{5} = \tan\Theta,$

$\Phi = \tan^{-1} \dfrac{1}{239}, \dfrac{1}{239} = \tan\Phi$ and

where $\tan 4\Theta = \dfrac{2\tan 2\Theta}{1 - \tan^2 2\Theta}$

$$\frac{2\left(\frac{5}{12}\right)}{1 - \left(\frac{5}{12}\right)^2} = \frac{120}{119} \text{ and}$$

$$\tan 2\Theta = \frac{2\tan\Theta}{1-\tan^2\Theta} = \frac{2\left(\frac{1}{5}\right)}{1 - \frac{1}{25}} = \frac{\frac{2}{5}}{\frac{24}{25}} = \frac{5}{12}$$

$$\frac{\tan 4\Theta - \tan\Phi}{1+\tan 4\Theta\tan\Phi} = \frac{\frac{120}{119}-\frac{1}{239}}{1+\frac{120}{119}\cdot\frac{1}{239}}$$

$$= \frac{120\,(239)-119}{(119)(239)+120}$$

$$= \frac{28561}{28561} = 1$$

hence $\boxed{4\tan^{-1}\frac{1}{5}-\tan^{-1}\frac{1}{239}=\frac{\pi}{4}}$

To show $\tan^{-1}\frac{1}{2}+\tan^{-1}\frac{1}{3}=\frac{\pi}{4}$, taking tangents on both sides

$$\frac{\tan\tan^{-1}\frac{1}{2}+\tan\tan^{-1}\frac{1}{3}}{1-\tan\tan^{-1}\frac{1}{2}\tan\tan^{-1}\frac{1}{3}} = \tan\frac{\pi}{4}.$$

L.H.S. $\dfrac{\frac{1}{2}+\frac{1}{3}}{1-\frac{1}{2}\cdot\frac{1}{3}} = \dfrac{\frac{5}{6}}{\frac{5}{6}}$ =1, *therefore*

$\boxed{\tan^{-1}\frac{1}{2}+\tan^{-1}\frac{1}{3}=\frac{\pi}{4}}$

To show that $\sin^{-1}\frac{1}{\sqrt{5}}+\cot^{-1}3=\frac{\pi}{4}$,

$\tan(\Theta+\Phi)=\tan\frac{\pi}{4}$

where $\Theta=\sin^{-1}\frac{1}{\sqrt{5}}$ and $\Phi=\cot^{-1}3$,

$\tan\Theta=\frac{1}{2}$, $\tan\Phi=\frac{1}{3}$,

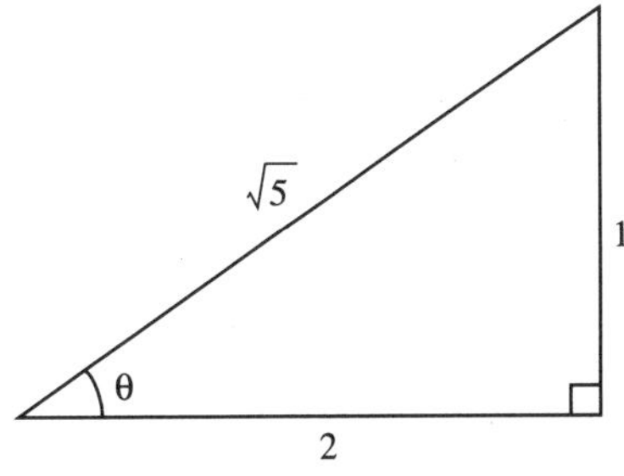

Fig. 2-I/78

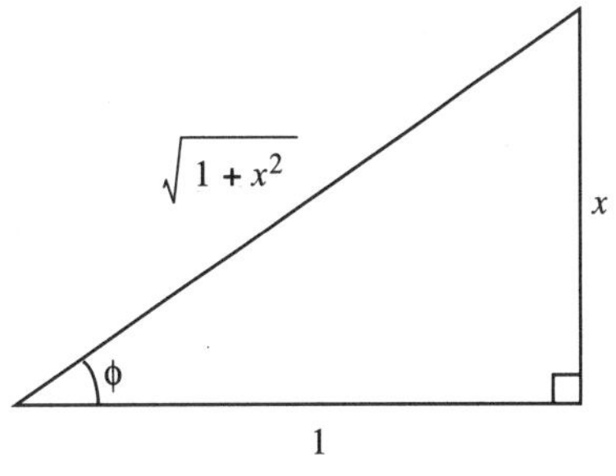

Fig. 2-I/79

$$\tan(\Theta+\Phi) = \frac{\tan\Theta+\tan\Phi}{1-\tan\Theta\tan\Phi}$$

$$= \frac{\frac{1}{2}+\frac{1}{3}}{1-\frac{1}{2}\cdot\frac{1}{3}} = \frac{\frac{5}{6}}{\frac{5}{6}} = 1$$

therefore $\boxed{\sin^{-1}\frac{1}{\sqrt{5}}+\cot^{-1}3=\frac{\pi}{4}}$

Worked Example 82

Evaluate the angle $\tan^{-1}2+\tan^{-1}3$.

Solution 82

Let $\Phi = \tan^{-1}2+\tan^{-1}3$. Taking tangents on both sides,

$$\tan\Phi = \tan(\tan^{-1}2+\tan^{-1}3)$$

$$= \frac{\tan\tan^{-1}2+\tan\tan^{-1}3}{1-\tan\tan^{-1}2.\tan\tan^{-1}3}$$

$$= \frac{2+3}{1-2.3} = \frac{5}{-5} = -1$$

$$\Phi = \frac{3\pi}{4} = \tan^{-1}(-1)$$

therefore $\boxed{\tan^{-1}2+\tan^{-1}3=\frac{3\pi}{4}}$

Worked Example 83

Evaluate the angle $\tan^{-1}3+\tan^{-1}4=\Phi$.

Solution 83

$\Phi=\tan^{-1}3+\tan^{-1}4$. Taking tangents on both sides, let $\tan^{-1}3=A$, $\tan^{-1}4=B$, hence $\tan A=3$, and $\tan B=4$, $\tan\Phi=\tan(\tan^{-1}3+\tan^{-1}4)$

$$= \tan(A+B) = \frac{\tan A + \tan B}{1 - \tan A \tan B}$$

$$= \frac{3+4}{1-3.4} = \frac{7}{-11}$$

$$\Phi = \tan^{-1}\left(\frac{7}{-11}\right) = 147^\circ\, 31'$$

$$\boxed{\Phi = 147^\circ\, 31'}$$

WORKED EXAMPLE 84

Solve the equation $\tan^{-1} x + \tan^{-1} 1 = \tan^{-1} 2$.

Solution 84

$\tan^{-1} x = \tan^{-1} 2 - \tan^{-1} 1$.

Taking tangents on both sides,

$\tan\tan^{-1} x = \tan(\tan^{-1} 2 - \tan^{-1} 1)$

$$x = \frac{\tan\tan^{-1} 2 - \tan\tan^{-1} 1}{1 + \tan\tan^{-1} 2 . \tan\tan^{-1} 1}$$

$$x = \frac{2-1}{1+2.1} = \frac{1}{3}.$$

$$\boxed{x = \frac{1}{3}}$$

WORKED EXAMPLE 85

Show that $\tan^{-1} 2 + \tan^{-1} \frac{1}{2} = \frac{\pi}{2}$, and in general $\tan^{-1} x + \tan^{-1} \frac{1}{x} = \frac{\pi}{2}$.

Solution 85

Let $\Phi = \tan^{-1} 2 + \tan^{-1} \frac{1}{2}$. Taking tangents on both sides

$$\tan\Phi = \frac{\tan\tan^{-1} 2 + \tan\tan^{-1} \frac{1}{2}}{1 - \tan\tan^{-1} 2 \tan\tan^{-1} \frac{1}{2}}$$

$$= \frac{2 + \frac{1}{2}}{1 - 2 \cdot \frac{1}{2}} = \frac{\frac{5}{2}}{0} = \infty.$$

Therefore $\boxed{\Phi = \frac{\pi}{2}}$.

In general, $\tan^{-1} x + \tan^{-1} \frac{1}{x} = \Phi$

$$\tan\Phi = \frac{\tan\tan^{-1} x + \tan\tan^{-1} \frac{1}{x}}{1 - \tan\tan^{-1} x \tan\tan^{-1} \frac{1}{x}}$$

$$= \frac{x + \frac{1}{x}}{1-1} = \frac{x + \frac{1}{x}}{0} = \infty$$

$$\boxed{\Phi = \frac{\pi}{2}}.$$

WORKED EXAMPLE 86

Simplify: $\cos(2\tan^{-1} x)$.

Solution 86

$\cos(2\tan^{-1} x)$.

Let $\tan^{-1} x = \Theta$, $\cos(2\tan^{-1} x) = \cos 2\Theta$,

$\tan\Theta = x$

$$\cos(2\tan^{-1} x) = \frac{1-t^2}{1+t^2}$$

$$= \frac{1-\tan^2\Theta}{1+\tan^2\Theta} = \frac{1-x^2}{1+x^2} \text{ where}$$

$$\cos 2\Theta = \frac{1-t^2}{1+t^2} \text{ where } t = \tan\Theta$$

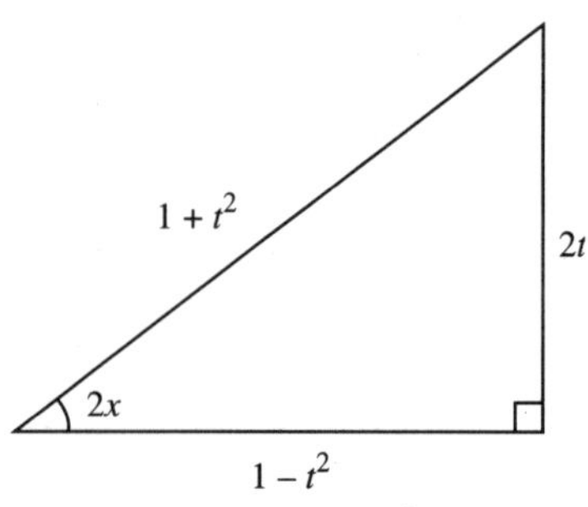

Fig. 2-I/80

$$\boxed{\cos(2\tan^{-1} x) = \frac{1-x^2}{1+x^2}}$$

WORKED EXAMPLE 87

Show that $\sin^{-1} x + \cos^{-1} x = \frac{\pi}{2}$.

Solution 87

Let $\Theta = \sin^{-1} x, x = \sin\Theta$, forming the right angle triangle where $\sin\Theta = \frac{x}{1}$, and

$$\Phi = \cos^{-1} x, \frac{x}{1} = \cos\Phi, \Theta + \Phi = \frac{\pi}{2},$$

therefore $\boxed{\sin^{-1} x + \cos^{-1} x = \frac{\pi}{2}}$.

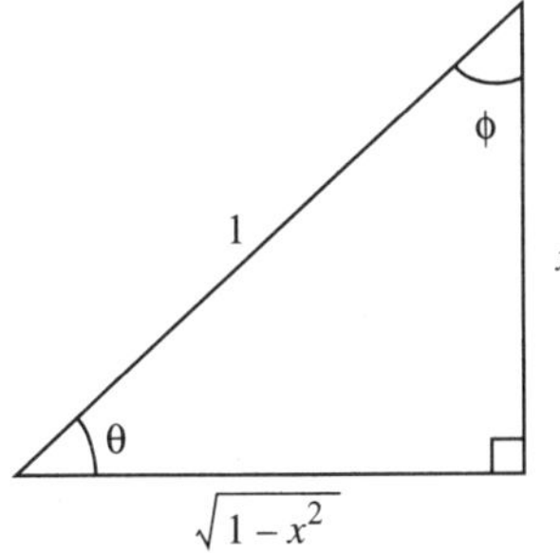

Fig. 2-I/81

Exercises 17

1. Write down the values of the following angles in the range $0° \le \Theta \le 360°$:

   (i) $\sin^{-1} 0$

   (ii) $\sin^{-1} 1$

   (iii) $\sin^{-1}\left(\frac{\sqrt{3}}{2}\right)$

   (iv) $\sin^{-1}\left(-\frac{1}{2}\right)$

   (v) $\sin^{-1}\left(\frac{1}{2}\right)$

   (vi) $\cos^{-1}\left(\frac{1}{2}\right)$

   (vii) $\cos^{-1}(-1)$

   (viii) $\cos^{-1}\left(\frac{\sqrt{3}}{2}\right)$

   (ix) $\cos^{-1}(0)$

   (x) $\cos^{-1}\left(-\frac{1}{2}\right)$

   (xi) $\tan^{-1} 1$

   (xii) $\tan^{-1}(\infty)$

   (xiii) $\tan^{-1}(0)$

   (xiv) $\tan^{-1}\left(-\sqrt{3}\right)$

   (xv) $\tan^{-1}\left(\frac{1}{\sqrt{3}}\right)$

   (xvi) $\sec^{-1}(-2)$

   (xvii) $\sec^{-1}(\infty)$

   (xviii) $\sec^{-1}\left(-\frac{2}{\sqrt{3}}\right)$

   (xix) $\sec^{-1}(2)$

   (xx) $\sec^{-1}(1)$

   (xxi) $\cot^{-1} 0$

   (xxii) $\cot^{-1}\left(-\sqrt{3}\right)$

   (xxiii) $\cot^{-1}(\infty)$

   (xxiv) $\cot^{-1}\left(\frac{1}{\sqrt{3}}\right)$

   (xxv) $\cot^{-1}(-1)$.

2. Simplify the following:

   (i) $\sin^{-1}(\sin x)$

   (ii) $\sin^{-1}(\cos x)$

   (iii) $\tan^{-1}(\tan x)$

   (iv) $\sec^{-1}(\sec x)$

   (v) $\cot^{-1}(\cot x)$

   (vi) $\mathrm{cosec}^{-1}(\mathrm{cosec}\, x)$

   (vii) $\cos^{-1}(\sin x)$

   (viii) $\cos^{-1}(\cos x)$

   (ix) $\cot^{-1}(\tan x)$

   (x) $\tan^{-1}(\cot x)$

   (xi) $\sec^{-1}(\mathrm{cosec}\, x)$

   (xii) $\mathrm{cosec}^{-1}(\sec x)$

   (xiii) $\sin(2\tan^{-1} x)$

   (xiv) $\sin(2\cot^{-1} x)$

   (xv) $\cos(2\cot^{-1} x)$.

3. Solve the following equations:

   (i) $\tan^{-1} 2 + \tan^{-1} 4 = \tan^{-1} x$

   (ii) $\tan^{-1} 2 + \tan^{-1} x = \tan^{-1} 3$

   (iii) $2\tan^{-1} x + \tan^{-1} 3 = \tan^{-1} 4$

   (iv) $2\tan^{-1} x + \tan^{-1} 1 = \tan^{-1} 3$

   (v) $\tan^{-1} 3 + 2\tan^{-1} x = \tan^{-1} 5$

   (vi) $\tan^{-1} 1 + \tan^{-1} 2 = \tan^{-1} x$.

4. Simplify the following expressions:

   (i) $\sin(\tan^{-1} x + \cot^{-1} x)$

   (ii) $\cos(\tan^{-1} x)$

   (iii) $\cos(2\tan^{-1} x)$

   (iv) $\cos(\tan^{-1} x + \cot^{-1} x)$

   (v) $\sin(\cot^{-1} x + 2\tan^{-1} x)$.

5. Evaluate the following expressions:

   (i) $\tan(\tan^{-1} 1 + \tan^{-1} 2 + \tan^{-1} 3)$

   (ii) $\tan\left(\tan^{-1}\frac{1}{2} + \tan^{-1}\frac{1}{3} + \tan^{-1}\frac{1}{4} + \tan^{-1}\frac{1}{1}\right)$

   (iii) $\tan^{-1}\frac{1}{2} + \tan^{-1}\frac{1}{3} + \tan^{-1}\frac{1}{4} + \tan^{-1}\frac{1}{5}$

   (iv) $\sin\left(\tan^{-1}\frac{1}{2} + \frac{\pi}{4}\right)$

   (v) $\cos\left(\tan^{-1}\frac{3}{4} + \frac{\pi}{2}\right)$.

6. Solve $\sin^{-1} x = \cos^{-1}\frac{3x}{2}$

   $\left(\textbf{Answer } x = \frac{2}{\sqrt{13}}\right)$

7. Show that $4\tan^{-1}\frac{1}{5} - \tan^{-1}\frac{1}{70} + \tan^{-1}\frac{1}{99} = \frac{\pi}{4}$

   Rutherford

8. Show that $5\tan^{-1}\frac{1}{7} + 2\tan^{-1}\frac{3}{79} = \frac{\pi}{4}$

   Euler

9. Solve $\tan^{-1}\frac{x+1}{x+2} - \tan^{-1}\frac{x-1}{x-2} = \cos^{-1}\frac{3}{\sqrt{13}}$

   (**Answer** $x = 1$)

10. Solve $\tan^{-1} x + \frac{1}{2}\sec^{-1} 5x = \frac{\pi}{4}$.

    $\left(\textbf{Answer } x = \frac{1}{3}\right)$

18

Three Dimensional Problems

Angle of Elevation

Referring to Fig. 2-I/82, the angle of elevation is α. Looking up to the top of a tower, the angle between the line of sight and the horizontal is called "the angle of elevation".

A theodolite is placed at a height h_1 and the height of the tower from the ground level is h_2.

A theodolite is an instrument used by surveyors to measure the angles of elevation and depression.

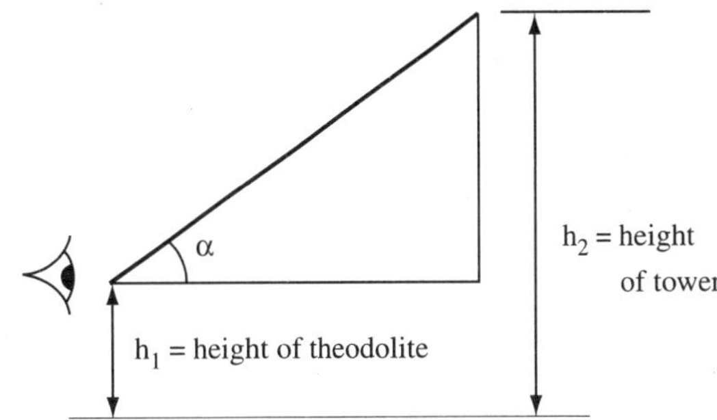

Fig. 2-I/82 Angle of elevation

Referring to Fig. 2-I/83, the angle of depression is β. Looking down from the top of a mountain, the angle between the horizontal to the line of sight is called "the angle of depression".

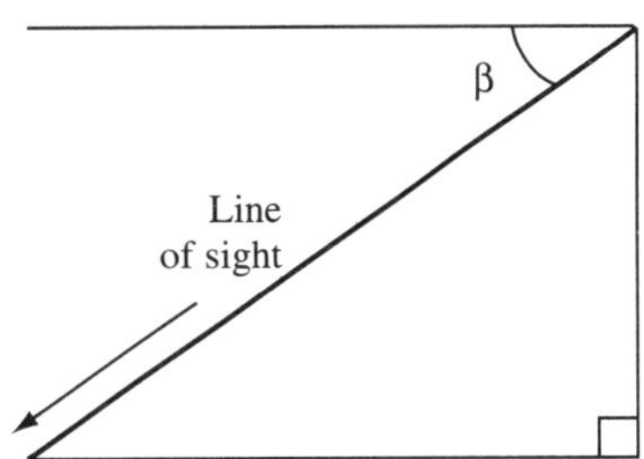

Fig. 2-I/83 Angle of depression

Bearings

The four cardinal directions are, North, South, East and West, as shown in Fig. 2-I/84.

NS and EW intersect.

The NE, SW, SE and NW directions are at 45° to the four cardinals.

A bearing of N 45° E is 45° from N to E:

A bearing of S 45° E is 45° from S to E:

A bearing of N 45° W is 45° from N to W:

A bearing of S 45° W is 45° from S to W:

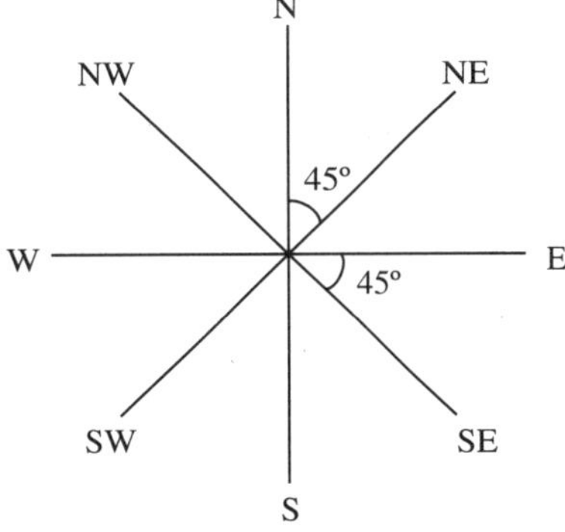

Fig. 2-I/84 The four cardinals

Bearings are always measured from N to S.

Bearings are also measured from N in a clockwise direction, the **NORTH** taken as the reference 0°.

NE is 045°, **E** is 090°, **SE** is 135°, **S** is 180°, **SW** is 225°, **W** is 270°, **NW** is 315°.

The bearings of **A, B, C** and **D** are 055°, 135°, 330° and 210° respectively, and these are shown in Fig. 2-I/85.

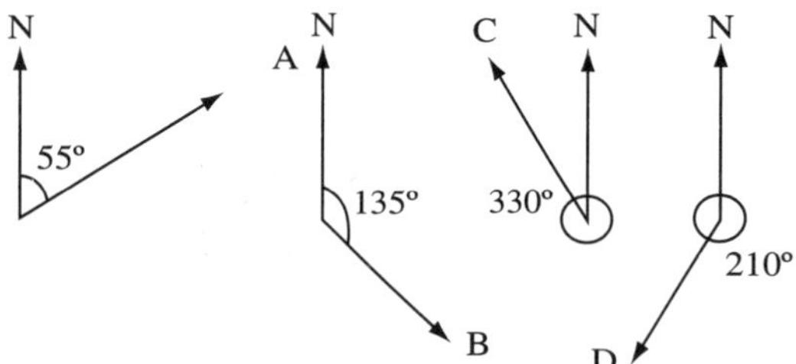

Fig. 2-I/85 The bearings

WORKED EXAMPLE 88

A tower is 75 m high. A surveyor measures the angle of elevation as 45° by means of a theodolite which stands 1.4 m above the ground.

Determine the distance between the surveyor and the tower.

If the surveyor moves 10 m further away from the tower and 10 m nearer to the tower, calculate the corresponding angles of elevation.

Solution 88

$$\Delta ATD,\ \tan 45° = \frac{75 - 1.4}{x}$$

$$x = \frac{73.6}{1} = 73.6 \text{ m}$$

$\boxed{x = 73.6 \text{ m}}$

the distance between the surveyor and the tower. From Fig 2-I/86

$$\tan\beta = \frac{73.6}{x+10} = \frac{73.6}{83.6},\ \beta = 41°\ 21'\ 36'',$$

$$\tan\alpha = \frac{73.6}{x-10} = \frac{73.6}{63.6},\ \alpha = 49°\ 10'\ 7''.$$

$\boxed{\beta = 41°\ 21'\ 36''}$ $\boxed{\alpha = 49°\ 10'\ 7''}$

WORKED EXAMPLE 89

A surveyor standing on top of a skyscraper 150 m high is in line with two points *A* and *B* whose angles of depression are 15° and 25° respectively.

Calculate the distance from *A* and *B* to the bottom of the skyscraper, and hence the distance *AB*, to three significant figures.

Solution 89

$$\tan 15° = \frac{150}{AK}$$

$$AK = \frac{150}{\tan 15°} = 559.81 \text{ m} \approx 560 \text{ m}$$

$$\tan 25° = \frac{150}{BK}$$

$$BK = \frac{150}{\tan 25°} = 321.68 \text{ m} \approx 322 \text{ m}$$

$$AB = 559.81 - 321.68 = 238.13 \text{ m}$$

$$AB = 560 - 322 = \underline{238 \text{ m}}.$$

$\boxed{AB = 238 \text{ m}}$

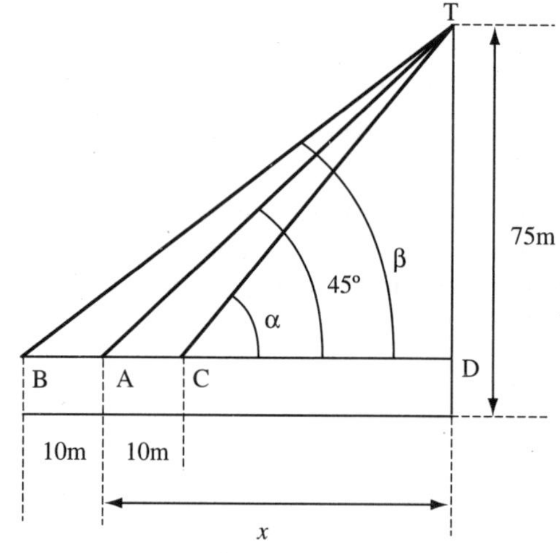

Fig. 2-I/86 Angle of elevation

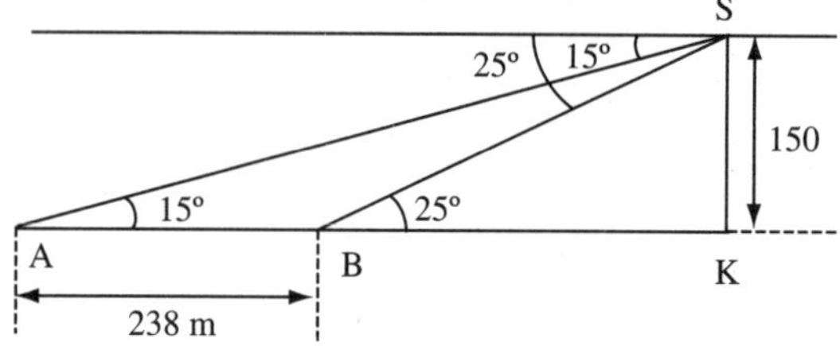

Fig. 2-I/87 Angle of depression

The Angle Between a Plane and a Line

Consider a rectangular plane *ABCD*, a line *VN* intersects this plane at *N*, Fig. 2-I/88.

The angle between the plane and the line *VN* is required.

VO is drawn perpendicular to the plane. The angle *VNO* is equal to Θ, the angle between a plane and a line.

The Angle Between Two Planes

The angle between a wall and the ceiling of a room is 90°.

The angle between a wall and the floor of a room is 90°, and the angle between the ceiling and the floor is 0°, assuming the planes of the ceiling and floor are parallel, and the walls are perpendicular to the ceiling and floor.

Two planes which are not parallel intersect in a straight line, Fig. 2-I/89 shows the angle between two planes. The line of intersection between the planes is *AB* where *CN* and *DN* are perpendicular to *AB*.

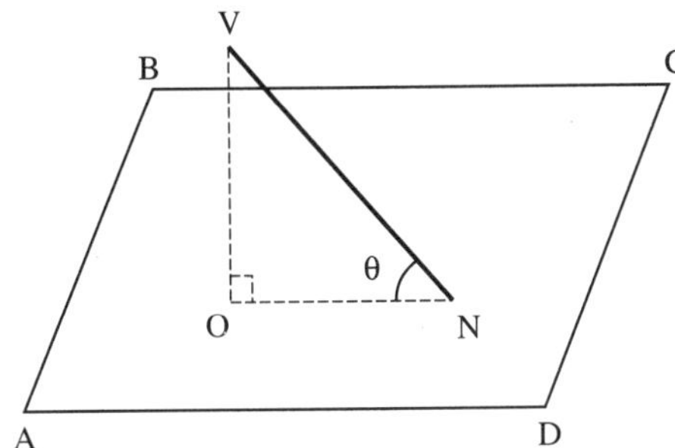

Fig. 2-I/88 The angle between the plane *ABCD* and the line *VN* is Θ.

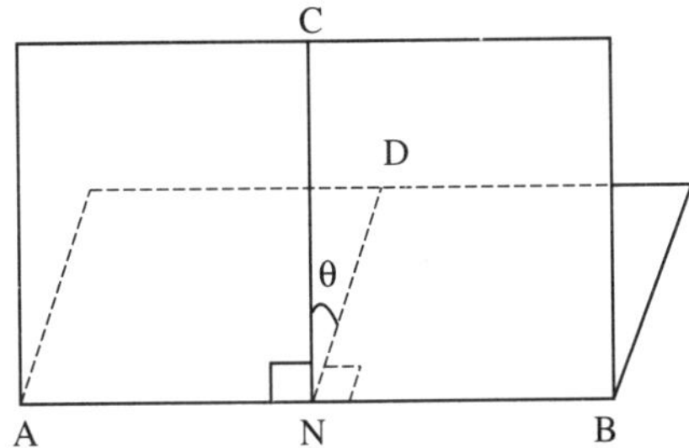

Fig. 2-I/89 The angle between the two planes is Θ, *CN* and *DN* are perpendicular to the line of intersection AB.

WORKED EXAMPLE 90

A rectangular box is shown in Fig. 2-I/90.

Calculate:

(i) the angle $\angle C'AD$,

(ii) the angle between the planes $A'D'C'B'$ and $A'D'BC$

(iii) the angle between $D'B$ and plane $ABCD$,

(iv) the angle between the planes $DD'\ BB'$ and $A'B'C'D'$ or $ABCD$,

(v) the length AC'.

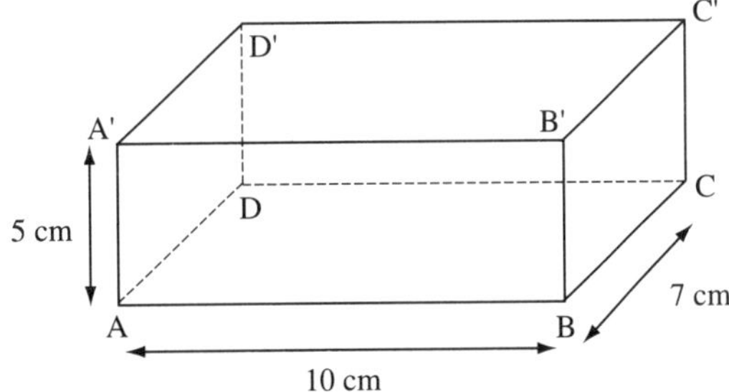

Fig. 2-I/90 A rectangular box

Solution 90

(i) From the right angled triangle $C'DC$,

$$(C'D)^2 = (CD)^2 + (CC')^2$$

$$= 10^2 + 5^2 = 100 + 25 = 125$$

$$C'D = 5\sqrt{5}\text{cm}$$

AD is perpendicular to the plane $CC'D'D$,

angle $C'DA = 90°$.

From the triangle $C'AD$ of Fig. 2-I/91.

$\tan\alpha = \dfrac{5\sqrt{5}}{7}$, $\alpha = 57°\ 57'$ to the nearest minute.

$$\boxed{\alpha = 5°\ 57'}$$

(ii) The planes $A'D'C'B'$ and $A'D'CB$ intersect in the line $A'D'$. From the triangle $A'AB$, the angle $A'AB = 90°$, therefore

$$A'B^2 = 5^2 + 10^2 = 25 + 100 = 125$$

$A'B = 5\sqrt{5}$ cm which is perpendicular to the line of intersection of the planes $A'B'C'D'$ and $A'D'CB$, $A'D'$.

The triangle $E'FF'$ is right angled at F', Fig. 2-I/92. The angle between the planes $A'D'C'B'$ and $A'D'CB$ is Θ and the cosine of the angle Θ is given by

$$\cos\Theta = \frac{E'F'}{E'F} = \frac{10}{5\sqrt{5}}$$

where $A'B = E'F = D'C = 5\sqrt{5}$

$$\cos\Theta = \frac{10}{5\sqrt{5}} = \frac{2}{\sqrt{5}} \times \frac{\sqrt{5}}{\sqrt{5}} = \frac{2}{5}\sqrt{5}$$

or $\Theta = \cos^{-1}\frac{2}{5}\sqrt{5}$

$\Theta = 26° 34'$ to the nearest minute.

$$\boxed{\Theta = 26° 34'}$$

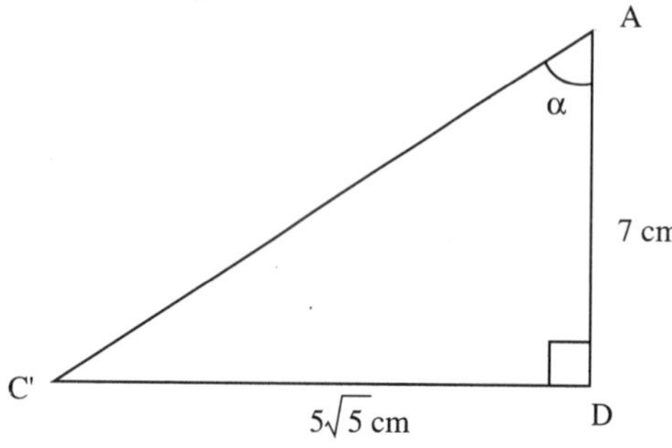

Fig. 2-I/91 The triangle $AC'D$

(iii) From the right angled triangle DAB

$$(DB)^2 = (AD)^2 + (AB)^2$$
$$= 7^2 + 10^2 = 49 + 100 = 149$$
$$DB = \sqrt{149}.$$

Angle $D'BD$ is required, let this be β,

$$\tan\beta = \frac{DD'}{BD} = \frac{5}{\sqrt{149}}$$

$$\boxed{\beta = 22°16'29''}$$

(iv) $D'B'$ is perpendicular to BB', the angle between the planes $DD'BB'$ and $A'\ B'\ C'\ D'$ or $ABCD$ is $90°$.

(v) From Fig. 2-I/90, $(AC')^2 = (AD)^2 + (C'D)^2$

$$AC' = \sqrt{7^2 + (5\sqrt{5})^2}$$
$$= \sqrt{49 + 125} = \sqrt{174} = 13.2 \text{ cm}$$

Alternatively – from the right angled triangle ACC'

$$\sqrt{(AC)^2 + (CC')^2} = AC',\ AC = DB = \sqrt{149}$$

$$AC' = \sqrt{(AC)^2 + (CC')^2}$$
$$= \sqrt{149 + 25} = \sqrt{174} = 13.2 \text{ cm}.$$

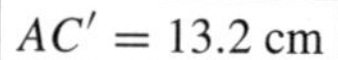

$$\boxed{AC' = 13.2 \text{ cm}}$$

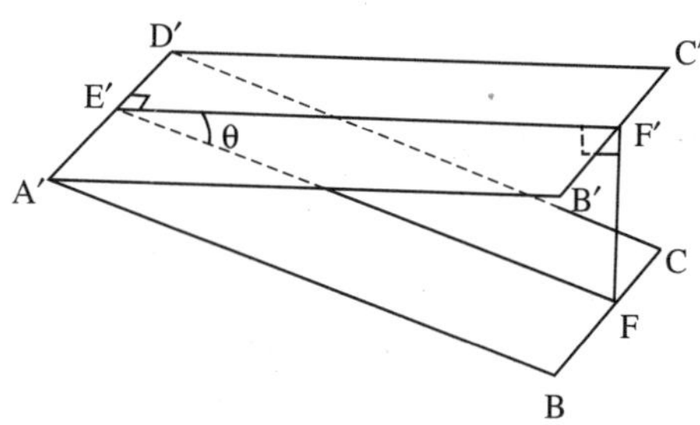

Fig. 2-I/92 The angle between the plane $A'D'C'B'$ and $A'D'CB$

WORKED EXAMPLE 91

A tetrahedron has a horizontal equilateral triangular base of side 5 cm, and the sloping edges are each 3 cm in length.

Calculate:

(i) the height of the tetrahedron

(ii) the inclination of a sloping edge to the horizontal.

(iii) the angle between two sloping faces.

Solution 91

ABC is the horizontal equilateral triangular base, *V* is the vertex, *VO* is the height of the tetrahedron: Fig. 2-I/93.

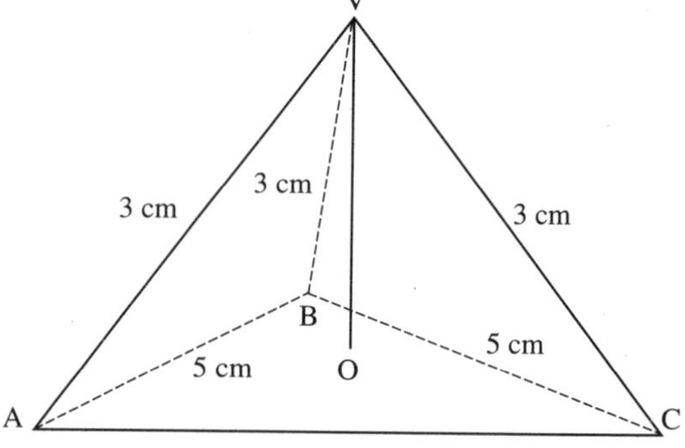

Fig. 2-I/93 A tetrahedron with horizontal equilateral triangular base.

(i) To find the height of the tetrahedron, first determine the median of the equilateral triangular base.

Let BN_1 be the median;

$x^2 + 2.5^2 = 5^2$, $x = \sqrt{25 - 6.25} = 4.33$ cm, the length of the median.

$$BO = \frac{2}{3} \cdot 4.33 = 2.89 \text{ cm},$$

$$h = \sqrt{3^2 - 2.89^2} = 0.81 \text{ cm}.$$

This can be checked otherwise. (Fig. 2-I/94),

$y = \sqrt{3^2 - 2.5^2} = 1.66 \text{ cm} = N_2V$ = median in VBA triangle,

$$N_20 = \frac{1}{3} \times 4.33 = 1.44 \text{ cm},$$

$$h = \sqrt{N_2V^2 - N_20^2} = \sqrt{1.66^2 - 1.44^2}$$

$= 0.81$ cm approximately.

$$\boxed{h = 0.81 \text{ cm}}$$

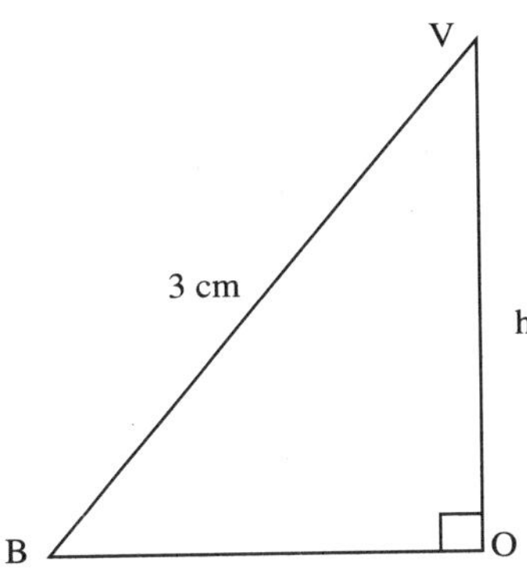

Fig. 2-I/94

(ii) To find the inclination of a sloping edge *(ABV)* to the horizontal plane (*ABC*):

The planes intersect in the line *AB*.

ON_2 is perpendicular to AB and VN_2 is perpendicular to AB. The angle between the two planes is that angle between the two lines ON_2 and VN_2,

$$\sin \Theta = \frac{h}{N_2V} = \frac{0.81}{1.66}$$

or $\Theta = 29° \, 12' \, 21'' = 29° \, 12'$ approximately.

$$\boxed{\Theta = 29° \, 12'}$$

(iii) The angle between two sloping faces. Two sloping faces are *ABV* and *BVC*, which intersect in the line *VB*.

Draw perpendicular lines from *A* and *C* to *VB*, Fig. 2-I/95.

Angle AMC = the angle between two sloping faces $= \alpha$.

$$AM = \sqrt{3^2 - VM^2}$$

$$= \sqrt{5^2 - (3 - VM)^2}$$

$$= \sqrt{9 - VM^2}$$

$$= 9 - VM^2 = 25 - 9 + 6VM - VM^2,$$

$6VM = 18 - 25 = -7$, the negative sign implies that M lies outside BV, therefore

$$AM = \sqrt{3^2 - MV^2}$$

$$= \sqrt{5^2 - (3 + VM)^2},$$

$$9 - MV^2 = 25 - 9 - 6VM - MV^2$$

$$6MV = 25 - 18$$

$$MV = \frac{7}{6}, AM = \sqrt{9 - \left(\frac{7}{6}\right)^2} = 2.764 \text{ cm}$$

applying the cosine rule

$$5^2 = 2.764^2 + 2.764^2 - 2(2.764)^2 \cos \alpha$$

$$\cos \alpha = \frac{2(2.764)^2 - 25}{2(2.764)^2}$$

$$= 1 - \frac{25}{2(2.764)^2}$$

$$= -0.63619$$

$$\alpha = 129° \, 30'.$$

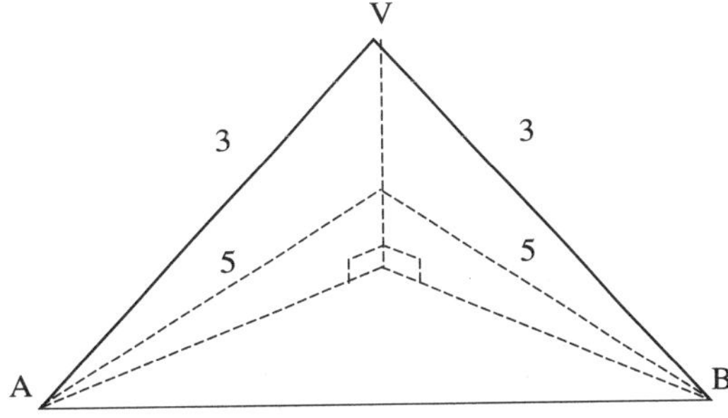

Fig. 2-I/95 Perpendicular lines are drawn to *VB* projected from *A* and *C*.

WORKED EXAMPLE 92

A tetrahedron has a horizontal equilateral triangular base of side a cm and the sloping edges are each of a cm lengths.

Calculate:

(i) the height of the tetrahedron;
(ii) the inclination of a sloping edge to the horizontal;
(iii) the angle between two sloping edges.

Solution 92

Fig. 2-I/96 shows the tetrahedron.

(i) The medians of ΔABC meet at O, where VO is the height of the tetrahedron.

$$BM = \sqrt{a^2 - \frac{a^2}{4}} = \sqrt{\frac{3a^2}{4}} = \frac{\sqrt{3}}{2}a$$

$$BO = \frac{2}{3}BM = \frac{2}{3}\frac{\sqrt{3}}{2}a = \frac{\sqrt{3}}{3}a.$$

$$h = \sqrt{a^2 - \frac{1}{3}a^2} = \sqrt{\frac{2}{3}a^2} = \sqrt{\frac{2}{3}}a.$$

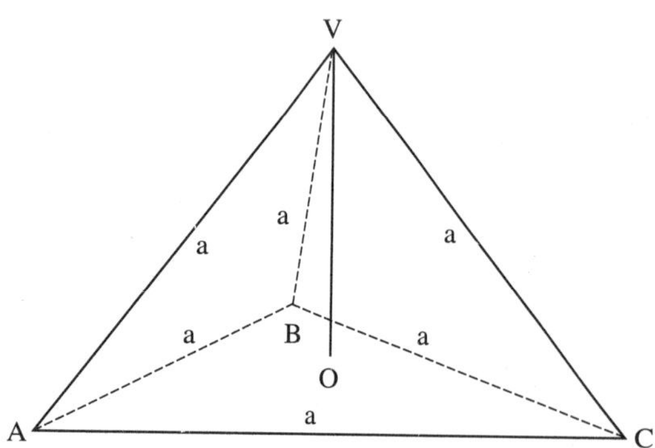

Fig. 2-I/96 A tetrahedron with a horizontal triangular base of side 'a' and sloping edges of side 'a'.

(ii) The planes AVB and ABC intersect in AB. ON is drawn perpendicularly to AB, and VN is drawn perpendicularly to AB. The angle between the two planes is that angle between the two lines ON and VN.

$$VN = \sqrt{a^2 - \frac{a^2}{4}} = \sqrt{\frac{3\,a^2}{4}} = \frac{\sqrt{3}}{2}a,$$

$$\sin\Theta = \frac{h}{VN} = \frac{\sqrt{\frac{2}{3}}a}{\sqrt{\frac{3}{4}}a} = \sqrt{\frac{2}{3}}\sqrt{\frac{4}{3}} = \frac{2\sqrt{2}}{3}$$

$$\Theta = \sin^{-1}\frac{2}{3}\sqrt{2} = 70^\circ\ 32'$$

$$\boxed{\Theta = 70^\circ\ 32'}$$

Fig. 2-I/97 shows the relevant triangles.

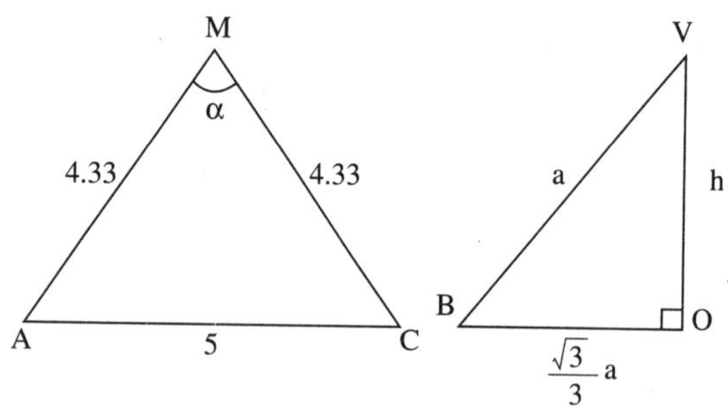

Fig. 2-I/97

(iii) *Draw* perpendicular lines from A and C to VB

$$AM = \sqrt{a^2 - VM^2}$$

$$= \sqrt{a^2 - (a - VM^2)} \Rightarrow a^2 - VM^2$$

$$= a^2 - \left(a^2 - 2aVM + VM^2\right)$$

$$a^2 - VM^2 = 2aVM - VM^2 \Rightarrow VM = \frac{a}{2}$$

$$AM = \sqrt{a^2 - \left(\frac{a}{2}\right)^2} = \frac{\sqrt{3}}{2}a = CM.$$

angle $AMC = \alpha =$ the required angle

$$a^2 = \left(\frac{\sqrt{3}a}{2}\right)^2 + \left(\frac{\sqrt{3}a}{2}\right)^2$$

$$-2\left(\frac{\sqrt{3}a}{2}\right)\left(\frac{\sqrt{3}a}{2}\right)\cos\alpha$$

$$\cos\alpha = \frac{\frac{6a^2}{4} - a^2}{\frac{3a^2}{2}} = \frac{1}{3}$$

$$\boxed{\alpha = 70^\circ\ 32'}$$

which agrees with answer of (ii), the angle between two sloping faces. Fig. 2-I/98 shows the relevant triangles.

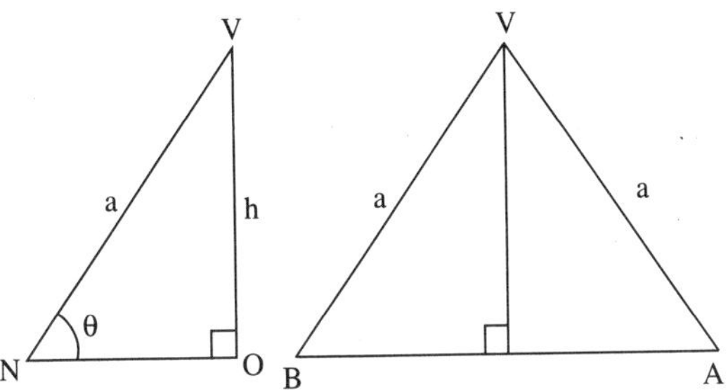

Fig. 2-I/98

The Angle Between Two Planes

$ABCD$ is a horizontal rectangle, $A'B'C'D'$ is a rectangle inclined at an angle α to the horizontal. Fig. 2-I/99 shows the two planes inclined at angle α.

The area $A'B'C'D'$

$$= (A'B') \times (B'C') = \frac{AB \times B'C''}{\cos\alpha} \text{ but}$$

$$\cos\alpha = \frac{B'C''}{B'C'} \text{ and } A'B' = AB,\ B'C'' = BC$$

$$\text{area } A'B'C'D' = \frac{\text{area } ABCD}{\cos\alpha}$$

$$\cos\alpha = \frac{\text{area } ABCD}{\text{area } A'\ B'\ C'\ D'} = \frac{\text{area projected}}{\text{area inclined}}.$$

This formula applies to any area inclined to the horizontal at an angle α.

Three vertical poles are placed at A, B and C at heights h_1, h_2, and h_3 respectively.

The angle between the plane of the triangle $A'B'C'$ and plane of the triangle ABC is given by

$$\alpha = \cos^{-1}\frac{\Delta ABC}{\Delta\, A'\ B'\ C'}.$$

The angle between the ellipse and the circle is given by

$$\alpha = \cos^{-1}\frac{\text{area circle}}{\text{area ellipse}}$$

Figs. 2-I/100 and 2-I/101 respectively show the areas of the triangles and those of the ellipse and the circle.

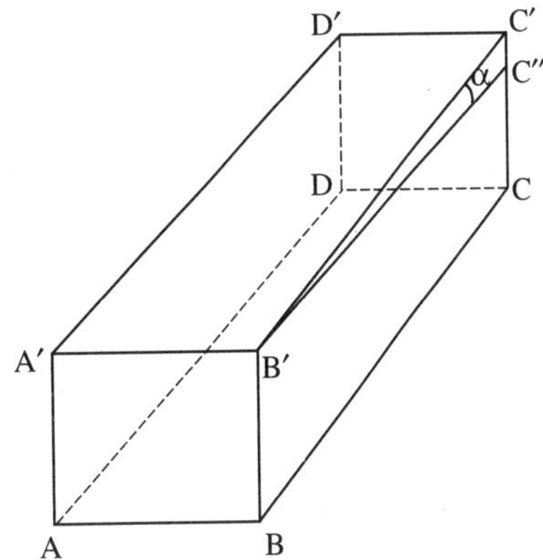

Fig. 2-I/99 Angle between two planes

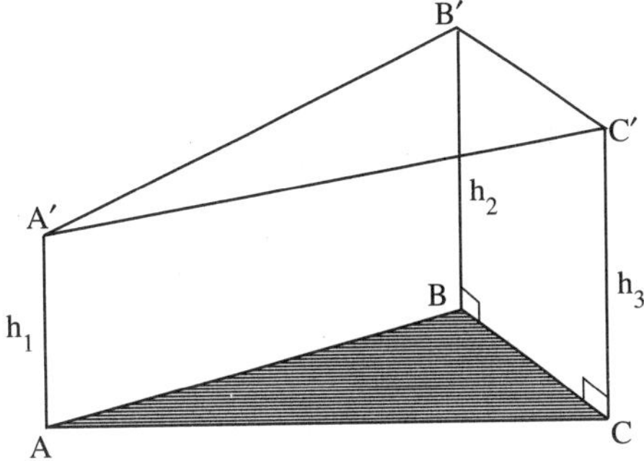

Fig. 2-I/100

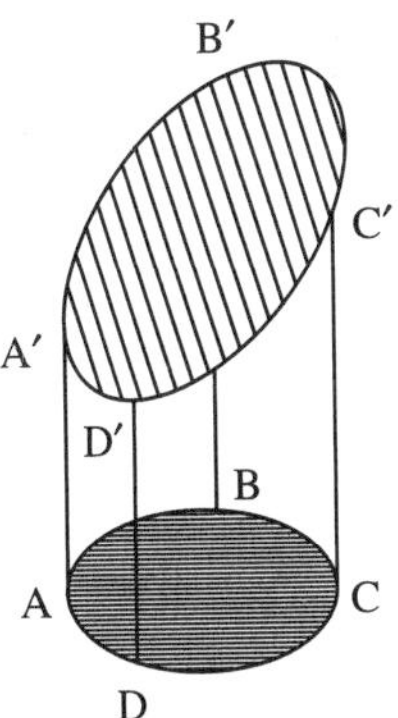

Fig. 2-I/101

Exercises 18

1. An equilateral triangle ABC, of side $2\sqrt{6}$, lies in a horizontal plane.

   Points A', B' and C' are vertically above A, B and C respectively at heights above the plane of 2 cm, 5 cm and 7 cm respectively.

   Calculate:

   (i) the area of the triangle ABC

   (ii) the area of the triangle $A'B'C'$

   (iii) the angle between the planes of the triangles $A'B'C'$ and ABC,

   (iv) the angle between the planes of the triangles $AB'C'$ and ABC,

2. A solid pyramid with a horizontal square base $ABCD$ of side 5 cm and sides 10 cm is shown in the following diagram;

   Calculate:

   (i) the height of V above the plane $ABCD$

   (ii) the angle of one of the faces with the horizontal;

   (iii) the volume of the solid;

   (iv) the total surface area;

   (v) the angle between the planes VAB and VAD.

   Ans.

   (i) 9.35 cm

   (ii) $75° 2'$

   (iii) 77.9 cm^3

   (iv) 121.8 cm^2

   (v) $93° 51'$

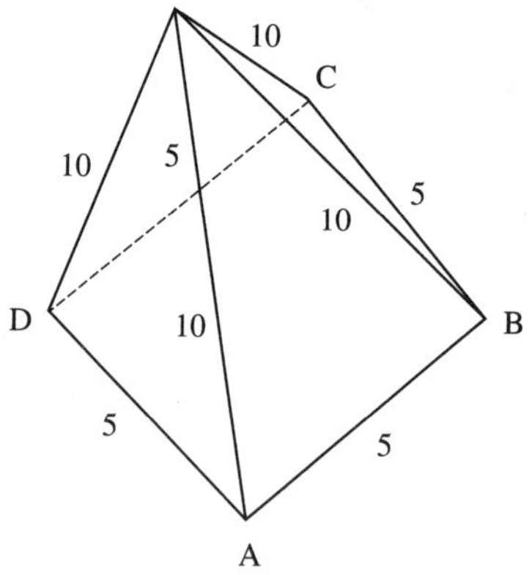

Fig. 2-I/102 A solid pyramid with a horizontal square base ABCD.

3. A, B and C are points equally spaced on the circumference of a horizontal circle of radius 5 cm. Points A', B' and C' are at heights 1 cm, 2 cm and 3 cm vertically above A, B and C respectively.

   Calculate:

   (i) the area of triangle ABC;

   (ii) the area of triangle $A'B'C'$;

   (iii) the angle between the two planes ABC and $A'B'C'$.

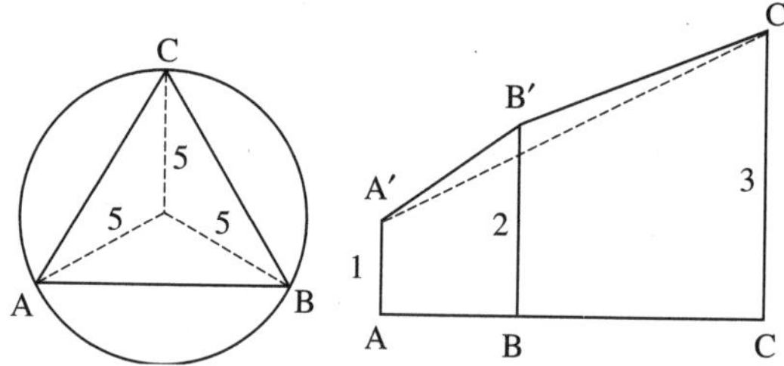

Fig. 2-I/103 $A'B'C'$ are at heights 1, 2 and 3 cm vertically above A, B and C respectively.

19

Small Angles

If x is a very small angle and expressed in radians, we can show that x lies between $\sin x$ and $\tan x$, **i.e.** $\sin x < x < \tan x$.

The area of the triangle ABC, knowing the sides a and b and the angle between the two sides a and b is $\frac{1}{2}ab\sin\Theta$.

The area of the triangle OAB is $\frac{1}{2}r^2\sin\Theta$.

The area of the sector OAB is $\frac{1}{2}r^2\Theta$.

If the angle is very small and is measured in radians, $\frac{1}{2}r^2\sin\Theta \approx \frac{1}{2}r^2\Theta$ or $\sin\Theta \approx \Theta$; this implies that the chord AB approaches the length of the arc AB and A approaches B.

Let Θ be such a small angle subtending an arc AB.

If OA is produced to OA' such that $A'B$ is perpendicular to OB the area of the triangle $OA'B = \frac{1}{2}r\,r\tan\Theta = \frac{1}{2}r^2\tan\Theta$, and the area of the sector $OAB = \frac{1}{2}r^2\Theta$.

It is obvious from the diagram that the area of the sector OAB lies between the two areas of the triangles OAB and $OA'B$

$$\frac{1}{2}r^2\sin\Theta < \frac{1}{2}r^2\Theta < \frac{1}{2}r^2\tan\Theta \text{ or}$$

$$\boxed{\sin\Theta < \Theta < \tan\Theta} \qquad (1)$$

Dividing each term of the inequalities by a positive quantity such as $\sin\Theta$ where Θ is a small positive angle, we have

$$1 < \frac{\Theta}{\sin\Theta} < \frac{\tan\Theta}{\sin\Theta} \text{ or } 1 < \frac{\Theta}{\sin\Theta} < \frac{1}{\cos\Theta} \text{ hence}$$

$\frac{1}{\cos\Theta}$ or $\sec\Theta$ is greater than 1.

If the angle Θ is very small, then $\sec\Theta$ approaches unity **i.e.** as $\Theta \to 0$ then

$\sec\Theta \to 1$, $\frac{\Theta}{\sin\Theta} > 1$, $\Theta > \sin\Theta$, when the angle Θ is very small.

i.e. as $\Theta \to 0$ $\boxed{\sin\Theta \approx \Theta}$ $\frac{\Theta}{\sin\Theta} \to 1$ or $\sin\Theta \to \Theta$, $\sin\Theta < \Theta < \tan\Theta$.

Considering again (1) and dividing each term by $\tan\Theta$ which is also positive

$$\frac{\sin\Theta}{\tan\Theta} < \frac{\Theta}{\tan\Theta} < 1, \qquad \frac{\Theta}{\tan\Theta} < 1,$$

$\Theta \to \tan\Theta$ as $\Theta \to 0$.

The limiting values are $\sin\Theta \approx \Theta$, but $\cos\Theta = 1 - 2\sin^2\frac{\Theta}{2}$

$$2\sin^2\frac{\Theta}{2} = 1 - \cos\Theta,$$

$$\cos\Theta = 1 - 2\sin^2\frac{\Theta}{2} \approx 1 - 2\left(\frac{\Theta}{2}\right)^2$$

$$\approx 1 - \frac{2\Theta^2}{4} \approx 1 - \frac{1}{2}\Theta^2$$

$$\boxed{\cos\Theta \approx 1 - \frac{1}{2}\Theta^2.}$$

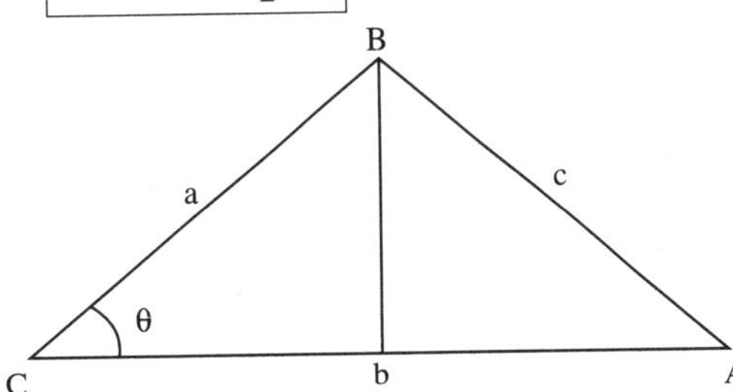

Fig. 2-I/104 The area of the triangle $A = \frac{1}{2}ab\sin\Theta$

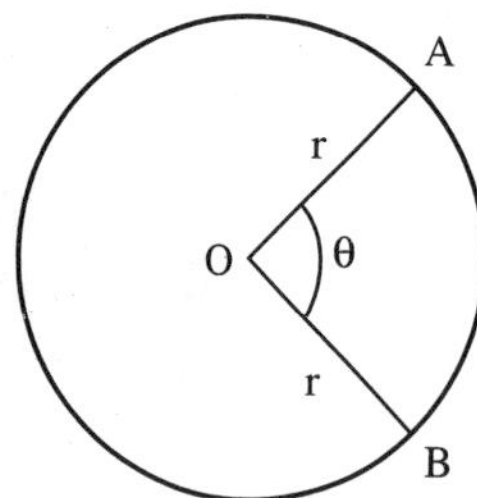

Fig. 2-I/105 The area of the sector OAB is $\frac{1}{2}r^2\Theta$

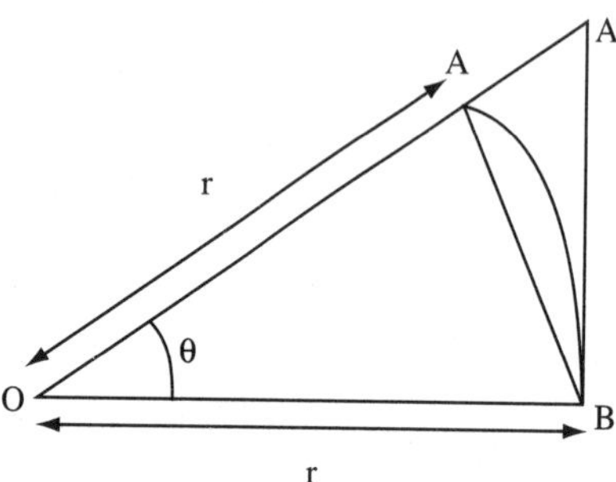

Fig. 2-I/106 $\sin\Theta < \Theta < \tan\Theta$

$\lim_{x\to 0} \frac{\sin x}{x} = \frac{\sin 0}{0} = \frac{0}{0}$ undeterminable.

Applying L'Hospital's rule, **i.e.** differentiating numerator and denominator separately

$$\lim_{x\to 0} \frac{\cos x}{1} = 1.$$

But we showed earlier that $\sin x \approx x$ as x is a very small angle and expressed in radians

$$\lim_{x\to 0} \frac{\sin x}{x} = \lim_{x\to 0} \approx \frac{x}{x} = 1$$

$\lim_{x\to 0} \frac{\tan x}{x} = \frac{\tan 0}{0} = \frac{0}{0}$ undeterminable but since x is small

$$\lim_{x\to 0} \frac{\tan x}{x} \approx \frac{x}{x} = 1.$$

Applying L'Hospital's rule again

$$\lim_{x\to 0} \frac{\sec^2 x}{1} = \frac{\sec^2 0}{1} = 1$$

but we showed earlier that $\tan x \approx x$ as x is a very small angle and expressed in radians.

Use of The Approximations

(i) $\sin x \approx x$

(ii) $\cos x \approx 1 - \frac{x^2}{2}$

(iii) $\tan x \approx x$.

Applying Maclaurin's theorem, it can be shown that

$$\sin x = x - \frac{x^3}{3!} + \frac{x^5}{5!} - \frac{x^7}{7!} + \qquad \ldots.(1)$$

where x is expressed in radians.

If x is a very small angle, and expressed in radians, then $\sin x \approx x$ where terms x^3 and higher are neglected.

Applying Maclaurin's theorem, it can be shown that

$$\cos x = 1 - \frac{x^2}{2!} + \frac{x^4}{4!} - \frac{x^6}{6!} + \qquad \ldots.(2)$$

where x is expressed in radians.

If x is a very small angle, expressed in radians, then $\cos x \approx 1 - \frac{1}{2}x^2$

where terms x^4 and higher are neglected.

Dividing the polynomial (1) by that of (2), we have $\tan x = x + \frac{1}{3}x^3 + \frac{1}{8}x^5$.

If x is a very small angle and expressed in radians, then $\tan x \approx x$.

Small Angles

Use of The Approximation

(i) $\sin x \approx x$

(ii) $\cos x \approx 1 - \frac{x^2}{2}$

(iii) $\tan x \approx x$.

The expansion of $\sin x$ as a polynomial in x is

$$\sin x = \frac{x}{1!} - \frac{x^3}{3!} + \frac{x^5}{5!} - \frac{x^7}{7!} + \ldots.$$

where x is expressed in radians.

If x is a very small angle and expressed in radians, then $\sin x \approx x$.

WORKED EXAMPLE 93

Find the value of $\sin 1'$.

Solution 93

The angle of $1'$ must be converted into radians,

$$1^\circ \equiv \left(\frac{\pi}{180}\right)^c$$

$$1' \equiv \left(\frac{\pi}{180 \times 60}\right)^{c} \equiv 2.9088821 \times 10^{-4} \text{ radians}$$

$\sin 1' \approx 0.000291^{c}$.

Worked Example 94

Solve the equation $\cos x = 0.99$ approximately.

Solution 94

$$\cos x \approx 1 - \frac{1}{2}x^2, \quad 1 - \frac{1}{2}x^2 = 0.99,$$

$$1 - 0.99 = \frac{1}{2}x^2$$

$x^2 = 0.02$, therefore $x = 0.1414213$ radians.

Worked Example 95

Find the value of $\cos 5'$.

Solution 95

$\cos x \approx 1 - \frac{x^2}{2}$, $5'$ must be expressed in radians.

$$5' \equiv \left(\frac{\pi}{180 \times 60} \times 5\right)^{c} = 1.454441 \times 10^{-3} \text{ radians}$$

$$\cos 5' = \cos(1.454441 \times 10^{-3})^{c}$$

$$\approx 1 - \frac{1}{2}(1.454441 \times 10^{-3})^2$$

$\cos 5' \approx 0.9999989$.

Worked Example 96

Find the value of $\cos 1°$.

Solution 96

$$1° \equiv \left(\frac{\pi}{180 \times 1}\right)^{c} = 0.0174532 \text{ radians}$$

$$\cos 0.0174532^{c} \approx 1 - \frac{(0.0174532)^2}{2}$$

$\cos 1° \approx 0.9998476$.

If we use a better approximation

$$\cos x \approx 1 - \frac{x^2}{2!} + \frac{x^4}{4!} = 1 - \frac{(0.0174532)^2}{2} + \frac{(0.0174542)^4}{24}$$

$$\cos 1° \approx 1 - 1.523071 \times 10^{-4} + 3.8662419 \times 10^{-9}$$

$$\approx 0.9999848 \text{ but}$$

$\cos 1° = 0.9998477$ from the calculator.

Worked Example 97

Find an approximate value for $\sin 46°$ without using calculators.

Solution 97

$$\begin{aligned}\sin 46° &= \sin(45° + 1°),\\ &= \sin 45° \cos 1° + \sin 1° \cos 45°\\ &= \frac{1}{\sqrt{2}}(\cos 1° + \sin 1°)\\ &= \frac{1}{\sqrt{2}}(0.9998476 + 0.0174532)\\ &= 0.7193403 \approx 0.71934\end{aligned}$$

$$\cos 1° = \cos\left(\frac{\pi}{180}\right)^{c} \approx 1 - \left(\frac{\pi}{180}\right)^2 \frac{1}{2} \approx 0.9998476$$

$$\sin 1° = \sin\left(\frac{\pi}{180}\right)^{c} \approx \frac{\pi}{180} \approx 0.0174532.$$

Worked Example 98

Find an approximate value for $\tan 29° 15'$.

Solution 98

$$\begin{aligned}\tan 29° 15' &= \tan(30° - 45')\\ &= \frac{\tan 30° - \tan 45'}{1 + \tan 30° \tan 45'}\\ &= \frac{\frac{1}{\sqrt{3}} - 0.0130899}{1 + \frac{1}{\sqrt{3}}0.0130899}\end{aligned}$$

$$\tan 45' = \tan\left(\frac{\pi}{180}\frac{45}{60}\right)^c \approx \frac{\pi}{180}\frac{45}{60}$$

$$= \frac{\pi}{240} = 0.0130899$$

$$\tan 29°15' = \frac{0.5773502 - 0.0130899}{1 + 0.0075575}$$

$$= \frac{0.5642603}{1.0075575} = 0.5600278$$

Worked Example 99

Find to five decimal places, approximate values for:

(i) $\cos 117°$

(ii) $\sin 5.02^c$

(iii) $\tan 177°$.

Use the formulae $\cos(A \pm B)$, $\sin(A \pm B)$, and $\tan(A \pm B)$.

Solution 99

(i) $\cos 117° = \cos(120° - 3°)$

$$= \cos 120° \cos 3° + \sin 120° \sin 3°$$

$$= \left(-\frac{1}{2}\right)\cos 3° + 0.866 \sin 3°$$

$$= -\frac{1}{2}0.9986292 + 0.866\,(0.0523598)$$

$$= -0.4540024 \approx -0.45400$$

$$\sin 3° = \sin\left(\frac{\pi}{180}\cdot 3\right)^c$$

$$= \sin\left(\frac{\pi}{60}\right) \approx \frac{\pi}{60} = 0.0523598$$

$$\cos 3° = \cos\left(\frac{\pi}{180}\cdot 3\right)^c$$

$$= \cos\left(\frac{\pi}{60}\right)^c \approx 1 - \frac{1}{2}\left(\frac{\pi}{60}\right)^2$$

$$= 0.9986292.$$

(ii) $\sin 5.02^c = \sin(5 + 0.02)^c$

$$= \sin 5^c \cos 0.02^c + \sin 0.02^c \cos 5^c$$

$$= (-0.9589242)(\cos 0.02) + \sin 0.02^c(0.2836621)$$

$$= (-0.9589242)(0.9998) + (0.02)(0.2836621)$$

$$= -0.9587324 + 0.005673242$$

$$= -0.95306 \text{ approx.}$$

$$\cos 0.02^c \approx 1 - \frac{1}{2}(0.02)^2$$

$$= 1 - \frac{1}{2}0.0004 = 1 - 0.0002$$

$$= 0.9998; \quad \sin 0.02^c \approx 0.02.$$

(iii) $$\tan 177° = \frac{\tan 180° - \tan 3°}{1 + \tan 180° \tan 3°}$$

$$= -\tan\left(\frac{\pi}{180}\times 3\right)^c = -\tan\left(\frac{\pi}{60}\right)^c$$

$$\approx -\frac{\pi}{60} = -0.0523598$$

$$\boxed{\tan 177° \approx -0.05236}$$

Worked Example 100

Find approximations when x is very small for the following expressions:

(i) $\dfrac{\cos 2x}{\sqrt{3 - \sin x}}$

(ii) $\dfrac{\tan 3x - \sin x}{1 - \cos 2x}$

(iii) $1 - \cos 2x + \sin 2x$.

Solution 100

(i) $$\frac{\cos 2x}{\sqrt{3 - \sin x}} \approx \frac{1 - 2x^2}{\sqrt{3 - x}}$$

(ii) $$\frac{\tan 3x - \sin x}{1 - \cos 2x} \approx \frac{3x - x}{1 - 1 + \dfrac{(2x)^2}{2}} = \frac{2x}{2x^2} = \frac{1}{x}$$

(iii) $1 - \cos 2x + \sin 2x \approx 1 - 1 + \frac{1}{2}(2x)^2$

$+2x = 2x^2 + 2x = 2x(1 + x).$

Exercises 19

1. Find to three decimal places the values of the following circular functions without using tables or calculators:
   (i) $\sin 2'$
   (ii) $\sin 15'$
   (iii) $\sin 1.5°$
   (iv) $\sin 0.15°$
   (v) $\cos 5'$
   (vi) $\cos 25'$
   (vii) $\cos 45'$
   (viii) $\cos 1.5°$
   (ix) $\tan 5'$
   (x) $\tan 18'$.

2. Find approximations when x is a very small angle and expressed in radians for the following expressions:
   (i) $\dfrac{1 - \tan 2x}{1 + \tan 2x}$
   (ii) $\cos 3x - \sin 3x$
   (iii) $\dfrac{\tan 2x - x}{\tan 2x + x}$
   (iv) $\dfrac{\cot 3x - \sec x}{\operatorname{cosec} 2x - \tan x}$
   (v) $\sec 3x - (\operatorname{cosec} x)\, 5x$.

3. Find, to three decimal places, approximate values for:
   (i) $\operatorname{cosec} 1°$
   (ii) $\sec 119°$
   (iii) $\tan 133°$
   (iv) $\cot 359°$
   (v) $\sin 33°$
   (vi) $\sin 3.01^{c}$
   (vii) $\tan 2.001^{c}$
   (viii) $\cos 5.01^{c}$
   (xi) $\operatorname{cosec} 0.05^{c}$
   (x) $\cot 1.001^{c}$.

   Use the compound angle formulae in the evaluation of the above.

4. Evaluate:
   (i) $\lim_{x\to 0} \dfrac{\sin 3x}{5x}$
   (ii) $\lim_{x\to 0} \dfrac{\cos 3x}{\sin 2x}$
   (iii) $\lim_{x\to 0} \dfrac{\tan x}{\sin x}$
   (iv) $\lim_{x\to 0} \dfrac{\tan x}{x}$
   (v) $\lim_{x\to 0} \dfrac{x}{\sin x}$
   (vi) $\lim_{x\to 0} \dfrac{\tan x + x}{\sec x}$
   (vii) $\lim_{x\to 0} \dfrac{\sec x + 1}{\sec x - 1}$
   (viii) $\lim_{x\to 0} \dfrac{\cot x + \sec x}{\operatorname{cosec} x - \tan x}$
   (ix) $\lim_{x\to 0} \dfrac{\operatorname{cosec} x - 1}{\operatorname{cosec} x + 1}$
   (x) $\lim_{x\to 0} \dfrac{\cot x - \tan x}{\cot x + \tan x}$

   (a) by employing the following approximations:

   $\sin x \approx x \quad \cos x \approx 1 - \dfrac{x^2}{2} \quad \tan \approx x.$

   (b) by employing L'Hospital's rule.

5. Evaluate the approximations in question (2) when:
   (a) $x = 1'$
   (b) $x = 0.01^{c}$
   (c) $x = 1°$.

6. Solve approximately the following equations:
   (i) $\sin \Theta = 0.001$
   (ii) $\sin \Theta = 0.01$
   (iii) $\cos \Theta = 0.999$
   (iv) $\tan \Theta = 0.005$
   (v) $\tan \Theta = 0.099$

7. Show that an angle x lies between its sine and its tangent ($\sin x < x < \tan x$).

8. Find, without using tables or calculators the value of sine, cosine, tangent, secant, cosecant and cotangent of:

   (i) $1'$

   (ii) $5'$

   (iii) $25'$

   (iv) $45'$

   (v) 1°.

9. By using suitable approximations for $\sin x$, $\cos x$ and $\tan x$, obtain an approximate value for solution of the following:

   (i) $\sin x + \cos x = 1$

   (ii) $x \cos x - \sin x = 0.9975$

   (iii) $\tan x + x \sin x = 1.75$

   (iv) $\sin x + x \tan x = 0.025$

   (v) $x \cot x - \sec x = 1.35$.

10. By using suitable approximations for $\sin x$ and $\cos x$, obtain an approximation in radians to the positive solution of the equation $\cos x - x \sin x = 0.9995$ when x is small.

20

Miscellaneous

1. Show that $\dfrac{\cos(A-B)}{\cos(A+B)} = \dfrac{\cot A + \tan B}{\cot A - \tan B}$.

2. Using the substitution of $t = \tan\dfrac{\Theta}{2}$, show that

   $\cos\Theta = \dfrac{1-t^2}{1+t^2}$ and $\operatorname{cosec}\Theta = \dfrac{1+t^2}{2t}$. Hence solve

   $5\cos\Theta - 2\sin\Theta = 3$ for $0° \leq \Theta \leq 360°$.

3. Prove the trigonometric identity

   $\tan\Theta + \cot\Theta = 2\operatorname{cosec} 2\Theta$.

4. Solve the trigonometrical equation

   $3\sin\Theta - 2\cos\Theta = 1$ when $0° < \Theta < 360°$.

5. Show that for all values of Θ

   $\sin\Theta + \sin\left(\Theta - \dfrac{2\pi}{3}\right) + \sin\left(\Theta + \dfrac{2\pi}{3}\right) = 0.$

6. Solve the equation $2\cos\Theta - 5\sin\Theta = 3$, giving all solutions between $0°$ and $360°$.

7. Using the same scales and axes, sketch the graphs of $y = \cos x$ and $y = 2\sin x$ between $0°$ and $360°$, and estimate the approximate solutions of the equation $\cos x = 2\sin x$.

8. If $\tan(A+B) = 3$, and $A = \frac{\pi}{4}$ calculate the value of $\tan B$.

   Express $\cos 2\Theta$ in terms of $\sin\Theta$ only.

   Express $\cot 2\Theta$ in terms of $\cot\Theta$ only.

   Deduce from the formulae

   $\sin 2A = 2\sin A\cos A$,

   $\cos 2A = \cos^2 A - \sin^2 A$ that

   $\tan\Theta = \dfrac{2t}{1-t^2}$ where $\tan\dfrac{\Theta}{2} = t$.

   Hence derive an expression for $\cos\Theta$ in terms of t.

21

C1 No Trigonometry

C2 Example 1

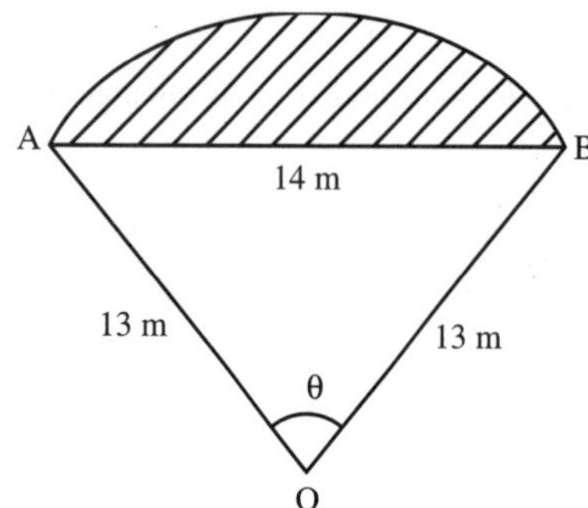

Fig. 1 shows a sector of a circle, radius 13 m. The chord *AB* is 14 m long.

(a) Show that $\cos\theta = \dfrac{71}{328}$

(b) Hence find the angle θ in radians, giving your answer to 3 decimal places.

(c) Calculate the area of the sector *AOB*.

(d) Calculate the area of the triangle *AOB*.

(e) Hence calculate the area of the segment (shaded area).

Solution 1

(a) Using the cosine rule

$$AB^2 = OA^2 + OB^2 - 2 \times OA \times OB \times \cos\theta$$

$$14^2 = 13^2 + 13^2 - 2 \times 13 \times 13 \times \cos\theta$$

$$328\cos\theta = 169 + 169 - 196$$

$$\cos\theta = \frac{71}{328}$$

(b) $\theta = 1.352605792^c = 1.353^c$ to 3 d.p.

(c) Area of the segment $= \dfrac{1}{2}r^2\theta$

$$= \frac{1}{2} \times 13^2 \times 1.352605792^c$$

$$= 114.2951894$$

$$= 114 \text{ m}^2 \text{ to 3 s.f.}$$

(d) Area of the triangle $= \dfrac{1}{2}r^2 \sin\theta$

$$\text{Area } \triangle AOB = \frac{1}{2} \times 13^2 \times \sin 1.352605792^c$$

$$= 82.49656572$$

$$= 82.5 \text{ m}^2 \text{ to 3 s.f.}$$

(e) Area of shaded area

$$= 114.2951894 - 82.49656672$$

$$= 31.79141857$$

$$= 31.8 \text{ m}^2 \text{ to 3 s.f.}$$

Example 2

(a) Find all the values of θ, to 1 decimal place, in the interval $0° \leq \theta < 360°$ for which

$$4\sin(\theta - 30°) = 1$$

(b) Find all the values of θ, to 1 decimal place, in the interval $0° \leq \theta < 360°$ for which $\sin^2(x + 30°) = \frac{1}{2}$.

Solution 2

(a) $4\sin(\theta - 30°) = 1$

$$\sin(\theta - 30°) = \frac{1}{4}$$

$$\sin(\theta - 30°) = \sin 14.47751219° \quad \ldots(1)$$

$$\sin(\theta - 30°) = \sin 165.5224878° \quad \ldots(2)$$

From(1) $\theta - 30° = 14.47751219°$

$$\theta = 44.47751219°$$

$$\theta = 44.5° \text{ to 1 d.p.}$$

From(2) $\theta - 30° = 165.5224878°$

$$\theta = 195.5° \text{ to 1 d.p.}$$

(b) $\sin^2(x + 30°) = \dfrac{1}{2}$

$$\sin(x + 30°) = \pm\frac{1}{\sqrt{2}}$$

$$\sin(x + 30°) = \frac{1}{\sqrt{2}} \quad \ldots(1)$$

$$\sin(x + 30°) = -\frac{1}{\sqrt{2}} \quad \ldots(2)$$

From(1) $\sin(x + 30°) = \sin 45° = \sin 135°$

$$x + 30° = 45°$$

$$x = 15°$$

$$x + 30° = 135°$$

$$x = 105°$$

From(2) $\sin(x + 30°) = -\dfrac{1}{\sqrt{2}}$

$$= \sin 225° = \sin 315°$$

$$x + 30° = 225° \Rightarrow x = 195°$$

$$x + 30° = 315° \Rightarrow x = 285°$$

Example 3

Solve, for $0 \le x \le 90°$, the equation

(a) $\cos(x - 20°) = \dfrac{\sqrt{3}}{2}$,

(b) $\sin 2x = 0.75$, giving your answers to 1 d.p.

Solution 3

(a) $\cos(x - 20°) = \dfrac{\sqrt{3}}{2} = \cos 30°$

$$x - 20° = 30°$$

$$\boxed{x = 50°}$$

(b) $\sin 2x = 0.75 = \sin 48.59037789° \quad \ldots(1)$

$$= \sin 131.4096221° \quad \ldots(2)$$

From (1) $x = 24.295188945°$

$$\boxed{x = 24.3°} \text{ to 1 d.p.}$$

From (2) $x = 65.70481105°$

$$\boxed{x = 65.7°} \text{ to 1 d.p.}$$

Example 4

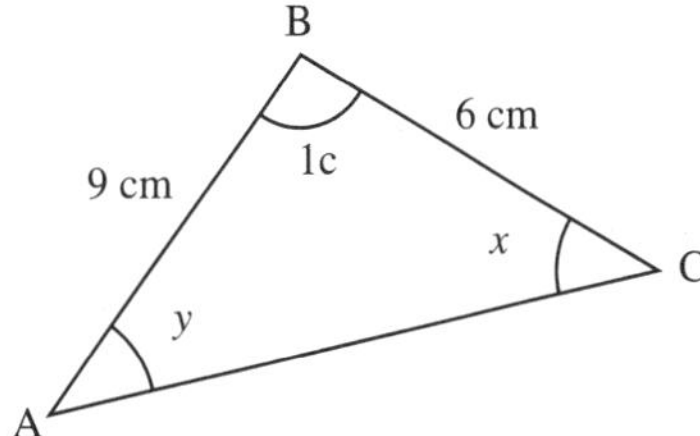

In the scalene triangle ABC, $AB = 9$ cm, $BC = 6$ cm and $A\hat{B}C = 1$ radian

(a) Find AC first and then find the value of $\sin x$, giving your answer to 3 s.f.

(b) Find the area of the triangle to 3 s.f.

Solution 4

(a) $\dfrac{AC}{\sin A\hat{B}C} = \dfrac{6}{\sin y} = \dfrac{9}{\sin x} \quad \ldots(1)$

From (1) $AC = \dfrac{9}{\sin x} \sin 1^c$

$$\sin x = \frac{9 \sin 1^c}{AC} \quad \ldots(2)$$

$$AC^2 = AB^2 + BC^2 - 2 \times AB \times BC \times \cos 1^c$$

$$= 9^2 + 6^2 - 2 \times 9 \times 6 \times \cos 1^c$$

$$= 81 + 36 - 108 \cos 1^c$$

$$= 58.64735097$$

$AC = 7.658155846 = 7.66$ cm

substituting in (2)

$$\sin x = \frac{9 \times 0.841470984}{7.658155846}$$

$$= 0.988911562$$

$$\sin x = 0.989$$

(b) $\text{Area} = \frac{1}{2} \times 9 \times 6 \sin 1^c = 22.71971659$

$$= 22.7 \text{ cm}^2 \text{ to 3 s.f.}$$

Example 5

(a) Given that $2 \sin \theta = 7 \cos \theta$, find the value of $\tan \theta$

(b) Find the values of θ in the interval $0° \leq \theta < 360°$ for which $4 \sin \theta = 14 \cos \theta$, giving your answer to 1 d.p.

Solution 5

(a) $2 \sin \theta = 7 \cos \theta$

$$\frac{\sin \theta}{\cos \theta} = \frac{7}{2} = 3.5$$

$$\tan \theta = 3.5$$

(b) $\tan \theta = \frac{14}{4} = \frac{7}{2} = 3.5 = \tan 74.0546041°$

$$= \tan 254.0546041°$$

$$\theta = 74.1°,\ 254.1°$$

Example 6

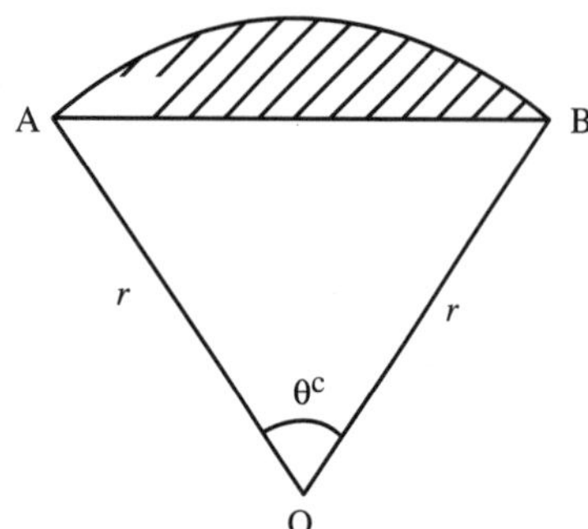

(a) Show that the length of arc $AB = r\theta$ and the area of the sector $= \frac{1}{2}r^2\theta$,

Write down the area of the triangle AOB, hence write down the formula for the area of the segment (shaded area).

(b)

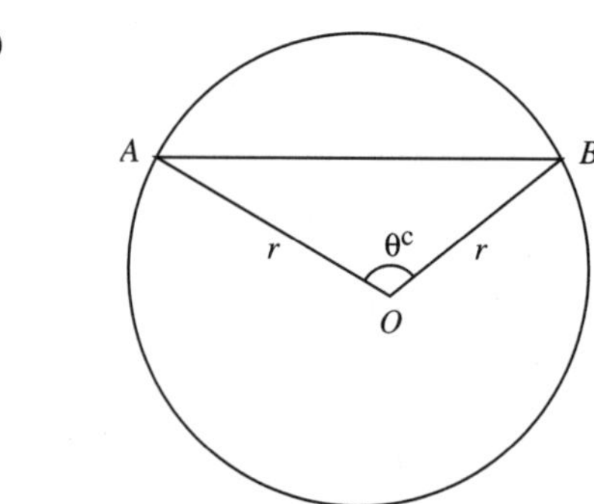

Determine the ratio of the area of the minor segment to that of the major segment. If this ratio is $\frac{1}{5}$, show that $\theta = \frac{\pi}{3} + \sin \theta$.

Solution 6

(a) The circumference of the circle is $2\pi r$, the length of arc s is given $s = 2\pi r \times \frac{\theta}{2\pi} = r\theta$.

The area of the circle is πr^2, the area of the sector $= \pi r^2 \times \frac{\theta}{2\pi} = \frac{1}{2}r^2\theta$

Area of $\Delta ABC = \frac{1}{2}r^2 \sin \theta$

Area of segment $= \frac{1}{2}r^2\theta - \frac{1}{2}r^2 \sin \theta$ where θ is in radians.

(b) $\dfrac{\text{Area of Minor segment}}{\text{Area of Major segment}}$

$$= \frac{\frac{1}{2}r^2\theta - \frac{1}{2}r^2 \sin \theta}{\frac{1}{2}r^2(2\pi - \theta) - \frac{1}{2}r^2 \sin(2\pi - \theta)}$$

$$= \frac{\theta^c - \sin \theta}{(2\pi - \theta) - \sin(2\pi - \theta)}$$

$$= \frac{\theta - \sin \theta}{(2\pi - \theta) + \sin \theta}$$

$$= \frac{1}{5}$$

$$5\theta - 5 \sin \theta = 2\pi - \theta + \sin \theta$$

$$6\theta = 2\pi + 6 \sin \theta$$

$$\theta = \frac{\pi}{3} + \sin \theta$$

Example 7

Solve $6\cos^2 x + \sin x - 5 = 0$, when the interval is $0 < x < 360$ where x is in degrees.

Solution 7

$$6\cos^2 x + \sin x - 5 = 0$$
$$6(1 - \sin^2 x) + \sin x - 5 = 0$$
$$6 - 6\sin^2 x + \sin x - 5 = 0$$
$$6\sin^2 x - \sin x - 1 = 0$$

$$\sin x = \frac{1 \pm \sqrt{1+24}}{12}$$
$$= \frac{1 \pm 5}{12}$$
$$\sin x = \frac{6}{12} = \frac{1}{2}$$
$$= \sin 30° = \sin 150°$$
$$x = 30°, 150°$$

Example 8

Solve

$$4\sin^2 x + 2(1+\sqrt{3})\cos x - (\sqrt{3}+4) = 0$$
$$4(1-\cos^2 x) + 2(1+\sqrt{3})\cos x - (\sqrt{3}+4) = 0$$
$$-4\cos^2 x + 2(1+\sqrt{3})\cos x - (\sqrt{3}+4) = 0$$
$$4\cos^2 x - 2(1+\sqrt{3})\cos x + \sqrt{3} = 0$$

$$\cos x = \frac{2(1+\sqrt{3}) \pm \sqrt{4(1+\sqrt{3})^2 - 16\sqrt{3}}}{8}$$

$$\cos x = \frac{2(1+\sqrt{3}) \pm \sqrt{4(1+2\sqrt{3}+3) - 16\sqrt{3}}}{8}$$

$$= \frac{2(1+\sqrt{3}) \pm \sqrt{16+8\sqrt{3} - 16\sqrt{3}}}{8}$$

$$= \frac{2(1+\sqrt{3}) \pm \sqrt{16 - 8\sqrt{3}}}{8}$$

$$= \frac{2(1+\sqrt{3}) \pm 2(1-\sqrt{3})}{8}$$

$$= \frac{2(1+\sqrt{3}) + 2(1-\sqrt{3})}{8}$$

$$\cos x = \frac{1}{2} \Longrightarrow x = 60°, 300°$$

or

$$\cos x = \frac{\cancel{2} + 2\sqrt{3} - \cancel{2} + 2\sqrt{3}}{8}$$

$$\frac{\sqrt{3}}{2} \Longrightarrow x = 30°, 330°.$$

C3

Notes

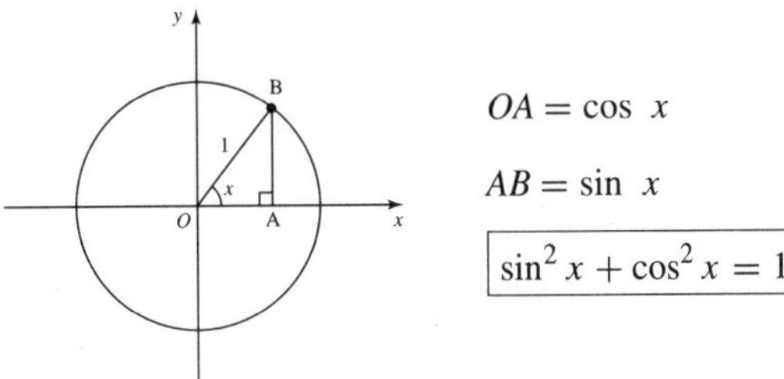

$OA = \cos\ x$

$AB = \sin\ x$

$$\boxed{\sin^2 x + \cos^2 x = 1}$$

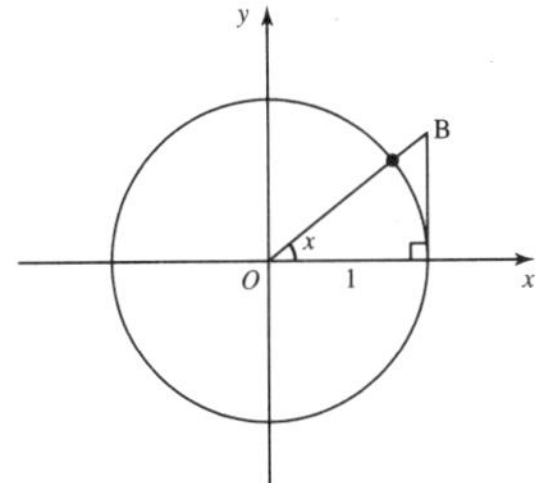

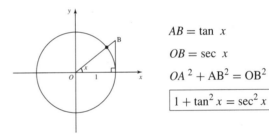

$AB = \tan\ x$

$OB = \sec\ x$

$OA^2 + AB^2 = OB^2$

$$\boxed{1 + \tan^2 x = \sec^2 x}$$

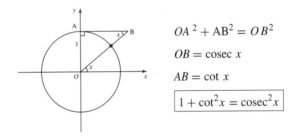

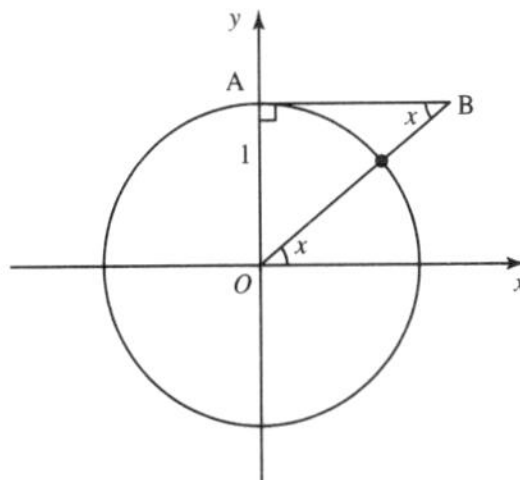

$OA^2 + AB^2 = OB^2$

$OB = \operatorname{cosec} x$

$AB = \cot\ x$

$$\boxed{1 + \cot^2 x = \operatorname{cosec}^2 x}$$

$$\sin x = \frac{1}{\operatorname{cosec} x} \Longrightarrow \sin x, \operatorname{cosec} x = 1$$

$$\cos x = \frac{1}{\sec x} \Longrightarrow \cos x, \sec x = 1$$

$$\tan x = \frac{1}{\cot x} \Longrightarrow \tan x, \cot x = 1$$

$\sin x$, $\cos x$, $\tan x$, are the reciprocals of cosec x, sec x, and cot x respectively cosec x, sec x, cot x are the reciprocals of $\sin x$, $\cos x$, $\tan x$ respectively

$\sin(A+B) = \sin A\cos B + \sin B\cos A$ show that

$$\sin(A-B) = \sin A\cos(-B) + \sin(-B)\cos A$$
$$= \sin A\cos B - \sin B\cos A$$
$$\cos(-B) = \cos B \text{ even function}$$
$$\sin(-B) = -\sin B \text{ odd function}$$

$\cos(A+B) = \cos A\cos B - \sin A\sin B$ show that

$$\cos(A-B) = \cos A\cos B - \sin A\sin B$$
$$\cos(A-B) = \cos A\cos(-B) - \sin A\sin(-B)$$
$$= \cos A\cos B + \sin A\sin B$$

since $\cos(-B) = \cos B$ even function

$\sin(-B) = -\sin B$ odd function

$$\tan(A+B) = \frac{\tan A + \tan B}{1 - \tan A\tan B}$$
$$\tan(A-B) = \frac{\tan A + \tan(-B)}{1 - \tan A\tan(-B)}$$

$\tan(-B) = -\tan B$ odd function

$$\tan(A-B) = \frac{\tan A - \tan B}{1 + \tan A\tan B}$$

$a\cos x + b\sin x \equiv r\cos(x - \propto)$

$a\cos x + b\sin x \equiv r\cos x\cos\propto + r\sin x\sin\propto)$

Equating the coefficients of $\cos x$ and $\sin x$

$$a = r\cos\propto$$

r a α b

$$b = r\sin\propto$$
$$\sqrt{a^2+b^2} = r$$
$$\tan\propto = \frac{a}{b}$$

Sketch the trigonometric functions $\sin x$, $\cos x$, $\tan x$, cosec x, sec x, cot arcsin x, arccos x, arctan x

Example 1

Show that

(i) $\sin 2x = 2\sin x\cos x$

(ii) $\cos 2x = \cos^2 x - \sin^2 x$

$$= 1 - 2\sin^2 x$$
$$= 2\cos^2 x - 1$$

(iii) $\sin 3x = 3\sin x - 4\sin^3 x$

(iv) $\cos 3x = 4\cos^3 x - 3\cos x$

Solution 1

(i) $\sin(A+B) = \sin A\cos B + \sin B\cos A$

$$\sin(x+x) = \sin x\cos x + \sin x\cos x$$
$$\sin 2x = 2\sin x\cos x$$

(ii) $\cos(A+B) = \cos A\cos B - \sin A\sin B$

$$\cos(x+x) = \cos x\cos x - \sin x\sin x$$
$$\cos 2x = \cos^2 x - \sin^2 x$$
$$= 1 - \sin^2 x - \sin^2 x$$
$$= 1 - 2\sin^2 x$$
$$= \cos^2 x - (1 - \cos^2 x)$$
$$= 2\cos^2 x - 1$$

(iii) $\sin(2x+x) = \sin 2x\cos x + \sin x\cos 2x$

$$= 2\sin x\cos^2 x + \sin x(1 - 2\sin^2 x)$$
$$= 2\sin x(1 - \sin^2 x) + \sin x - 2\sin^3 x$$
$$= 2\sin x - 2\sin^3 x + \sin x - 2\sin^3 x$$
$$= 3\sin x - 4\sin^3 x$$

(iv) $\cos(2x+x) = \cos 2x\cos x - \sin 2x\sin x$

$$= (2\cos^2 x - 1)\cos x - 2\sin^2 x\cos x$$
$$= 2\cos^3 x - \cos x - 2(1 - \cos^2 x)\cos x$$
$$= 2\cos^3 x - \cos x - 2\cos x + 2\cos^3 x$$
$$= 4\cos^3 x - 3\cos x$$

Example 2

Given that $\sin x = \frac{\sqrt{3}}{8}$, find the exact value of $\sin 3x$.

$(\sin 3x = 3\sin x - 4\sin^3 x)$

Solution 2

$\sin 3x = 3\sin x - 4\sin^3 x$

$$\sin 3x = 3\left(\frac{\sqrt{3}}{8}\right) - 4\left(\frac{\sqrt{3}}{8}\right)^3$$

$$= \frac{3\sqrt{3}}{8} - \frac{12\sqrt{3}}{512}$$

$$= \frac{3\sqrt{3}}{8} - \frac{3}{128} = \frac{48\sqrt{3}}{128} - \frac{3}{128}$$

$$= \frac{3}{128}(16\sqrt{3} - 1)$$

Example 3

$\cos 3x = 4\cos^3 x - 3\cos x$

If $\cos x = \frac{1}{\sqrt{2}}$, Find the exact value of $\cos 3x$.

Solution 3

$$\cos 3x = 4\left(\frac{1}{\sqrt{2}}\right)^3 - 3\left(\frac{1}{\sqrt{2}}\right)$$

$$= \frac{4}{2\sqrt{2}} - \frac{3}{\sqrt{2}}$$

$$= \frac{2}{\sqrt{2}} - \frac{3}{\sqrt{2}} = -\frac{1}{\sqrt{2}}$$

Example 4

Sketch the function $y = \cos x^\circ + \sin x^\circ$.

Solution 4

$\cos x^\circ + \sin x^\circ \equiv r\sin(x + \propto)$.

$\cos x^\circ + \sin x^\circ \equiv r\sin x^\circ \cos \propto + r\sin \propto \cos x^\circ$

$$1 = r\cos \propto$$

$$1 = r\sin \propto$$

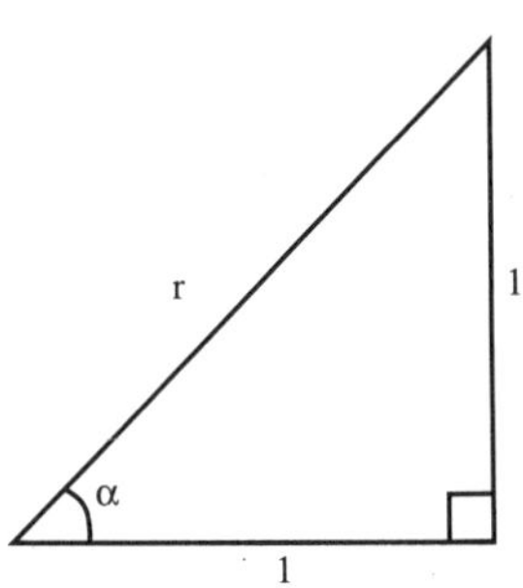

$$r = \sqrt{1^2 + 1^2} = \sqrt{2}$$

$$\tan \propto = \frac{1}{1}$$

$$\propto = 45^\circ$$

$$y = \sqrt{2}\sin(x + 45)^\circ$$

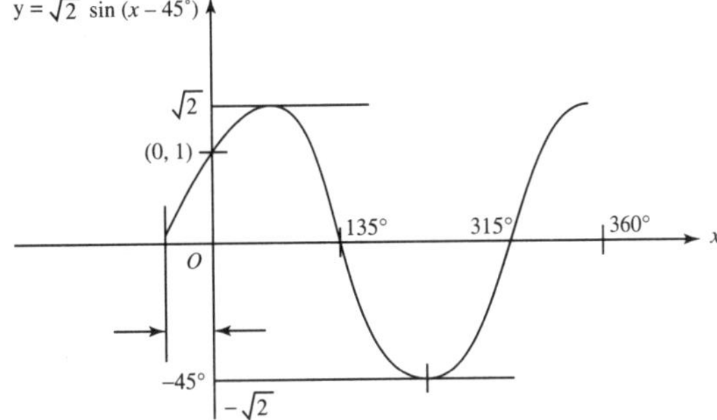

Example 5

Prove that $\cot^2 x - \tan^2 x \equiv \operatorname{cosec}^2 x - \sec^2 x$

Solution 5

$$\cot^2 x - \tan^2 x = \operatorname{cosec}^2 x - 1 - (\sec^2 x - 1)$$

$$= \operatorname{cosec}^2 x - 1 - \sec^2 x + 1$$

$$= \operatorname{cosec}^2 x - \sec^2 x$$

Example 6

Prove that

$$\frac{\cot x - \tan x}{\operatorname{cosec} x - \sec x} = \frac{\operatorname{cosec} x + \sec x}{\cot x + \tan x}$$

Solution 6

Cross multiply

$\cot^2 x - \tan^2 x = \operatorname{cosec}^2 x - \sec^2 x$ see example 5.

Example 7

(a) Prove that

$$\cot^4\theta - \operatorname{cosec}^4\theta = -(\cot^2\theta + \operatorname{cosec}^2\theta)$$

(b) Solve

$$\operatorname{cosec}^2\theta + \cot^2\theta = 2 - \cot\theta \text{ for } 0^\circ < \theta < 180^\circ$$

Solution 7

(a) $\cot^4\theta - \text{cosec}^4\theta$

$= (\cot^2\theta - \text{cosec}^2\theta)(\cot^2\theta + \text{cosec}^2\theta)$

$= (\text{cosec}^2\theta - 1 - \text{cosec}^2\theta)(\cot^2\theta + \text{cosec}^2\theta)$

$= (-1)(\cot^2\theta + \text{cosec}^2\theta)$

$= -(\cot^2\theta + \text{cosec}^2\theta)$

(b) $\text{cosec}^2\theta + \cot^2\theta = 2 - \cot\theta$

$1 + \cot^2\theta + \cot^2\theta = 2 - \cot\theta$

$2\cot^2\theta + \cot\theta - 1 = 0$

$$\cot\theta = \frac{-1 \pm \sqrt{1+8}}{4}$$

$$= \frac{-1 \pm 3}{4}$$

$\cot\theta = -1$

$= \cot 135°$

$\theta = 135°$

$\cot\theta = \frac{1}{2}$

$= \cot 63.43494882°$

$\theta = 63.4°$

Notes

C3 Differentiation $\sin x$, $\cos x$, $\tan x$, $\sin kx$, $\cos kx$, $\tan kx$, $\cos x^2$, $\tan^2 2x$ This is dealt with in the Differential calculus book.

C4 Integration $\sin x$, $\cos x$, $\sin kx \cos kx$ This is dealt in the integral calculus book.

FP1 Polar coordinates (r, θ)

$\theta = \propto$, $r = p\sec(a - \theta)$

$r = a$, $r = 2a\cos\theta$, $r = k\theta$,

$r = a(1t\cos\theta)$, $r = a(3 + 2\cos\theta)$

$r = a\cos 2\theta$, $r^2 = a^2\cos 2\theta$

The ability to find tangent parallel to, or at night angles to, the initial line is expected

$$\int_\alpha^\beta \frac{1}{2}r^2 d\theta.$$

This is dealt with in the cartesian and polar curve sketching book

FP2 $x = a\cos t$, $y = b\sin t$, $x = a\sec t$ $y = b\tan t$

Intrinsic coordinates (s, ψ)

$\frac{dy}{dx} = \tan\psi \frac{dx}{ds} = \cos\psi$,

$\frac{dy}{ds} = \sin\psi$ reduction formulae

$$\int_0^{\frac{\pi}{2}} \sin^n x dx$$

FP3 Maclaurin and Taylor series $\sin x \cos x$ (Series Expansions). Dealt with in the calculus Books.

Miscellaneous

1. A vertical pole BAO stands with its base O on a horizontal plane, where $BA = c$ and $AO = b$. A point P is situated on the horizontal plane at distance x from O and the angle $APB = \Theta$.

   Prove that $\tan \Theta = \dfrac{cx}{x^2 + b^2 + bc}$

   As P takes different positions on the horizontal plane, find the value for x for which Θ is greatest.

   Ans. $\sqrt{b^2 + bc}$.

2. In the tetrahedron $VABC$ the angles ACB, VAC and VBC are $60°$, α and β respectively, $AB = d$ and VC is perpendicular to the plane ABC.
   Show that

   $$VC = \frac{d}{(\cot^2\alpha + cot^2\beta - \cot\alpha\cot\beta)^{\frac{1}{2}}}.$$

   If $\tan\alpha = \dfrac{3}{4}$ and $\tan\beta = \dfrac{1}{2}$, find:

   (i) the area of the triangle ABC,
   (ii) the volume of the tetrahedron $VABC$,
   (iii) the tangent of the angle between the planes VAB and ABC.

   Ans.
   (i) $\dfrac{\left(3\sqrt{3}d^2\right)}{14}$;
   (ii) $\dfrac{\left(3\sqrt{3}d^3\right)}{28\sqrt{7})}$;
   (iii) $\sqrt{\frac{7}{12}}$.

3. (a) Express $\cos x + 2\sin x$ in the form $R\cos(x - \alpha)$ where R is positive. Hence or otherwise, solve the equation $\cos x + 2\sin x = 1.52$ for $0° \le x \le 360°$.

   Ans. $\sqrt{5}\cos(x - 63°\ 26')$, $x = 120°\ 37'$.

   (b) An equilateral triangle ABC is drawn on a plane inclined at $5°$ to the horizontal. AB is horizontal at a level lower than that of point C and $AB = 10$ cm. Point P is the foot of the perpendicular from C to the horizontal plane through A. The midpoint of AB is M.

   Find (i) the length of CM (ii) the inclination of AC to the horizontal.

   Ans.
   (i) 8.66 cm
   (ii) $4°\ 20'$.

4. The perimeter of a triangle is 42 cm, one side is of length 12 cm and the area is $21\sqrt{15}\ \text{cm}^2$. Find the lengths of the other sides and show that the cosine of the smallest angle is $\dfrac{11}{16}$.

   Ans. 14 cm, 16 cm.

5. Find all the solutions in the interval $0 \le x \le \pi$ of the equation $\sin 2x - \sin x = 0$

   Ans. $0°$, $180°$, $60°$.

6. Prove that the general solution of the equation $\sec\Phi + \operatorname{cosec}\Phi = 2\sqrt{2}$ can be expressed as $\Phi = \dfrac{2k\pi}{3} + \dfrac{\pi}{4}$, where k is integral.

7. An observer on a ship A travelling due north at $7\ \text{km}\ h^{-1}$ sees another ship B which appears to him to be travelling south-east at $12\sqrt{2}\ \text{km}\ h^{-1}$,

   Calculate:

   (i) the speed of B
   (ii) the bearing on which B is travelling

   Ans.
   (i) $22.5\ \text{km}\ h^{-1}$
   (ii) $147.8°$.

8. Express $\dfrac{(3\sin 2x - 2\sin 3x)}{\sin x}$ in terms of $\cos x$.

   For what range of values of x in the interval $0 \le x \le \pi$ is $3\sin 2x$ greater than $2\sin 3x$?

   Ans. $6\cos x - 8\cos^2 x + 2$, $0^c < x < 1.82^c$.

9. The lines OA, OB and OC are mutually perpendicular, and are each of unit length. M is the mid-point of OA.

Calculate:

(i) the area of the triangle ABC;

(ii) the angle between the lines AC and BM;

(iii) the length of the perpendicular from M to the plane ABC.

Ans. (i) $\frac{1}{2}\sqrt{3}$

10. Prove that for all values of Θ,

$$2\cos\Theta\cos\frac{\Theta}{2} - 2\cos 2\Theta\cos\frac{\Theta}{2} = \cos\frac{\Theta}{2} - \cos\frac{5\Theta}{2}.$$

Hence show that $\frac{\pi}{5}$ and $\frac{3\pi}{5}$ are roots of the equation $\cos\Theta - \cos 2\Theta = \frac{1}{2}$.

11. Given that $\sin^{-1}x$, $\cos^{-1}x$ and $\sin^{-1}(1-x)$ are acute angles

(i) prove that $\sin\{\sin^{-1}x - \cos^{-1}x\} = 2x^2 - 1$,

(ii) solve the equation $\sin^{-1}x - \cos^{-1}x = \sin^{-1}(1-x)$.

Ans. $\frac{1}{4}\left[\sqrt{17}-1\right]$.

12. A tetrahedron has a horizontal equilateral triangular base of side 6 cm and the sloping edges are each of length 4 cm.

(i) Find the height of the tetrahedron.

(ii) Find the inclination of a sloping edge to the horizontal.

(iii) Show that the sloping faces are inclined to one another at an angle $\cos^{-1}\left(-\frac{1}{7}\right)$.

Ans. (i) 2 cm; (ii) 30°.

13. Express $4\sin 2x + 3\cos 2x$ in the form $R\sin(2x + \alpha)$ where R is positive and α is an acute angle measured in degrees.

Hence find the values of x, between 0° and 360° for which $4\sin 2x + 3\cos 2x = 2.49$.

Ans. $5\sin(2x + 36°52')$; $56°38'$, $176°30°$, $236°38'$, $356°30'$.

14. Solve the following equations giving your answers in the range 0° to 360°:

(i) $\sec^2\Theta - 3\tan\Theta - 5 = 0$,

(ii) $\cos 4x + \cos 2x - \sin 4x + \sin 2x = 0$.

Ans.

(i) 76°, 135°, 256°, 315°

(ii) 30°, 45°, 90°, 150°, 210°, 225°, 270°, 330°

15. If $\tan(x+y) = a$ and $\tan(x-b) = b$, *express* $\dfrac{\sin 2x + \sin 2y}{\sin 2x - \sin 2y}$ in terms of a and b.

Show that $\tan 2y = \dfrac{a-b}{1+ab}$ and by using this result, or otherwise, obtain an expression for $\tan(x+3y)$ in terms of a and b.

Ans. $\frac{a}{b}$; $\dfrac{2a - b + a^2b}{1 - a^2 + 2ab}$.

16. Find all solutions in the interval $0 < N < 2\pi$ of the equation $\sin x = \cos 2x$.

17. Given that $A + B + C = 2\pi$, prove that:

(i) $\sin\frac{A}{2} = \frac{1}{2}\sin(B+C)$

(ii) $\cos\frac{A}{2} = -\frac{1}{2}\cos(B+C)$

(iii) $\sin A + \sin B + \sin C = 4\sin\frac{A}{2}\sin\frac{B}{2}\sin\frac{C}{2}$.

18. For those values of x which satisfy the equation $8\sin x + \cos x = 4$, calculate:

(i) the possible values of $\tan\frac{1}{2}x$.

(ii) the possible values of $\cos x$. If, in addition, $-\frac{\pi}{2} < x < \frac{\pi}{2}$, calculate, in radians, the values of x which satisfies the given equation, giving your answers to two decimal places.

Ans.

(i) 3, $\frac{1}{5}$

(ii) $\frac{12}{13}$, $-\frac{4}{5}$; 0.39.

19. (a) Find the general solution of the equation $2\sqrt{3}\sin^2\Theta - \sin 2\Theta = 0$.

20. Given that $4\sin 2y = 3\sin 2x$ and $4\sin^2 y - 3\sin^2 x = 2$, show that $\cos 2x = \frac{1}{9}$ and find the value of $\cos 2y$. Hence, or otherwise, find the angles x and y lying in the interval (0°, 180°), giving your answers to the nearest 0.1°.

21. Show that $\operatorname{cosec} 2x - \cot 2x = \tan x$.

Deduce, or find otherwise the exact value of $\tan 75°$, expressing your answer in the form $a + b\sqrt{3}$, where a and b are integers.

22. Find all solutions of the equation $4 \tan 2x = \cot x$, for which $0° < x < 360°$, giving your answers to the nearest $0.1°$.

23. Solve for x the equation $\cos 2x + \sin x = 0$, giving in radians in the form $k\pi$ all values of x lying between 0 and 2π.

24. Find all the values of Θ in the range $0° < \Theta < 180°$ which satisfy the equation $\tan 3\Theta = \sqrt{3}$. Express $\tan 3\Theta$ in terms of $\tan \Theta (= t)$, and hence write this equation as a cubic equation in t. Deduce that $\tan 20° \tan 40° \tan 80° = \sqrt{3}$.

    Write down another relation connecting the tangents of these three angles.

25. (a) Let $x = 2\cos\Theta + 3\cos 2\Theta$, $y = 2\sin\Theta + 3\sin 2\Theta$.

    Show that $(x-3)\cos\Theta + y\sin\Theta = 2$
    $y\cos\Theta - (x+3)\sin\Theta = 0$ and hence eliminate Θ from these equations.

    (b) Eliminate t from the equations

$$\left.\begin{aligned} a^2 + at + t^2 &= 0 \\ b^2 + bt + t^2 &= 0 \\ c^2 + ct + t^2 &= 0 \end{aligned}\right\} \text{ factorising your result as far as possible.}$$

26. Find the general solution of the equation
$$\cos\Theta + \sin\Theta = \frac{1}{2}\sqrt{6}$$

27. (a) Obtain the general solution for x of the equation $\cos 2x = -\frac{2}{3}\sqrt{3}$, giving your answer in radians.

    (b) Find, as Θ varies in $(0, \pi)$ the greatest and least values of x and of y, where $x = 17 + 5\sin 2\Theta + 12\cos 2\Theta$, $y = 17 + 5\sin^2\Theta + 12\cos^2\Theta$

28. The angles of elevation of P, the top of a vertical pole PQ, from three points A, B and C, lying in a straight line in the horizontal plane through Q, are $30°, 45°$ and $60°$ respectively (Fig. 2-M/1). If $AB = BC = 20$ m, find PQ correct to three significant figures.

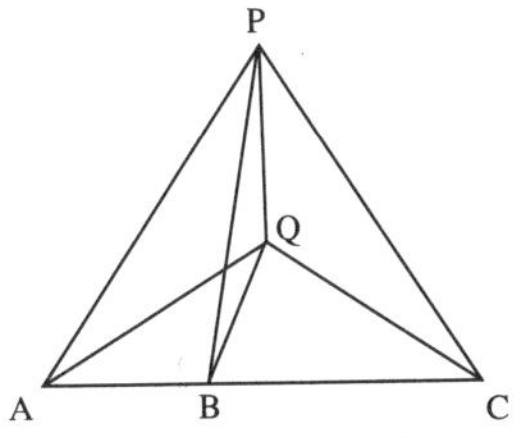

Fig. 2-M/1

29. Solve the simultaneous equations $\cos A + \cos B = \frac{2k}{3}$, $\cos A \cos B = -\frac{k^2}{3}$ to find $\cos A$ and $\cos B$ in terms of k.

    Find the range of values of k for which A and B exist.

30. Express the function $4\cos x - 6\sin x$ in the form $R\cos(x + a)$ where R is positive and $0° < \alpha < 360°$.

    Hence find the coordinates of the point on the graph of $y = 4\cos x - 6\sin x$ for $0° \leq x \leq 360°$, where y has its minimum value.

    Sketch the graph. State the values of x where the curve crosses the x-axis.

31. A plane is inclined at angle α to the horizontal and a line PQ on the plane makes an acute angle β with PR which is a line of greatest slope on the plane. Show that the inclination Θ of PQ to the horizontal is given by $\sin\Theta = \sin\alpha\cos\beta$.

    Show that the angle Φ between the vertical plane through PQ and the vertical plane through PR is given by $\cos\Phi\cos\Theta = \cos\alpha\cos\beta$.

32. The triangle ABC has altitudes AD, BE and CF. Show that $EF \sin C = AE \sin A$ and deduce that $EF = BC\cos A$.

    If $AB = 3$, $BC = 4$ and $BE + EF = 5$, find the angle A in degrees and minutes.

33. In the triangle ABC the angle B is obtuse; $\sin A = \frac{3}{5}$ and $\sin B = \frac{12}{13}$. Without using tables or calculator, find:

    (i) $\cos C$,

    (ii) $\tan \frac{1}{2}$ A.

34. Express $\sin x - 2\cos x$ in the form $R\sin(x - \alpha)$, where R is positive and α is acute. Hence, or otherwise,

    (i) find the set of possible values of $\sin x - 2\cos x$.

    (ii) solve the equation $\sin x - 2\cos x = 1$ for $0 \leq x \leq 360°$

35. A man walks due north. When he is at a point A, he sees a pole on a bearing of $40°$. After walking 200 m he is at the point B from which the bearing of the pole is $70°$.

Find, to the nearest metre, the distance of the pole from:

(i) the man's path,

(ii) the mid-point of AB.

36. A chord AB divides a circle of radius a and centre O into two segments.

The perimeter of the minor segment is 4a and the angle AOB is 2Θ radians. Show that $\sin\Theta = 2-\Theta$.

Find graphically the value of Θ to 2 significant figures.

37. The roots of the equation $x^2 - px - c = 0$ are α and β.

(i) Show that $\alpha^3 + \beta^3 = p(p^2 + 3c)$ and find a quadratic equation whose roots are α^3 and β^3.

(ii) Given that α and β satisfy the equation $\tan^{-1}\left(\frac{x}{c}\right) + \tan^{-1}(x) - \tan^{-1} c$, where $c \neq 0$, show that $pc + 1 + c = 0$.

38. Express $4\sin 2x + 3\cos 2x$ in the form $R\sin(2x + \alpha)$ where R is positive and α is an acute angle measured in degrees. Hence find the values of x between $0°$ and $360°$ for which $4\sin 2x + 3\cos 2x = 2.49$

39. Solve the following equations giving your answers in the range $0°$ to $360°$:

(i) $\sec^2\Theta - 3\tan\Theta - 5 = 0$

(ii) $\cos 4x + \cos 2x - \sin 4x + \sin 2x = 0$

40. For those values of x which satisfy the equation $8\sin x + \cos x = 4$,

Calculate:

(i) the possible values of $\tan\frac{1}{2}x$,

(ii) the possible values of $\cos x$.

If, in addition, $-\frac{\pi}{2} \leq x \leq \frac{\pi}{2}$, calculate, in radians the value of x which satisfies the given equation, giving your answer to two decimal places.

41. Prove the identity $\tan\Theta + \cot\Theta = \operatorname{cosec} 2\Theta$. *(2 marks)*

Find, in radians, all the solutions of the equation $\tan x + \cot x = 8\cos 2x$ in the interval $0 < x < \pi$. *(4 marks)*

Ans. $\frac{\pi}{24}, \frac{5\pi}{24}, \frac{13\pi}{24}, \frac{17\pi}{24}$.

42. Express $2\cos(x - \pi)$ in the form $a\cos x + b\sin x$. Using the small angle approximations for $\sin x$ and $\cos x$. Show that, if x is small enough for x and higher powers to be ignored,

$$\sqrt{\left(2\cos\left(x - \frac{\pi}{3}\right)\right)} = 1 + \frac{\sqrt{3}}{2}x + kx^2.$$

where x is a constant. State the value of k.

Ans. $\cos x + \sqrt{3}\sin x, k = -\frac{5}{8}$.

43. Find, in radians, the general solution of the equation $6\tan^2\Theta = 4\sin^2\Theta + 1$.

Ans. $n\pi \pm \frac{\pi}{6}$

44. Prove the identity $\sin 3A \equiv 3\sin A - 4\sin^3 A$.

Hence show that $\sin 10°$ is a root of the equation $8x^3 - 6x + 1 = 0$. *(5 marks)*

45. Find all the solutions in the interval $0° \leq \Theta \leq 360°$ of the equation $\sin\Theta - \cos\Theta = k$ when

(a) $k = 0$ *(3 marks)*

(b) $k = 1$ *(4 marks)*

Ans. $45°, 225°$, (b) $90°, 180°$.

46. The function f is defined by $f(x) = \sin 2x + 2\cos^2 x$, where x is real and measured in radians.

(a) Find the general solution of the equation $f(x) = 0$. *(5 marks)*

(b) Prove that $1 - \sqrt{2} \leq f(x) \leq 1 + \sqrt{2}$. *(5 marks)*

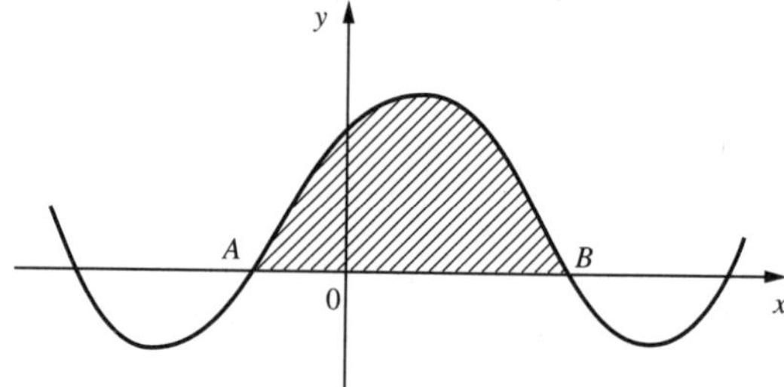

Fig. 2-M/2

Fig. 2-M/2 shows part of the curve with equation $y = \sin 2x + 2\cos^2 x$. Find the area of the shaded region, giving your answer in terms of π.

(6 marks)

Ans. (a) $(2\pi + 1)\frac{\pi}{2}$, $n\pi + \frac{3}{4}\pi$; $1 + \frac{3}{4}\pi$

47. Solve the equation $\sqrt{3}\tan\Theta - \sec\Theta = 1$, giving all solutions in the interval $0° < \Theta < 360°$

(6 marks)

Ans. 60°, 180°

48. Assuming the identities $\sin 3\Theta \equiv 3\sin\Theta - 4\sin^3\Theta$ and $\cos 3\Theta \equiv \cos^3\Theta - 3\cos\Theta$, prove that $\cos 5\Theta \equiv 5\cos\Theta - 20\cos^3\Theta + 16\cos^5\Theta$.

(5 marks)

(a) Find the set of all values of Θ in the interval $0 < \Theta < \pi$ for which $\cos 5\Theta > 16\cos^5\Theta$

(6 marks)

(b) Find the general solution, in radians, of the equation $\cos x + 3\cos 3x + \cos 5x = 0$

Ans. (a) $\frac{\pi}{3} < \Theta < \frac{\pi}{2}$; $\frac{2\pi}{3} < \Theta < \pi$;

b) $\frac{2n\pi}{3} \pm \frac{\pi}{6}$.

49. Fig. 2-M/3 shows that a square-based pyramid in which $AB = BC = CD = DA = 1$ m and $AE = BE = CE = DE = 2$ m.

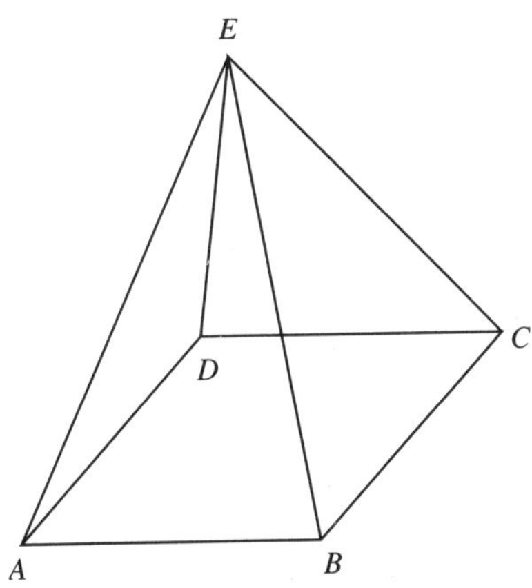

Fig. 2-M/3

Calculate

(a) the height of the pyramid, giving your answer correct to 2 decimal places.

(3 marks)

(b) the acute angle, to the nearest degree, between the line AE and the plane $ABCD$

(2 marks)

(c) the acute angle, to the nearest degree, between the planes ADE and $ABCD$.

(3 marks)

Ans. (a) 1.87 m;

(b) 69°;

(c) 75°.

50. Fig. 2-M/4 shows a ladder AC of length L leaning against the vertical side DF of a house.

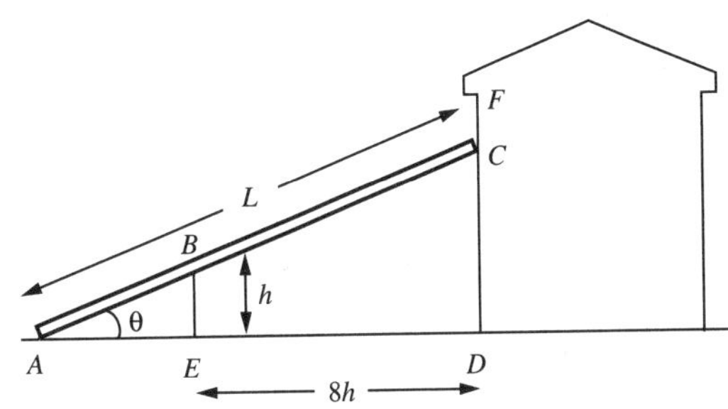

Fig. 2-M/4

The ladder, which is inclined at an angle Θ to the horizontal AD, also rests on the top of a vertical wall BE of height h which is situated at a distance $8h$ from the house.

Show that

$L = h\,\text{cosec}\,\Theta + 8h\sec\Theta$ *(2 marks)*

Prove that L has a stationary value when $\Theta = \tan^{-1}\frac{1}{2}$ and find this stationary value in terms of h.

(6 marks)

Ans. $5\sqrt{5}$ h.

51. By considering $\cos(\Theta + 2\Theta)$, show that $\cos 3\Theta = 4\cos^3\Theta - 3\cos\Theta$ *(3 marks)*

The variable satisfies the equation $x^3 - 3x - 1 = 0$. By putting $x = 2\cos\Theta$, and using the above result, show that $\cos 3\Theta = \frac{1}{2}$.

Find the three values of Θ between 0° and 180° which satisfy this equation. *(4 marks)*

Hence calculate, correct to 2 decimal places the three roots of the equation $x^3 - 3x - 1 = 0$.

(2 marks)

Ans. 20°, 100°, 140°. Roots are 1.88, −0.35, −1.53.

52. By expanding $\cos(\Theta - 60°)$, express $7\cos\Theta + 8\cos(\Theta - 60°)$ in the form $13\sin(\Theta + \alpha)$, where $0° < \alpha < 90°$, and state the value of α to the nearest 0.1°. *(5 marks)*

Hence find the solutions of the equation

$7\cos\Theta + 8\cos(\Theta - 60°) = 6.5$, in the interval $0° < \Theta < 360°$, giving your answers to the nearest 0.1°. *(3 marks)*

Ans. $13\sin(\Theta + 57.8°)$; 92.2°, 332.2°.

53. Find, in radians in terms of π, the general solution of the equation $\cos\Theta = \sin 2\Theta$.

Ans. $\Theta = 2n\pi \pm \frac{\pi}{2}$; $\Theta = 2n\pi + \frac{\pi}{6}$;

$\Theta = 2n\pi + \frac{5\pi}{6}$

54.

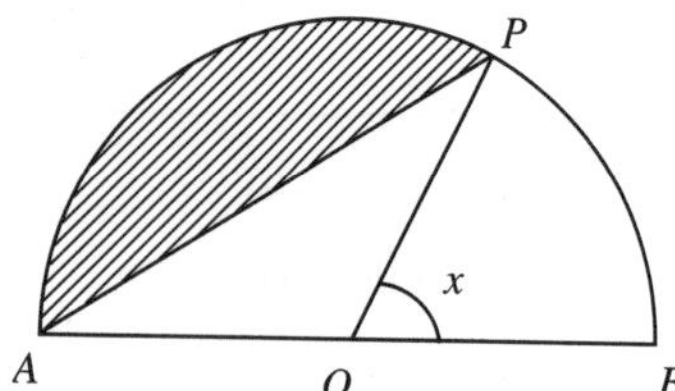

Fig. 2-M/5

Figure 2-M/5 shows a semicircle with O the mid-point of the diameter AB. The point P on the semicircle is such that the area of sector POB is equal to the area of the shaded segment. Angle POB is x radians.

(a) Show that $x = \frac{1}{2}(\pi - \sin x)$.

The iterative method based on the relation $x_{n+1} = \frac{1}{2}(\pi - \sin x_n)$ can be used to evaluate x.

(b) Starting with $x_1 = 1$ perform two iterations to find the values of x_2 and x_3, giving your answers to two decimal places. *(5 marks)*

(Ans. $x_2 = 1.15$; $x_3 = 1.11$)

55. Given that $0 \leq x \leq 270°$, find the values of x for which (a) $\tan^2 x° = 3$, (b) $\cos 2x° = -0.5$. *(6 marks)*

Ans. (a) 60°, 120°, 240°

(b) 60°, 120°, 240°.

56.

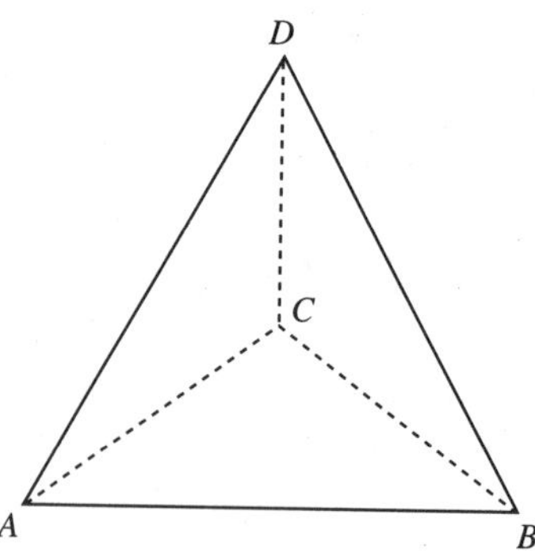

Fig. 2-M/6

The tetrahedron $ABCD$ has each edge of length $2a$ and the base ABC rests on a horizontal plane, as shown in Fig. 2-M/6.

(a) Show that the height of D above ABC is $\frac{2}{3}a\sqrt{6}$.

(b) Calculate the acute angle between the plane DAB and the horizontal, giving your answer to the nearest tenth of a degree. *(12 marks)*

Ans. (b) 70.5°.

57. The equation $8\cos x = 31x$ has a root near $x = 0$.

Use the approximation $\cos x = 1 - 0.5x^2$ to estimate the value of this root. *(5 marks)*

Ans. $\frac{1}{4}$

58. Find the positive constance R and the acute angle A for which $\cos x + \sin x = R\cos(x - A)$.

(a) Find the general solution of the equation $\cos x + \sin x = 1$.

(b) Deduce the greatest value of $\sin x + \cos x$. *(12 marks)*

Ans. (a) $2n\pi$ or $2n\pi \pm \frac{\pi}{2}$

(b) $\sqrt{2}$

59. Show that $\cos\left(2x - \frac{\pi}{4}\right) \equiv \frac{1}{\sqrt{2}}\cos 2x + \sin 2x$ and find an express for $\cos\left(x + \frac{\pi}{4}\right)$ in terms of $\sin x$ and $\cos x$.

Hence show that if x satisfies the equation

$\cos x\cos\left(x + \frac{\pi}{4}\right) - \cos\left(2x - \frac{\pi}{4}\right) = 0$, then either $\sin x = 0$ or $\tan x = 3$. Hence find the general solution of the equation

$\cos x \cos\left(x + \frac{\pi}{4}\right) - \cos\left(2x - \frac{\pi}{4}\right) = 0$ giving your answer in radians. *(14 marks)*

Ans. $\frac{1}{\sqrt{2}}(\cos x - \sin x), x = n\pi, x = n\pi + 1.25^c$.

60.

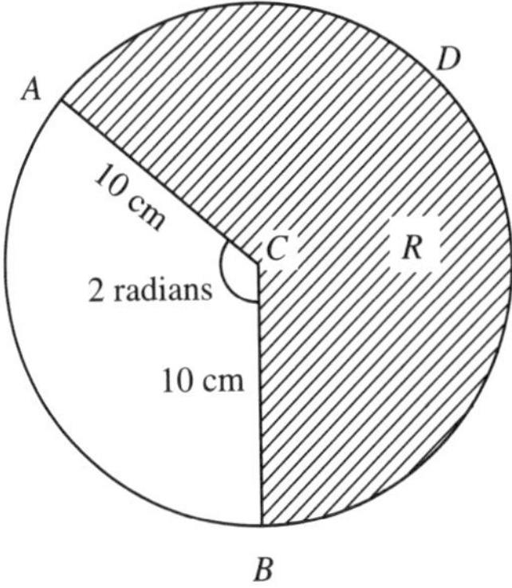

Fig. 2-M/7

Figure 2-M/7 represents a circle of radius 10 cm and centre C. Points A and B are taken on the circumference of the circle so that $<ACB = 2$ radians. The shaded region R is bounded by the radii CA and CB and the major arc ADB, as shown.

Calculate

(a) the perimeter of R (b) the area of R (c) the area in cm^2 of Δ CAB, giving your answer to 1 decimal *(9 marks)*

Ans. (a) 20π cm

(b) $100(\pi - 1)$ cm^2

(c) 45.5 cm^2.

61. The tetrahedron $PQRS$ has a horizontal triangular base PQR and $PQ = PR = 12$ cm. The vertex S is above the level of PQR and $SQ = SR = 10$ cm, $SP = 8$ cm.

(a) Show that the perpendicular distance from S to the lane PQR is $\sqrt{57}$ cm. Find, to the nearest degree, the acute angle between.

(b) the edge SQ and the horizontal.

(c) the plane SQR and the horizontal. *(15 marks)*

Ans. (b) 49°

(c) 71°.

62. Solve the equation $9\cos^2 x - 6\cos x - 0.21 = 0$, $0° \le x \le 360°$, giving each answer in degrees to 1 decimal place. *(9 marks)*

Ans. 45.6°, 314.4°, 91.9°, 268.1°.

63. (a) Show that $7\cos x - 4\sin x$ may be expressed in the form $R\cos(x + \alpha)$, where R is $\sqrt{65}$ and $\tan\alpha = \frac{4}{7}$.

(b) Find, in radians to 2 decimal places, the smallest positive value of x for which $87\cos x - 4\sin x$ takes its maximum value.

(c) Find, in radians to 2 decimal places, the two smaller positive values of x for which $7\cos x - 4\sin x = 4.88$.

The curve C has equation $y = (7\cos x - 4\sin x + 4)^{\frac{1}{2}}$.

(d) Take corresponding values of y at $x = 0, \frac{\pi}{6}, \frac{\pi}{3}$ and for the curve C and use the trapezium rule to find an estimate for the area of the finite region bounded by the curve C, the y-axis and the x-axis for $0 \le x \le \frac{\pi}{2}$ giving your answer to 1 decimal place. *(18 marks)*

Ans. (b) 5.76

(c) 0.4, 4.84

(d) 3.4

64. Given that $-90 < x < 90$ find the values of x for which

(a) $4\sin^2 x° = 3$

(b) $\sec(2x - 15°) = 2$ *(10 marks)*

Ans. (a) 60°, 120°, −60°, −120°

(b) 37.5°, −37.5°

65.

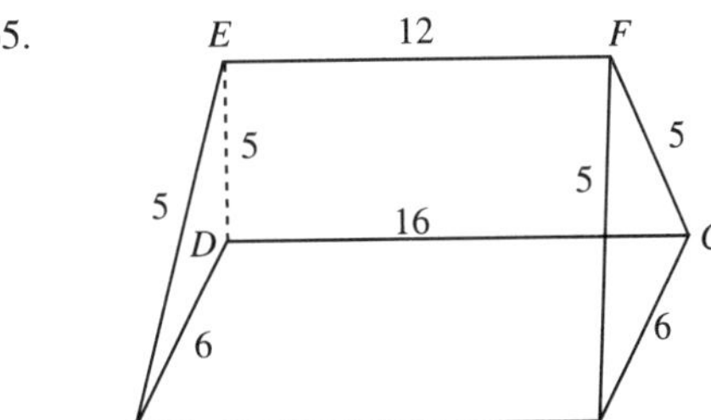

Fig. 2-M/8

A tent is erected, as shown in Fig. 2-M/8. The base $ABCD$ is rectangular and horizontal and the top edge EF is also horizontal.

The lengths, in metres, of the edges are

$AE = BF = CF = DE = 5$.

$AB = CD = 16, AD = BC = 6, EF = 12$.

(a) Calculate the size of $<ADE$, giving your answer to the nearest degree.

(b) Show that the vertical height of EF above the base ABCD is $2\sqrt{3}$ m.

Calculate, to the nearest degree, the size of the acute angle between

(c) the face ADE and the horizontal

(d) the edge AE and the horizontal.

(15 marks)

Ans. (a) $53° 8'$

(c) 60°

(d) 43.9°

66. $8 \cos x - 15 \sin x \equiv R \cos (x + A)$

Find

(a) the positive constant R,

(b) the acute angle A, giving your answer in degrees to 1 decimal place.

(c) Hence, or otherwise, find the maximum value of $8 \cos x - 15 \sin x$.

(d) Find the value of x, in the range $0° \leq x \leq 360°$, which will give the maximum value, giving your answer in degrees to 1 decimal place.

Ans. 17

(b) 61.9°

(c) 17

(d) 258.1°.

67. Find the general solution of the equation $\cos 2x = \cos 3x$, giving your answer in radians in terms of π. *(5 marks)*

Ans. $x = 2xn\pi$, or $2n\pi + 1.26^c$, or $2n\pi + 2.51^c$.

Answers

Exercise 1

1. (i) 0.5235987^c
 (ii) 0.7853981^c
 (iii) 0.2617993^c
 (iv) 1.3089966^c
 (v) 1.8325957^c.

2. (i) 0.2196706^c
 (ii) 0.7344927^c
 (iii) 0.9869836^c
 (iv) 1.5536339^c
 (v) 1.63337292^c.

3. (i) $18°$
 (ii) $45°$
 (iii) $60°$
 (iv) $240°$
 (v) $157.5°$.

4. (i) $57.29578°$
 (ii) $114.59156°$
 (iii) $171.8874°$
 (iv) $180°$
 (v) $401.07046°$.

Exercise 2

1. (i) 0.1000^c
 (ii) 0.5054^c
 (iii) 1.0472^c

2. (i) 9.424 cm
 (ii) 12.566 cm
 (iii) 19.897 cm
 (iv) 56.549 cm
 (v) 65.345 cm.

3. (i) 55.0 cm
 (ii) 7.85 cm
 (iii) 15.7 cm.

4. (i) 6.55 cm^2
 (ii) 9.60 cm^2
 (iii) 9.82 cm^2
 (iv) 29.5 cm^2
 (v) 67.0 cm^2.

5. 0.641^c

6. 98.1 cm

7. 261.8 cm/s

8. 30 cm

9. 60 cm^2

10. 57.3 cm

11. (i) 12.57 cm
 (ii) 45.52 cm^2.

12. (i) 16.58 cm
 (ii) 56.03 cm^2.
 (iii) 35.1, 153.4 cm

13. 0.028 cm^2, 282.46 cm^2.

Exercise 3

1. (i) $-\frac{\sqrt{2}}{\sqrt{3}}, \frac{1}{\sqrt{3}}, \sqrt{3}, -\frac{1}{\sqrt{2}}, -\sqrt{2}$

 (ii) $-\frac{\sqrt{2}}{\sqrt{3}}, -\frac{1}{\sqrt{3}}, -\sqrt{3}, \frac{1}{\sqrt{2}}, \sqrt{2}.$

2. (i) $-5, \frac{5}{\sqrt{26}}, -\frac{1}{\sqrt{26}}, -\sqrt{26}, \frac{\sqrt{26}}{5}$

(ii) $-5, -\frac{5}{\sqrt{26}}, \frac{1}{\sqrt{26}}, \sqrt{26}, -\frac{\sqrt{26}}{5}$.

3. (i) $-\frac{1}{\sqrt{2}}, -\frac{1}{\sqrt{2}}, 1, 1, -\sqrt{2}$

(ii) $-\frac{1}{\sqrt{2}}, \frac{1}{\sqrt{2}}, -\sqrt{2}, -\sqrt{2}, \sqrt{2}$.

4. (i) $-\frac{7}{50}, -\frac{1}{\sqrt{50}}, \sqrt{50}, -\frac{1}{7}, -\frac{\sqrt{50}}{7}$

(ii) $-\frac{7}{50}, -\frac{1}{50}, \sqrt{50}, -\frac{1}{7}, -\frac{\sqrt{50}}{7}$.

5. $-\frac{\sqrt{3}}{2}, \frac{1}{2}, 2, -\frac{1}{\sqrt{3}}, -\frac{2}{\sqrt{3}}$.

6. $-\frac{\sqrt{3}}{2}, \frac{1}{\sqrt{3}}, -2, -\frac{3}{\sqrt{3}}, \sqrt{3}$.

7. (i) third and fourth

(ii) first and second

(iii) second and fourth

(iv) second and third

(v) second and third

(vi) second and fourth.

8. (i) $\cos\alpha$

(ii) $\sin\alpha$

(iii) $\operatorname{cosec}\alpha$

(iv) $\cot\alpha$

(v) $\tan\alpha$

(vi) $\sec\alpha$.

9. (i) $\cos\alpha$

(ii) $\sin\alpha$

(iii) $-\cot\alpha$

(iv) $-\tan\alpha$

(v) $-\operatorname{cosec}\alpha$

(vi) $-\sec\alpha$.

10. (i) $\sin\alpha$

(ii) $-\cos\alpha$

(iii) $-\tan\alpha$

(iv) $-\cot\alpha$

(v) $-\sec\alpha$

(vi) $\operatorname{cosec}\alpha$.

11. (i) $-\sin\alpha$

(ii) $-\cos\alpha$

(iii) $\tan\alpha$

(iv) $\cot\alpha$

(v) $-\sec\alpha$

(vi) $-\operatorname{cosec}\alpha$

(vii) $-\cos\alpha$

(viii) $-\sin\alpha$

(ix) $\cot\alpha$

(x) $\tan\alpha$

(xi) $-\operatorname{cosec}\alpha$

(xii) $-\sec\alpha$

(xiii) $-\cos\alpha$

(xiv) $\sin\alpha$

(xv) $-\cot\alpha$

(xvi) $-\tan\alpha$

(xvii) $-\sec\alpha$

(xviii) $\operatorname{cosec}\alpha$.

12. (i) $-\sec\alpha$

(ii) $\cot\alpha$

(iii) $\cot\alpha$

(iv) $-\tan\alpha$

(v) $-\sin\alpha$

(vi) $-\cos\alpha$

(vii) $-\sec\alpha$

(viii) $-\sec\alpha$

(ix) $-\cot\alpha$

(x) $\cos\alpha$.

13. (i) -1
(ii) $-\sqrt{2}$
(iii) $-\dfrac{1}{\sqrt{2}}$
(iv) 1
(v) $\dfrac{1}{2}$
(vi) $\dfrac{\sqrt{3}}{2}$
(vii) $\dfrac{1}{\sqrt{2}}$.

Exercise 4

1. 1
2. $\dfrac{1}{2}$
3. $-\sin 10°$
4. $\dfrac{1}{2}$
5. $\dfrac{\sqrt{3}}{2}$
6. $\cos(3\alpha + \beta)$
7. $\cos 6x$
8. $\sin 6x$
9. $\dfrac{1}{\sqrt{3}}$
10. $\cot 75°$
11. $\cot 15°$
12. ∞
13. $\tan 2x$
14. $\cot 3\alpha$
15. $\sqrt{3}$
16. 0.259, 0.966, 0.268, 1.035, 3.73, 3.86
17. (i) -0.866
(ii) -0.5
(iii) 0.3865
(iv) -1
(v) $\sqrt{2}$
18. (i) $\dfrac{\cot A \cot B + 1}{\cot B - \cot A}$
(ii) $\dfrac{\tan A - \tan B}{1 + \tan A \tan B}$
19. (i) $\sin 105°$
(ii) $\tan 1°$
(iii) 0
(iv) $\cos 80°$
(v) $\cos 4°$
(vi) ∞
(vii) $\cos 75°$
(viii) 0.866
(ix) $\tan 110°$
(x) $\sin 10°$
20. 0.993, -0.231, -0.121, 0.973
21. $4 \sin x \cos x - 8 \sin^3 x \cos x$.
$\cos^4 x + \sin^4 x - 6 \sin^2 x \cos^2 x$.
22. (i) $\cos x$
(ii) $-\cot 2x$
(iii) $-\sin 3x$.

Exercise 5

1. (i) $2 \sin \dfrac{A+B}{2} \cos \dfrac{A-B}{2}$
(ii) $2 \cos \dfrac{A+B}{2} \cos \dfrac{A-B}{2}$
(a) $\tan \dfrac{A+B}{2}$
(b) $\cot \dfrac{A+B}{2}$
2. (i) $2 \sin \dfrac{P-Q}{2} \cos \dfrac{P+Q}{2}$

(ii) $-2\sin\dfrac{P-Q}{2}\sin\dfrac{P+Q}{2}$

(a) $-\cot\dfrac{P+Q}{2}$

(b) $-\tan\dfrac{P+Q}{2}$.

3. (i) $\tan\dfrac{\theta-\phi}{2}\cot\dfrac{\theta+\phi}{2}$

(ii) $\tan\dfrac{\theta+\phi}{2}\cot\dfrac{\theta-\phi}{2}$

(iii) $\cot\dfrac{\theta-\phi}{2}$

(iv) $-\tan\dfrac{\theta-\phi}{2}$.

4. (i) $\dfrac{b}{a}$

(ii) $\dfrac{1}{b}$

(iii) $-ab$

(iv) $\dfrac{b(1-a^2)}{a(1-b^2)}$.

5. $4\cos x\sin\dfrac{5}{2}\cos\dfrac{x}{2}$

6. $4\cos x\cos\dfrac{5}{2}x\cos\dfrac{x}{2}$

7. (i) $2\cos 2x\sin 4x$

(ii) $-2\sin 2x\cos 5x$

(iii) $-2\sin 4x\sin x$

(iv) $2\cos x\cos 8x$

(v) $2\cos x\sin 8x$.

Exercise 6

1. $\dfrac{1}{2}\cos 10° - \dfrac{1}{4}$
2. $\dfrac{\sqrt{3}}{4}$
3. $\dfrac{1}{2}\cos 10°$
4. $\dfrac{1}{2}\cos 50°$
5. $\dfrac{1}{2}\cos 5\alpha + \dfrac{1}{2}\cos 3\alpha$
6. $\dfrac{1}{2}\cos 4y + \dfrac{1}{2}\cos 2y$
7. $\dfrac{1}{2}\sin 2x + \dfrac{1}{2}\sin 2y$
8. $\cos 12x + \cos 2x$
9. $\cos 2x - \cos 8x$
10. $\cos 5t - \cos 7t$
11. $\sin 2x - \dfrac{\sqrt{3}}{2}$
12. $\sin 2A - \sin 2B$
13. 0.5
14. $1 + \sin 20°$
15. $\sin 80° - \sin 10°$
16. $\sin 56° - \sin 10°$
17. $\sin 2° + \sin 8°$
18. $\cos 3x - \cos 13x$
19. $5\cos 10y + 5\cos 4y$
20. $10\sin 14y - 10\sin 4y$.

Exercise 7

1. $2\sin x\cos x$
2. $\cos^2 x - \sin^2 x = 2\cos^2 x - 1$
   $= 1 - 2\sin^2 x$
3. $\dfrac{2\tan x}{1-\tan^2 x}$
4. (i) $2\sin 2A\cos 2A$

   (ii) $2\cos^2 2A - 1 = \cos^2 2A - \sin^2 2A$
   $= 1 - 2\sin^2 2A$

   (iii) $\dfrac{2\tan 2A}{1-\tan^2 2A}$

5. (i) $-\sqrt{3}$
   (ii) $\sin 12x$
   (iii) $\cos 6x$
   (iv) $\sqrt{3}$
   (v) $\cos 8x$
   (vi) $\tan x$
   (vii) $\sec 2x$
   (viii) 0.5
   (ix) -0.5
   (x) $\sin x$.

Exercise 8

1. (i) $\dfrac{1-\tan\frac{x}{2}}{1-\tan\frac{x}{2}}$
   (ii) $\tan\dfrac{x}{2}$

2. $\cot^2 x$

3. (i) $-\dfrac{\sqrt{3}}{2}$ second quadrant, $\dfrac{\sqrt{3}}{2}$ third quadrant
   (ii) $\sqrt{3}$
   (iii) $\dfrac{1}{2}$

4. (i) $2\sin 2x\cos 2x$
   (ii) $2\cos^2 2x - 1 = \cos^2 2x - \sin^2 2x$
   $= 1 - 2\sin^2 2x$
   (iii) $\tan 4x = \dfrac{2\tan 2x}{1-\tan^2 2x}$

5. (i) $2\sin 8x\cos 8x$
   (ii) $2\cos^2 8x - 1$
   (iii) $\dfrac{2\tan 8x}{1-\tan^2 8x}$

Exercise 9

1. (i) $\dfrac{1+t^2}{t^2-4t+1}$
   (ii) $\dfrac{1+t^2}{1-t^2}$
   (iii) $\dfrac{1+t^2}{2t}$
   (iv) $\dfrac{1+t^2}{3t^2+1}$

2. (i) $\dfrac{1+t}{1-t}$
   (ii) $\cot x$

3. $x = 45°$

4. $x = 99.1°$, $x = 321.4°$

5. $\dfrac{19-5t^2}{-5+19t^2}$

6. $\cos^2 x$

7. $\tan\dfrac{x}{2}$

Exercise 10

1. $5\sin(x + 53.13°)$
2. $\sqrt{2}\sin(x - 45°)$
3. $\sqrt{5}\sin(x - 26.57°)$.
4. $\sqrt{5}\cos(x - 39.23°)$
5. $\sqrt{14}$
6. 5
7. $a = 11.3$, $b = 6.5$
8. $a = b = 10.61$.

Exercise 11

Exercise 12

1. $\dfrac{a^2}{m^2} + \dfrac{b^2}{n^2} = 1$
2. $p^2 + q^2 = 1$
3. $mn = 1$
4. $\left(p + \dfrac{3}{2}q\right)^2 + \left(p - \dfrac{3}{2}q\right)^2 = 1$

5. $\left(\frac{7}{2}x + \frac{5}{\sqrt{2}}y\right)^2 + \left(\frac{7\sqrt{3}}{2}x - \frac{5}{\sqrt{2}}y\right)^2$

$= \left[\frac{35}{2\sqrt{2}}\left(1+\sqrt{3}\right)\right]^2$

6. $1 + \left(\frac{m+n}{2}\right)^2 = \left(\frac{2}{m-n}\right)^2.$

Exercise 13

(i) $x = 200.93°, 339.08°$

(ii) 198.21°, 341.79°

(iii) 78.46°, 281.54°

(iv) 161.57°, 341.57°

(v) 5.71°, 185.71°

(vi) 224.4°, 315.57°

(vii) 72.54°, 287.46°

(viii) 120°, 240°

(ix) 0°, 90°, 180°, 270°, 360, 75.52°, 284.48°

(x) 0°, 180°, 360°, 75.52°, 248.48°

(xi) 86.87°, 193.13°

(xii) 229.24°

(xiii) 22.98°, 157.02°, 219.82°, 320.18°

(xiv) 150°, 330°

(xv) 60°, 180°, 300°

(xvi) 11.95°, 168.05°

(xvii) 28.15°, 118.15°, 208.15°, 298.15°

(xviii) 54.74°, 234.74°, 125.26°, 305.26°

(xix) 150°, 330°

(xx) 30°, 210°, 150°, 330°

(xxi) 60°

(xxii) 225°

(xxiv) 285°, 345°, 105°, 165°

(xxv) 90°, 225°

(xxvi) −30°

(xxvii) 70.53°, 289.47°

(xxviii) 30°, 150°

(xxix) 0°, 360°, 40°, 160°, 280°

(xxx) 64.64°, 221.56°.

Exercise 14

(i) $x = 0°, 360°, y = 0°, 360°$

(ii) $x = 45°$ or $315°$, $y = 45°, 315°$

(iii) $x = 30°$ or $330°$

(iv) 60°, 300°

(v) $x = 120°, y = 120°; x = 240°, y = 240°$

(vi) $x = 60°$ or $300°$; $y = 30°$ or $330°$

(vii) $x = 45°$ or $135°$; $y = 45°$ or $315°$

(viii) $x = 30°$ or $210°$; $y = 60°$ or $240°$. If $x = 60°$ or $240°$ then $y = 30°$ or $210°$.

(ix) $x = 70° 32'$ or $289° 28'$; $y = 30°$ or $150°$,
$x = 60°$ or $300°$; $y = 19° 18'$ or $160° 32'$

(x) $x = 26° 34'$ or $206° 34'$, $y = 45°$ or $225°$,
$x = 45°$ or $225°$; $y = 63° 26'$, or $243° 26'$

Exercise 15

1. 120°

2. 8.66°, 96° 35′

3. (i) $\sqrt{\frac{2}{5}}, \sqrt{\frac{3}{5}}, 1; \frac{3}{\sqrt{15}}, \frac{2}{\sqrt{10}}, 0.$

4. (i) $\frac{4}{\sqrt{30}}, \frac{2}{\sqrt{18}}, \frac{1}{\sqrt{18}}, \sqrt{\frac{7}{15}}, \frac{\sqrt{7}}{3}, \sqrt{\frac{17}{18}}$

5. (i) $\frac{4}{3\sqrt{2}}, \frac{2}{\sqrt{6}}, -\frac{1}{\sqrt{6}}; \frac{1}{3}, \frac{1}{\sqrt{3}}, \sqrt{\frac{5}{6}}.$

Exercise 16

1. At A, $x = 18°$ or 0.324^c, at B, $x = 81°$ or 1.414^c,

2. $x = 43.5°$ or $x = 180°$.

3. (i) $A\,(-0.88, -2.09^c)$, $B\,(-0.62, -0.68^c)$;
$C\,(0.04, 3.12^c)$

(ii) $A\,(0.64, -0.945^c)$, $B\,(0.28, 1.31^c)$

(iii) $A\,(3.8, 1.313^c)$, $B\,(1.55, 4.14^c)$.

4. (i) $A\left(\frac{5\pi}{6}, \frac{1}{2}\right) \quad x = \frac{5\pi}{6}$

(ii) $B\left(\frac{3\pi}{4}, 0.707\right)$

(iii) $x = \frac{2\pi}{5}, y = 0; x = \frac{\pi}{3}, y = -0.21.$

5. (i) 0.75 m
   (ii) 1.05 m
   (iii) 1.57 m
   (iv) 3.14 m
   (v) 6.28 m.

6. Graphs

7. Graph

8. Graphs

9. $x = 101.5°$

10. $15°, 75°, 105°, 165°$

11. (i) $115.3°, x = 318.4°$
    (ii) $x = 95°, x = 298°$
    (iii) $x = 0°, 90°, 360°$

12. (i) $x = 75°, y = 3; x = 30°, y = -3;$
    $x = 0, y = 2.598$
    (ii) $x = 30°, y = 0, x = 150°, y = 0.$
    (iii) $x = 0, y = -0.866; x = 40°, y = 0.$

13. (i) $A(-105°, 3), B(-15°, -3), C(75°, 3);$
    (ii) $D(-120°, 2), E(60°, 2);$
    (iii) $\pm 1, H(-50°, 1), J(70°, 1), G(-110°, -1)$
    $I(10°, -1), K(130°, -1)$
    (i) Crosses the x-axis at $-150°, -60°, 30°$, and $120°$, and the y-axis at -2.598
    (ii) $-30°, 150°$, and the y-axis at -1
    (iii) $x = -140°, -80°, -20°, 40°, 100°, 160°$,
    $y = -0.866.$

14. (i) $\sqrt{2}\sin\left(x - \frac{\pi}{3}\right)$
    (ii) $5\sin\left(x - 53°\,8'\right)$
    (iii) $\sqrt{10}\cos\left(2x + 71°\,34'\right)$
    (iv) $\sqrt{52}\sin\left(3x + 56°\,19'\right)$
    (v) $14.93\cos\left(2x - 59°\,45'\right)$
    (vi) $14.03\cos\left(2x - 16°\,16'\right)$
    (vii) $\sqrt{65}\sin\left(x - 65°\,15'\right)$
    (viii) $5\sin\left(x + 53°\,8'\right)$

Exercise 17

1. (i) $0°, 180°, 360°$
   (ii) $90°$
   (iii) $60°, 120°$
   (iv) $210°, 330°$
   (v) $30°, 150°$
   (vi) $60°, 300°$
   (vii) $180°$
   (viii) $30°, 330°$
   (ix) $\frac{\pi}{2}, \frac{3\pi}{2}$
   (x) $120°\ 240°$
   (xi) $\frac{\pi}{4}$
   (xii) $\frac{\pi}{2}$ or $\frac{3\pi}{2}$
   (xiii) $0°, 180°, 360°$
   (xiv) $120°, 300°$
   (xv) $30°, 210°$
   (xvi) $120°, 240°$
   (xvii) $\frac{\pi}{2}, \frac{3\pi}{2}$
   (xviii) $150°, 210°$
   (xix) $60°, 300°$
   (xx) $0°, 360°$
   (xxi) $90°, 270°$
   (xxii) $150°, 330°$
   (xxiii) $0°, 180°, 360°$
   (xxiv) $60°, 240°$
   (xxv) $60°, 240°$
   (xxvi) $\frac{3\pi}{4}, \frac{7\pi}{4}$.

2. (i) $\sin^{-1}(\sin x) = x$
   (ii) $\sin^{-1}(\cos x) = \frac{\pi}{2} - x$
   (iii) $\tan^{-1}(\tan x) = x$
   (iv) $\sec^{-1}(\sec x) = x$
   (v) $\cot^{-1}\cot x = x$
   (vi) $\text{cosec}^{-1}(\text{cosec}\, x) = x$

(vii) $\cos^{-1}(\sin x) = \frac{\pi}{2} - x$

(viii) $\cos^{-1}(\cos x) = x$

(ix) $\cot^{-1}\tan x = \frac{\pi}{2} - x$

(x) $\tan^{-1}\cot x = \frac{\pi}{2} - x$

(xi) $\sec^{-1}(\operatorname{cosec} x) = \frac{\pi}{2} - x$

(xii) $\operatorname{cosec}^{-1}\sec x = \frac{\pi}{2} - x$

(xiii) $\sin(2\tan^{-1} x) = \frac{2x}{1+x^2}$

(xiv) $\cot^{-1} x = \theta, \cot\theta = x.$

(xv) $\cos 2\cot^{-1} x = \frac{x^2-1}{x^2+1}$

3. (i) $x = -\frac{6}{7}$

(ii) $x = \frac{1}{7}$

(iii) $x = 0.04$ or 26.04

(iv) $x = \sqrt{5} - 2$ or $x = -(2+\sqrt{5})$

(v) $x = -16.062$ or $x = 0.062$

(vi) $x = -3.$

4. (i) $\sin(\tan^{-1} x + \cot^{-1} x) = 1$

(ii) $\tan\Theta = x$

(iii) $\cos(2\tan^{-1} x) = \frac{1-x^2}{1+x^2}$

(iv) $\cos(\tan^{-1} x + \cot^{-1} x) = 0$

(v) $\sin(\cot^{-1} x + 2\tan^{-1})$

$$x = \frac{x^2 - 1 + 2\sqrt{1+x^2}}{(1+x^2)^{\frac{3}{2}}}$$

5. (i) 0

(ii) -4

(iii) $\frac{14}{5}$

(iv) $\frac{3}{\sqrt{10}}$

(v) $\frac{-3}{5}.$

6. $\frac{2}{\sqrt{3}}$

9. $x = 1$

10. $x = \frac{1}{3}.$

Exercise 18

1. (i) $6\sqrt{3}$

(ii) 14.9

(iii) $45^\circ 47'$

(iv) $55^\circ 49'$

(v) $45^\circ 47'$

2. (i) 9.35 cm

(ii) $75^\circ 2'$

(iii) 80.7 cm^3

(iv) 121.8 cm^2

(v) $93^\circ 71'$

3. (i) 32.5 cm^2

(ii) 33.35 cm^2

(iii) $12^\circ 58'$

Exercise 19

1. (i) 0.001

(ii) 0.004

(iii) 0.026

(iv) 0.003

(v) 0.9999989

(vi) 1.000

(vii) 1.000

(viii) 1.000

(ix) 0.002

(x) 0.005.

2. (i) $\frac{1-2x}{1+2x}$

(ii) $1 - 3x - \frac{9}{2}x^2$

(iii) $\frac{1}{3}$

(iv) $\dfrac{2(1-\frac{1}{2}x^2-3x)}{3\left(1-\frac{1}{2}x^2\right)(1-2x^2)}$.

(v) $\dfrac{\frac{49x^2}{2}-4}{1-\frac{9x^2}{2}}$.

3. (i) 57.296
(ii) −2.063
(iii) −1.072
(iv) −57.296
(v) 0.545
(vi) 0.131
(vii) −2.179
(viii) 0.293
(ix) 20.000
(x) 0.641.

4. (a) (i) $\frac{3}{5}$
(ii) ∞
(iii) 1
(iv) 1
(v) 1
(vi) 0
(vii) ∞
(viii) 1
(ix) 1
(x) 1
(b) (i) $\frac{3}{5}$
(ii) ∞
(iii) 1
(iv) 1
(v) 1
(vi) 0
(vii) ∞
(viii) 1
(ix) 1
(x) 1.

5. (a) (i) 0.99883371
(ii) 0.9973816
(iii) $\frac{1}{3}$
(iv) 0.6661
(v) −4
(b) (i) 0.961
(ii) 0.9696
(iii) $\frac{1}{3}$
(iv) 0.647
(v) −3.9996
(c) (i) 0.933
(ii) 0.946
(iii) $\frac{1}{3}$
(iv) 0.632
(v) −3.9986.

6. (i) $0° 3'27''$
(ii) $0° 34'23''$
(iii) $2° 33'44''$
(iv) $0° 17'11''$
(v) $5° 40'20''$

8. Sine
(i) 2.91×10^{-4}
(ii) 1.454×10^{-3}
(iii) 7.272×10^{-3}
(iv) 0.0131
(v) 0.0174532

cosine
(i) 0.9999999
(ii) 0.9999999
(iii) 0.9999736
(iv) 0.999143
(v) 0.9998477

tangent

(i) 2.9088821×10^{-4}

(ii) 1.454441×10^{-3}

(iii) 7.2722052×10^{-3}

(iv) 0.0130899

(v) 0.0174533

secant

(i) 1.0000001

(ii) 1.0000011

(iii) 1.0000264

(iv) 1.0000857

(v) 1.0001523

cosecant

(i) 3436.4201

(ii) 687.75791

(iii) 137.51375

(iv) 76.335878

(v) 57.296083

contagent

(i) 3437.7468

(ii) 687.5494

(iii) 137.0987

(iv) 323.6351

(v) 57.295775.

9. (i) 2^c or 0

(ii) -1.26^c

(iii) 0.914 or -1.914

(iv) -1.024 or 0.024

(v) ± 2.7775.

10. ± 0.0183.

Exercise 20

2. $\theta = 34° 20'$ or $242° 4'4.49° 98'$ or $162° 24'$

6. $347° 56'$ or $235° 39'$

7. $\tan^{-1} 0.5$

8. $\cos 2\Theta = 1 - 2\sin^2\Theta$, $\cot 2\theta = \dfrac{\cot^2\theta - 1}{2\cot\theta}$.

2. TRIGONOMETRY

Index

Appendix Trigonometry Syllabus

C_2

The sine and cosine rules, and the area of a triangle in the form $\frac{1}{2}ab \sin C$.

Radian measure, including use for arc length and area of sector.

Sine, cosine and tangent functions. Their graphs, symmetries and periodicity.

Knowledge and use of $\tan\theta = \dfrac{\sin\theta}{\cos\theta}$, and $\sin^2\theta + \cos^2\theta = 1$.

Solution of simple trigonometric equations in a given interval.

In the triangle ABC

$$\frac{a}{\sin A} = \frac{b}{\sin B} = \frac{c}{\sin C}$$

$$\text{area} = \tfrac{1}{2}ab \sin C$$

Use of the formulae $s = r\theta$ and $A = \frac{1}{2}r^2\theta$ for a circle.

Knowledge of graphs of curves with equations such as $y = 3\sin x$, $y = \sin(x + \pi/6)$, $y = \sin 2x$ is expected.

Candidates should be able to solve equations such as

$\sin\left(x - \frac{\pi}{2}\right) = \frac{3}{4}$ for $0 < x < 2\pi$,

$\cos(x + 30°) = \frac{1}{2}$ for $-180° < x < 180°$,

$\tan 2x = 1$ for $90° < x < 270°$,

$6\cos^2 x° + \sin x° - 5 = 0$ for $0 \le x < 360°$,

$\sin^2\left(x + \dfrac{\pi}{6}\right) = \frac{1}{2}$ for $-\pi \le x < \pi$.

C_3

Knowledge of secant, cosecant and cotangent and of arcsin, arccos and arctan. Their relationships to sine, cosine and tangent. Understanding of their graphs and appropriate restricted domains.

Knowledge and use of $\sec^2\theta = 1 + \tan^2\theta$ and $\operatorname{cosec}^2\theta = 1 + \cot^2\theta$.

Knowledge and use of double angle formulae; use of formulae for $\sin(A \pm B)$, $\cos(A \pm B)$ and $\tan(A \pm B)$ and of expressions for $a\cos\theta + b\sin\theta$ in the equivalent forms of $r\cos(\theta \pm a)$ or $r\sin(\theta \pm a)$.

Angles measured in both degrees and radians.

To include application to half-angles. Knowledge of the t $\left(\tan\frac{1}{2}\theta\right)$ formulae will *not* be required.

Candidates should be able to solve equations such as $a\cos\theta + b\sin\theta = c$ in a given interval, and to prove simple identities such as $\cos x\cos 2x + \sin x\sin 2x \equiv \cos x$.

Trigonometry Formulae

$\sin(A \pm B) = \sin A \cos B \pm \cos A \sin B$

$\cos(A \pm B) = \cos A \cos B \mp \sin A \sin B$

$\tan(A \pm B) = \dfrac{\tan A \pm \tan B}{1 \mp \tan A \tan B} \left(A \pm B \neq \left(k + \tfrac{1}{2}\right)\pi\right)$

$\sin A + \sin B = 2 \sin \dfrac{A+B}{2} \cos \dfrac{A-B}{2}$

$\sin A - \sin B = 2 \cos \dfrac{A+B}{2} \sin \dfrac{A-B}{2}$

$\cos A + \cos B = 2 \cos \dfrac{A+B}{2} \cos \dfrac{A-B}{2}$

$\cos A - \cos B = -2 \sin \dfrac{A+B}{2} \sin \dfrac{A-B}{2}$

$\cos^2 A + \sin^2 A = 1$

$\sec^2 A = 1 + \tan^2 A$

$\mathrm{cosec}^2 A = 1 + \cot^2 A$

$\sin 2A = 2 \sin A \cos A$

$\cos 2A = \cos^2 A - \sin^2 A$

$\tan 2A = \dfrac{2 \tan A}{1 - \tan^2 A}$

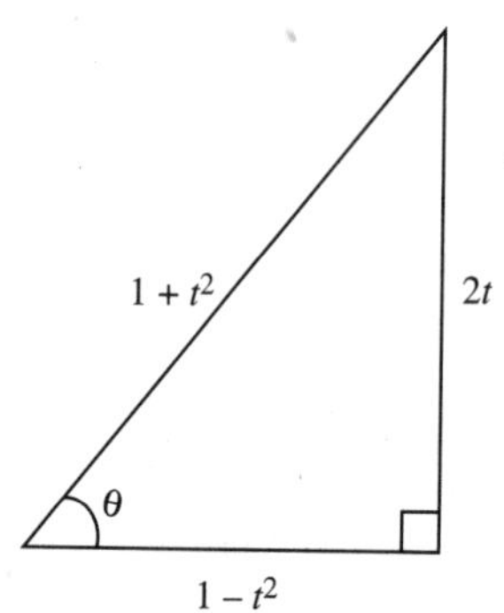

For $t = \tan \dfrac{\theta}{2}$; $\sin\theta = \dfrac{2t}{1+t^2}$, $\cos\theta = \dfrac{1-t^2}{1+t^2}$

In ΔABC,

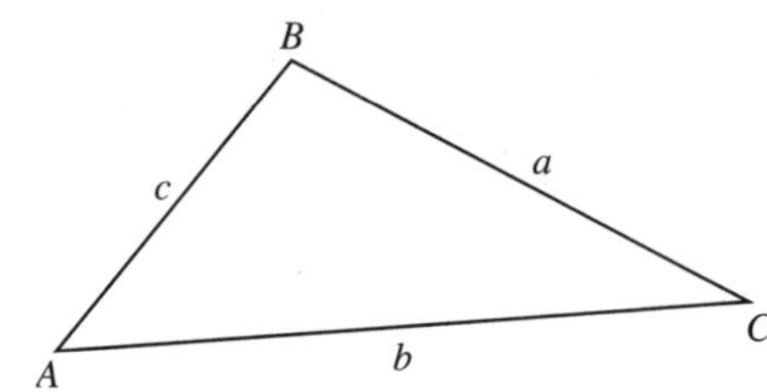

$\dfrac{a}{\sin A} = \dfrac{b}{\sin B} = \dfrac{c}{\sin C}$

$a^2 = b^2 + c^2 - 2bc \cos A$

$\sin x = x - \dfrac{x^3}{3!} + \dfrac{x^5}{5!} - \ldots + (-1)^r \dfrac{x^{2r+1}}{(2r+1)!} + \ldots$
for all x

$\cos x = 1 - \dfrac{x^2}{2!} + \dfrac{x^4}{4!} - \ldots + (-1)^r \dfrac{x^{2r}}{(2r)!} + \ldots$ for all x